MYTH, LEGE

FOLKLORE

American Indians: Folk Tales and Legends

AMERICAN INDIANS
Folk Tales and Legends

Keith Cunningham
Northern Arizona University

WORDSWORTH EDITIONS
in association with
THE FOLKLORE SOCIETY

FLS books

This edition published 2001 by Wordsworth Editions Limited
Cumberland House, Crib Street, Ware, Hertfordshire SG12 9ET
in association with FLS Books, The Folklore Society,
c/o The Warburg Institute, Woburn Square, London WC1H 0AB

Editor FLS Books: Jennifer Chandler

ISBN 1 84022 505 X

Typeset by Antony Gray
Printed and bound in Great Britain by
Mackays of Chatham plc, Chatham, Kent

This exciting new series is made possible by a unique partnership between Wordsworth Editions and The Folklore Society.

Among the major assets of The Folklore Society is its unparalleled collection of books, in the making since 1878. The library and archives have, over the years, formed an invaluable specialist resource. Now, Wordsworth Editions, which is committed to opening up whole areas of culture through good-looking, good-value books and intelligent commentary, make these riches widely available.

Individual introductions by acknowledged experts place each work in historical context and provide commentaries from the perspective of modern scholarship.

PROFESSOR W. F. H. NICOLAISEN
President, The Folklore Society

Simply to Kathryn

Contents

INTRODUCTION 15

1 *Abenaki*
Heroic Deeds of Glooscap 25
Why the Porcupine and Toad Have No Noses 25

2 *Achomawi*
Pine Marten Marries the Bead Sisters 27
Kangaroo Rat Races with Coyote and Others 28

3 *Acoma*
The Flaming Horse 30
Kaupata 36
The Kobictaiya Are Challenged to the Test of Lightning 40
The Windows of the Fox 41
The Travels of Salt Woman 43
Paiyatyamo and Yellow Woman 46
Greasy Boy Recovers His Wife 50
Careful Burden Carrier 56

4 *Arapaho*
On the War Path 60
The Woman and the Buffalo 61
The Man Who Gets Advice from the Skunk 61
The Origin of the Pleiades 61
Origin of the Buffalo 62
The Mother's Head 62
Origin of the Medicine Arrows 63
The Frog and the Woman 64
How a Bird and an Alligator Saved Two Children 64
The Cannibal and the Fox 65
Bad Robe Resurrecting a Buffalo 66
The Bear Girl 67

Why the Bear Has a Short Tail 67
The Alligator Boy 68
The Boy Who Was Carried off by the Wind 68

5 *Blackfoot*
Legend of Red Coulee 70
The Legend of Sheep Creek 70
Legend of Tongue Creek 71

6 *Carrier*
The Giant's Grandson 73
A Big Frog 88
The Trickster 88
Coming of the White Man 98
Caribou Man and the Sekani 98
Origin of the Crest Sleepy 100
The Revenge of the Mountain Goats 101
The Flood 105
The Dead Woman's Son 107
The Man Who Ate His Wives 112
The Origin of the Tribes 115
The Monstrous Bear 116
The Bear Wife 118
Porcupine 119

7 *Cheyenne*
Falling Star 122

8 *Chipewyan*
Naba-Cha 130
Big Bird Story 134
White Bear Story 135

9 *Comanche*
Origin of Death 137

10 *Coos*
The Country of the Souls 139
The Underground People 141
The Woman Who Married The Merman 142
The Revenge on the Sky People 143
The Man Who Married the Bird 146

11 *Cree*

The Birth of Lake Mistassini 148
The Painted Canoe 148
The Story of Katonao 149
The Biter Bit 150
Chichipischekwan (Rolling Head) 151
The Flight of Wesakaychak 153
The Younger Boy Becomes a Wolf 155
Wesakaychak Destroys the Great Moose 157
Wisakitcax and Buzzard 159

12 *Eskimo*

The Woman Who Was Fond of Intestines 161
A Sea Otter Story 165
The Sad Woman 166
The Man and Woman Who Became Sea Otters 167
The Woman Who Became a Bear 168
The Old Man of the Volcano 169
An Aleut with Two Wives 172
Woman Without a Nose 173
The Woman with One Eye 175
The Boy with Seal Flippers 175
Ughek 176
The Brother and Sister Who Became Hair Seals 178
The Loon and the Blind Man 178

13 *Flathead*

Coyote Makes Spokane Falls 183
Coyote and the Woman 183
Coyote and the Medicine Trees 184
Coyote and the Crying Baby 184
Coyote and Rock 185
Coyote in the Buffalo Country 186
Coyote and the Two Shells 188
Coyote Kills the Giant 189
Coyote and Fox Separate 190
Coyote and the Little Pig 191

14 *Fox*

Dispersion 193
The Blackhawk War 195
The Origin of the Sauks and Foxes 197
Witchcraft 199

15 *Hopi*
The Emergence 200
After the Emergence 203
Witch and Coyote Establish Death 206
Birth of the Twins 209
The Twins Slay Kwatoko 210
Early Monsters 213
The Twins Slay Chaveyo and Giant Elk 214
Pyuukanhoya Slays Chaveyo and the Nataska 216
Salyko 217
The Jamestown Weed Maids (Toothed Vagina) 219
Kwatoko, the Woman Stealer 222
The Sipapu Is Sought by the Birds 225
The Migrations of the Eagle Clan 226
The Migrations of the Horn Clan 228

16 *Huron*
The Making of the World 232

17 *Iroquois*
Three Brothers Who Followed the Sun under the Sky's Rim 235

18 *Mandan*
No Tongue 238

19 *Mojave*
Story of the Flood 245
Fire Myth 247

20 *Navajo*
Origin of the People 248
Coyote Makes Songs for the Hills 261
Coyote Burns Up Her Children 262
Mock Plea 262
Coyote at the River 262
Coyote Sets Fire to the Earth 263
Coyote Plays Dead 263
Coyote Invites Wildcat to Eat 264
Coyote and Wildcat Scratch Each Other 265
Origin of the Manygoats Clan 265

21 *Ojibwa*
An Adventure of Wenabuzu 267

22 *Papago*
Montezuma 269
Some of Coyote's Adventures 280

23 *Piegan*
The Woman Who Turned into a Bear 282
Old Man and the Geese 285
How the Beaver Bundle Was Introduced 285

24 *San Luisenos*
Creation Myth 291

25 *Shasta*
Origin of Death 292
The Dead Brought Back from the Other World 292
Urutsmaxig 293
The Race with Thunder 297
The Captive of the 'Little Men' 298
Coyote and the Rogue-River People 299

26 *Shawnee*
Huron Legend of the Snake Clan 302
Legendary Origin of the Kickapoos 303

27 *Shoshone*
Cosmology 304
The Star Husband 304
Weasels and Owl 306
The Eye-Juggler 306

28 *Sioux*
Ben Kindle's Winter Count 309

29 *Tahltan*
The Man with the Toothed Penis 311
The Three Sister Rocks 311
Story of Dcandui 312
Story of Gonexhataca, The Snail 313
The Sisters Who Married Stars 314
The Man Who Fooled the Cannibal Giant 316
Story of the War between the Tahltan and the Taku 316
The Woman Stolen by the Ducine 320
The Story of Tcizqa; or The Hunter Who Could Not Kill Game 320
The Deserted Woman 321

The Cannibal Women Who Lured Men 322
Big-Man and the Boy 323
The Bad Man and His Son-in-Law 326

30 *Tewa*
Water Jar Boy 328
Tewa Goat 330

31 *Ute*
Nowintc's Adventures with the Bird Girls and Their People 331
Coyote Juggles His Eyes and Becomes Blind 345

32 *Western Mono*
The Making of the World 348
A Visit to the World of the Dead 349
Walking Skeleton 349
The Adventures of Haininu and Baumegwesu 354
The Coyote Called 'Another One' 360

33 *Winnebago*
The Man Who Visited the Thunderbirds 362
Origin of the Thunderbird Clan and of Their Spirit Abode 374

34 *Yavapai*
Origin Story 380
The Burning of the World 395
The Human Bear 399
The Laughing Wives 403
Coyote Resurrects Mountain Lion 404
Coyote Juggles His Eyes 406
Bat's Wives 406

35 *Zuni*
The Flood 408
The Hopi Boy and the Sun 408
Lanco Blala 413
Santu 421
Juan Without Fear 422
The Rebellion Against the Spaniards 430

ACKNOWLEDGEMENTS 433

MORE INFORMATION about The Folklore Society 441

Introduction

Although some tribes gained a measure of protection from their geographic isolation, the Native American pre-contact population of the contiguous United States, estimated to have been over 300,000, fell to less than 150,000 by 1850 and dropped below 16,000 by 1900. The native populations of Canada and Alaska met similar fates. The years between the establishment of the American Folklore Society and its publication *Journal of American Folklore* in 1888 and the 1940s were the twilight years of many Native American tribes but the golden years of Native American narrative collection leading to the publication of a rich corpus of American Indian stories in the *Journal*.

This period of time began with the end of a century. It was a period of time when the American national consciousness began to see what had been lost and what was in danger of being lost as a result of the American experience and expansion. As a response to this widespread realisation of loss, the federal government established national parks and monuments to preserve the wilderness, and painters, photographers, novelists, museums, and individuals sought to preserve images and objects of a land and people conquered and controlled and brought to the edge of oblivion. The widespread realisation that the American West of the popular imagination and the American Indian were both rapidly disappearing and might soon be forgotten, too, lent a sense of urgency to folklore collection activities of those who knew and loved the storytellers, the stories, or the idea of preservation.

There was a rush to collect the narratives of the American Indian. Many people who knew Native Americans through their business activities or their travels sought to record the stories they had collected intentionally or accidently. Recording the lore of the American Indian was a specific goal of the American Folklore Society included in its charter when it was established in 1888, and a new generation of interested scholars sought out native groups with the expressed purpose of collecting and writing down their narratives so that they would not disappear

They were a fascinating group, these researchers and accidental collectors. They were professional anthropologists-college professors and graduate students, employees of The United States of America Bureau of Ethnography (an addition to the federal government that institutionalized a national ethnography effort concentrating upon Native Americans), free-lance scholars who supported their own work or secured support from museums or benefactors, traders to the Indians, missionaries from a wide variety of Christian groups, military personnel, travellers, authors, journalists and other interested individuals. Many wrote books considered classics in anthropology. Some of them were never heard from again. Many had long teaching careers in American colleges and universities. One of them was murdered in the South Seas before his American Indian collection was published. Others continued to live their lives and careers as before their research was published. But, they all had memories and stories.

Many of the professional cultural researchers were directly connected with the American Folklore Society and published in *Journal of American Folklore* as did many of the nonprofessional collectors. The list of editors and officers of *Journal of the American Folklore* and the American Folklore Society from these years reads like an honours list of the most important and distinguished anthropologists of the time, and, under their leadership, the *Journal of American Folklore* published a large number of collections of American Indian narratives.

Some of the articles these collectors and scholars edited or wrote included varying degrees of interpretation and theory, and their stories, these wonderful stories, were used as principle or supporting data for many, many later studies. Ethnopoetics, the Boasian method, the historical-geographical method, solar mythology, the pattern theory of culture, paradigmatic and syntagmatic structuralism, functional analysis, the idea of the trickster, and Freudian and Jungian interpretations of folklore were then or later inspired by and based upon or applied to this rich corpus, but the publication of these stories was motivated by a desire to record and preserve them rather than by an attempt to explicate them or use them as data for theoretical analysis. The unwritten rules of academic publishing of cultural studies of the time, unlike those of today, were such that many articles published were straightforward field collections with widely varying degrees of collaborative information. Even articles that were chiefly theoretical usually included extensive collections of narratives reported completely rather than as summaries. *Journal of American Folklore* in these early years was indeed a journal *of* folklore rather than a journal *about* folklore. There are advantages to this approach to publishing folklore, not the least of which is the fact that these stories these storytellers and collectors loved, worked, and sometimes died to record are published and therefore can find new audiences and new appreciations.

This book includes a very broad sample of 274 American Indian stories collected from 35 cultural or tribal groups (as designated by the collectors) out of the incredible corpus of narratives published in *Journal of American Folklore* in this period, a Zuni myth my wife Kathy and I collected but have not previously published and a Navajo clan origin legend collected by one of my students. The selections, like the original articles, present a rare set of glimpses into other peoples' behaviours, material culture, customs, arts and crafts, beliefs and world views in another time through their stories.

In the twentieth century, the stories, their contexts and the stories about how they were collected were largely lost, and American Indian tales were expropriated by Euro-American culture, cleaned up mightily and are today known to most non-Indian peoples, if at all, either as data in theoretical monographs or as sweet little children's stories. This bowdlerization is a sad, strange fate for one of the world's great narrative traditions and world views that bristled with life in all its awe.

There are many different kinds of stories here. Although myth and legend are the most common types of stories, many other narrative forms recognised by folklorists, including folk tale, trickster tale, cultural hero saga, personal experience story, and family story are represented.

There are also some narrative forms not generally known to their collectors' worlds at the time they were collected. 'Ben Kindle's Winter Account' (Chapter 28) recorded from the Oglala Sioux, for example, is a collecting of a living traditional annual calendar that recounted and preserved a major event for each year of its existence from 1759 to 1925, the year of its collection. The calendar is a part of a larger Native American tradition wide spread in the Southwest but probably originating in Mexico, and it is very interesting to see what sorts of item from each year were considered to be important enough to remember.

There are in this wealth of stories narrative elements that are similar to many worldwide folk, popular culture, or art story so that readers will be struck by tales that seem to echo Hansel and Gretel, Jack and the Beanstalk, The Three Little Pigs, Titus Andronicus, Jesus Christ, Lysistrata, classic mythology and many others. Some of these similarities represent the end product of borrowing. Other familiar sounding stories have no known link to the European tales they resemble and simply attest to the wide appeal of a good story well told.

There are also a number of recurring tale elements or plots that are typical of the groups' oral traditions included in this American Indian corpus. The eye juggler motif, the star husband tale, and the account of the separation and reunion of the genders are stories collected from a number of tribal groups. More generally, many tribes had stories featuring the same or similar characters – Coyote, twin war gods, ogres, and cultural heroes, that were told in many American Indian traditions in versions with culturally specific elements.

The stories follow a set of complex narrative rules about when and where and how they could be told. Many stories were seen as having seasonal connections and could only be told at certain times of the year. Some were performed individually, many were performed in four night storytelling cycles. There were stories than included songs and singing. Some performances required the audience to respond in unison with a traditional phrase to begin the storytelling or at recurring points in the narrative. There were often traditionalised beginnings and endings. The conventions are interesting and important in themselves because they offer us a way to understand and experience unfamiliar ways of telling the story of man.

By elaborate descriptions and simple references, the stories recreate physical worlds of peoples and times long passed away. The stories usher us into houses and show us cooking utensils, dresses, and shirts, shoes, hair styles, clothing, music, and food-and hunger. The stories tell us a great deal about how the people lived and what objects formed and informed their days.

Some of the tribes whose narratives are represented in this collection have flourished. Some have the largest number of members now than at any other time in their history. As the early collectors feared, however, many of the Indian tribes they knew have completely disappeared leaving behind only their stories. The list is long. The stories, furthermore, are removed from us by time. These are stories from eighty to one hundred and twenty years ago; they show worlds long forgotten and gone.

Many others of the stories live still. There are stories surviving in cultural borrowings across tribes and across time and loss. In the almost twenty years Kathy and I have spent conducting research with Native Americans, we have heard contemporary Native Americans tell Navajo coyote stories and Zuni myths that have clear antecedents in these stories told and collected eighty to a hundred years ago. It is also interesting that some elements that were of minor importance in older stories have become the centre of newer tales and that, as we discovered in our research on Navajo jokes, new Native American narrative forms have come into existence or been adopted since these great collections were made.

There are many stories here that have a timeless cross-cultural appeal. There are jokes and puns and parables that speak as powerfully to us today as they did to their original audiences long ago. When Kathy and I read the stories, with great difficulty chose the ones we wished to include in this compilation, entered them into our computer and compared them with ones we had experienced during our fieldwork with Native Americans, we discovered that various ones reached out to us and instantly became a part of us and our references. Elsie Clews Parsons collected the story 'Water Jar Boy' from a Tewa informant and published it in 1926 in volume nineteen of the *Memoirs of the American Folklore Society*. Gladys Reichard recognized it as a classic story and republished it in *Journal of American Folklore* in 1943 after a conversation with Joseph Campbell. Her report of the conversation was that Joseph Campbell pointed out that folklorists report all stories they collect and said he would prefer to see the 'good stories'. She selected 'Water Jar Boy' as one of those good stories. 'Water Jar Boy' (Chapter 30, p. 328) is indeed a 'good story' and was especially appropriate to publish in response to a request from a Jungian such as Joseph Campbell. The story includes all the elements of the human experience from the mysteries of conception, to the struggle to become an individual self, the reintegration of the masculine and feminine facets of the psyche, and life after death – all told with high drama, humour and compassion in just a few minutes.

The stories speak cross-culturally to audiences other then those that are their natural, original listeners. They also spoke and continue to speak to the people for whom whey were intended and to their decedents.

I was pleased last year when I looked out over my American Folklore class at Northern Arizona University and saw a Navajo student because he, and others like him, represent the only chance that Native American stories will continue to be collected since most Native American tribal groups have closed their groups to outside researchers. Lukai Nez proved to be an excellent student, collected and reported a contemporary Navajo clan origin story (Chapter 20, p. 265) – with the wonderful twist that it was the story of the Manygoats clan, his clan. His story, and his loving attention to it, clearly demonstrate that some American Indian narrative traditions continue also to flourish and speak to the children's children's children of their original audiences. Each one of these stories, too, encompasses its own, often unwritten history of cultural interaction within itself.

Kathy and I sat with Kuiceyetsa – regal descendent of a priestly family, the embodiment and personification of all that was good and right at and of Zuni – at her kitchen table with her husband Max – leader of the people, the greatest political figure and wisest man I have ever known – and recorded her telling her version of 'Boy and Girl Rocks,' a narrative that is a major part of the Zuni myth tradition and is reported later in the book from a much earlier recorded telling (Chapter 35, p. 408):

'Well, as they say, you know (pause) a long time ago (pause) our grandfathers told us that was a floody (pause) and uh, it, you know, began to rain, and it rained and rained and – so they had to go to a higher place, and they couldn't think of any place to go except up there (points to Towayalane) up to the top of Towayalane, and they uh, they, uh, but the water still kept coming, and it just – they didn't know *what* to do, so they uh the priest had two small children. They were (pause) maybe just like her (pats her granddaughter leaning up against her – a child I adored and whose children I would adore later as I adored her now) growing up. They didn't know any boys or anything like that (pause) and they – the whole village cut prayer plumes for, for them, and when they got through, they got them in a basket – one for the boy and one for the girl – they dressed them up nice and, uh, then they sent them to the edge, and they were praying that the water would stop, and they sent these children down (pause) a boy and a girl. (pause) And as they carried these prayer sticks down, well, the water started receding, and it didn't rise anymore till they reached the bottom. Then the water stopped, and it stayed, and then it got dryer and dryer and so in place of those two children that were sacrificed, they became rocks and those are the two rocks you see up close to Towayalane.

'That's the way I heard it, you know, from my grandparents and parents. I guess they had a legend about the sacrifice offering they had to make of this boy and girl that formed those two rocks up there. That's what I have been told.'

The story of course had great symbolic meaning like 'Water Jar Boy', speaks to as many listeners and was open to as many interpretations. It obviously had great meaning for Kuiceyetsa, as my students's story of the origin of his clan had for him, and, judging by its persistence over centuries, a similar degree of meaning for Zuni and Zunis in general.

It also had and has great meaning for the collector.

Earlier, Helen – Kuiceyetsa's daughter, she who arranged for a tribal bone presser to treat me after my disabling back surgery and give me a reason to return from illness and pain, she who personally treated Kathy's crushed foot for four hours with psychic massage after her terrible automobile accident and gave her temporary relief and lasting hope, she whom I loved and with whom Kathy and I shared much laughter and many tears, she whom I gave a pseudonym based upon Poe's poem never knowing her end would be as dark as her name's source – led Kathy and me on a hike to the place traditionally considered best for viewing Boy and Girl Rock after my surgery and before Kathy's accident. It was a long, slow climb up the steep trail, and I had trouble keeping up with Helen and Kathy. I stopped to catch my breath, and looked back at the village below. Kathy stopped. When Helen saw that we had stopped, she stopped, too, and turned toward us with a quizzical expression. Kathy pointed toward the village and said, 'There sure is a good view of the town from here.'

Helen looked and said, 'Yeah, you can see the village from here; I hadn't noticed. Come on. Here we are.' We followed her up a low mound of earth to the spot and looked and realised the hike had been, consciously or unconsciously, timed to arrive at this spot at this moment. Boy and Girl Rock towered over the plain as they stood alongside the sheer, steep face of Towayalane framed by other rock formations in the foreground against the golden blue sky bathed at the perfect angle in the holy, ethereal luminosity that is Western light. 'But,' Helen said as she pointed toward them and smiled, 'this is sure the place to see Zuni.'

The end of the story? First Max, then Kuiceyetsa, died. Zuni power shifted, Helen disappeared, the granddaughter went into exile. A part of me died with Max and Kuiceyetsa. A part of me was lost with Helen. I, too, am exiled. Yet – Boy and Girl Rock still stand in that aching purity of light that is forever. Through this book, their story is to be read again. By those readings, readers insure that the story is remembered but also assure that Kuiceyetsa and Max are not forgotten, that Helen is not lost, that the little girl and the woman she became remain, that love is enough and all that is, that Zuni is a part of me still, that Zuni becomes a part of them now. That is the end of the story about the story. It is about time. After three books and many tellings, I lay it down and return it to the light.

Each narrative in the book is undergirded by similar contexts and stories of interactions of performers and audiences, cultures and personalities, collectors and informants, long dead – and by contents with similar deep personal and cross-cultural appeal and meaning – and waits silently with infinite patience for readers to experience it and their relationships with it. Each story embodies a world view and way of life and relationships recorded by their teller and collectors. They are flesh made word. The tales evince and call forth a world view that all the Western world separates into sets of twos – holy and unholy, substance and dream, conscious and unconscious – is one.

Helen and the American Indian view of the unity of all things, furthermore included time as well as objects and substances as a part of 'all' and recognised and lived the collective unconscious as well as the unconscious and the conscious in it their worlds, world views and stories – all one.

Stories of giants, monsters, mermen, cannibals, talking animals – and hunger. Stories of individuals, families, clans, tribes – and a vast cast of legendary and mythic heroes. Sex, violence, cruelty, crudity, magic, mystery, majesty – twilight tales unfolding lives and dreams in a narrative universe.

Story worlds. The logic of dreams. Water Jar Boys, rolling heads and walking skeletons. Memories, sensations, images, hopes, fears past and future. Dream, not-dream in which all lives.

It's all there waiting for readers to quicken it.

Enter the dream.

KEITH CUNNINGHAM
Professor of English and Folklore
Northern Arizona University

American Indians: Folk Tales and Legends

CHAPTER 1

Abenaki

Heroic Deeds of Glooscap

Glooscap, who seems to have been a spiritual knight-errant, found, on descending the St John, that a beaver of enormous size and of bad disposition had built a dam across the river at the Falls. His pond included Kennebeccasis Bay, where his house was. In order to put an end to his evil doings, Glooscap seized his handspike, 'Split Rock,' which is yet to be seen, broke down the dam, and killed the beaver and all of his family, with the exception of one which had escaped up river some hundreds of miles. He threw two rocks in the river to head him off. These are now known by the Indians as the 'Tobique Rocks'.

About half a mile below Boar's Head you will see in the cliff the form of a man's head surrounded by curly hair. This is Glooscap's image, and it was here that he first came to the St John River, when he went down to destroy the beaver's dam. Not far from the mouth of the St John, on the shore of the Bay of Fundy, between Manawagonish and the mouth of the Musquash, Glooscap left his pack, and when he came back to look for it he found a sable gnawing at it. Now you can see this pack turned to a great rock, in which is the hole made by the sable. Glooscap also killed a great moose below Lubec, in the State of Maine, and you can yet see all of its entrails turned to stone.

We used to go down the river in our canoes to Lepreau for cranberries in the autumn, and as we were passing Glooscap's face and head we always threw tobacco into the water as an offering, so that we might have a calm time going and returning.

Why the Porcupine and Toad Have No Noses

The turtle, who was Glooscap's uncle, becoming proud of his prowess, had induced the porcupine and toad to join in with him in opposition to Glooscap. To frustrate the doings of these councils, Glooscap turned himself into an old squaw. After entering the door, he saw another squaw in the shape of a porcupine sitting on one side, while another in the shape of a toad sat opposite. Turning to the porcupine, he said, 'What does all this mean?'

To which the reply was made, that it was not worthwhile for him to know. So, thrusting out his hand, with two of his fingers he took off the porcupine's nose. He then in a rage passed over to the toad, when, receiving the same reply, he treated her in a similar manner. This is the reason why you see no nose on either of these animals.

So soon as Glooscap was gone, the porcupine said to the toad, 'Where is your nose?' Whereupon the toad, looking at the porcupine, said, 'Where is yours?' Upon which they both concluded that it was Glooscap with whom they had been speaking.

CHAPTER 2

Achomawi

Pine Marten Marries the Bead Sisters

The two Bead girls were sent by their mother to marry Cocoon Man's son. He was wrapped up and put away. He had never been outside, and had never eaten anything. The Bead sisters came from a place far off in the ocean. They came on the water, brought by the wind, and they always sang the song of the wind. It took just one day for them to reach Cocoon Man's house. His daughters liked the two girls and gave them food. All the men were out hunting, and the daughters sent the two girls into the sweat house and told them to sit by Pine Marten's bed.

They could not get Cocoon Man's son, the one their mother had sent them for. Cocoon Man would not listen to it, so they took Pine Marten, and stayed three days with him. At the end of that time they wanted to go home. Pine Marten asked all his people for blankets and shells to give his wives to carry home. They started. Cocoon Man made a trail to the west to walk on. He sent his words out west, put his hand out west and east to make a trail, and immediately it was open. Cocoon Man sat on the ground in the centre, and made a rainbow reaching from the place where he sat to the home of the girls.

The company started. Weasel went with Pine Marten up to the top of the rainbow, and the women went under it. While they were travelling, Weasel made a flute out of a reed, and made sweet music that sounded through the world and was heard by every living being.

The two sisters walked on the lower rainbow, the reflection, and reached home safely. Next year Pine Marten had children. He made a boy of bead shells, and from a round shell which he threw into his wife a girl was born. In the spring of the second year, he came back on the same trail that Cocoon Man had made. His children grew very fast. Then he left his boy at home, and sent his girl to her grandmother in the ocean. The boy stayed with Cocoon Man. The third year he had two sons and two daughters.

Now Pine Marten's wife took one son and one daughter to her mother in the ocean; and Pine Marten kept one son and one daughter, and they lived with him at Fall River.

Kangaroo Rat Races with Coyote and Others

Two Kangaroo Rat women, a mother and her daughter, lived near Coyote's place. Now the people at this place hunted all the time, but never sent any meat to the old woman. She said, 'It is best to get a man to hunt for us. I do not like these people; they are too proud.' Her daughter said, 'I will run a race with these men, and I'll bet myself against a man. I'll win and have a husband.'

The next morning the girl went over to Coyote's house when the men were just through breakfast. She went on top of the sweat-house and called out, 'I want to run a race with one of your boys; today I feel like running.'

Coyote said, 'All right. The chief men always run first. I will run with you first.' He went out, and they started towards the north, and ran until he fell down dead.

The girl came home, and that night Cocoon Man said, 'I know what she is trying to do. When women want to marry us, they always kill us first. These are bad women.'

Next day she came to the house and asked again to run with a man.

Badger ran with her. He ran northward, turned to come back, reached a mountain-top, and died. Next day Silver Fox went out to run with her. He ran far to the north, came back halfway, and fell dead. Ground Squirrel ran, came halfway home, and died. Kangaroo Rat was coming home slowly. She came more slowly each time. First she had always returned in the middle of the morning, but this time she was back about noon. The mother thought, 'My daughter will fail. I am afraid she gets tired too easily.' The girl ran the next day with Wolf, but he died, and she reached home still later.

Now she had killed all but three men. Pine Marten ran the next day. They kept together. The girl thought he was going to win; but when he came into the valley and almost reached home, he fell dead. The last men left were Weasel and his brother from the mountain. They were angry because Pine Marten had been killed. They were going to take an otter-skin quiver. One of the brothers was to rest in it; so when the other became tired, this one would jump out and carry the tired one. When then the other one had rested and was fresh, he would jump out and take his turn. Thus they would run and carry each other alternately. The two looked just alike, and the girl thought she was running with one. The mountain brother of Weasel sang. They ran near the girl all the time. They found the bones of Coyote, picked them up, and put them in the otter skin quiver. They came to the other bones and picked them up also. While they were picking up the bones, the girl, thinking she had beaten Weasel, turned and looked back. He called out, 'Don't look back. I can outrun you. Girls cannot run fast.' She was frightened at his words, and ran on as fast as possible. When one brother was tired, the other one came out, and the first went into the quiver. Weasel called out, 'Run fast, I am going to beat you.' Now the girl began to give out. While Weasel was running, she thought she noticed a difference in the song, and looked back. He called out, 'Go on fast!' It was near sundown now. The old woman saw them coming. The two Weasel brothers as one, reached the sweat house first. The young women went with them to their sweat house and did not go back to her mother. That evening they put the bones in water, and the food all came to life. The girl went in the morning to her mother's house to get roots, and the men went hunting. She always sent plenty of meat to her mother after that.

CHAPTER 3

Acoma

The Flaming Horse

A man had eleven sons and he said to them, 'Seven suns from today I shall divide my property among you.' The youngest son was stupid. He went to his oldest brother and he said, 'When is seven suns, and from where does he come?'

'Seven suns is coming from the east.'

The youngest brother did not want his oldest brother to see that he did not understand, so he said, 'I am going out to meet him. When our father divides his property, take charge of my share until I return.'

The youngest son started out on his trip. He went to the east. On his way he met Chief Barefoot. He asked the boy where he was going. 'I am going to meet Seven Suns.'

'Well, in six more suns it will be here. It is coming right down this road. Why do you want to find this Seven Suns?'

'My father is to divide his property in seven suns and I am going to meet it. I could not wait for it and I am on the road.' Chief Barefoot wished him good luck and they went on.

They met another man who asked him where he was going. 'I am on my way to meet Seven Suns.'

'Why do you want to meet this Seven Suns?'

'My father is to divide his property in seven suns and I am going to meet it.' They told each other goodbye and the boy went on. He travelled for a long time.

He came to Chief Black Cloud. Chief Black Cloud had a daughter, Yellow Corn. All the men came to present themselves to be chosen as a husband for his daughter. Yellow Corn did not choose any of them. She turned them all away. Chief Black Cloud was tired of this, and he said to his daughter, 'You have turned away too many men. The next man who comes, whether he is rich or poor, wise or foolish, you must marry him.' The next man who came to Chief Black Cloud's was the youngest son. The Chief said to him. 'Would you like to marry my daughter?'

'I was looking for a job. Is that the job you have for me? Yes, I can marry your daughter.'

'All right, we'll see what my daughter says.' They went into the house and called his daughter. All the Chief's men were there, and Chief Black Cloud said to them, 'This is the husband for my daughter.'

His daughter said, 'Yes, I will marry him if he will answer three questions.'

The Chief's men said, 'Yes, he shall answer three questions.'

The Chief's daughter asked him the first question. She said, 'Where is the beginning of the fountain (i.e. of its basin) and where is its end?'

The boy answered and said, 'That is a hard question. Let me think today and tonight, and in the morning I will answer your question.' The council agreed and they separated until the morning. The boy paid no attention to the question that he had to answer. When night came they told him to take his blankets and go on the roof to sleep. They did not ask him to stay in the neat, clean rooms of the house. He climbed the ladder and went to sleep. He slept all night. Toward morning he awoke and he heard a large and a small bird talking on the edge of the roof. The larger bird said, 'That is not a hard question. The fountain is a circle. The starting place is the ending place, and that is all there is to it.'

The boy got out of his blankets and climbed down the ladder. He washed his face and hands and got ready for breakfast. They ate breakfast and the council was called together. They met in the council room. They said, 'Can you answer the question: "Where is the beginning of the fountain and where is its end?" ' The boy gave the answer he had learned from the birds. So the question was answered and the Chief's daughter asked him the second question: 'When the Chief's wife, my mother, died, where was she buried, and when the Chief wept at the grave which eye dropped the first tear?'

The boy said, 'This is a hard question. Let me think today and tonight, and in the morning I shall answer.' The council agreed and they separated until the morning.

All day the boy worked around the place. At night they told him to take his blankets and sleep on the roof. He climbed the ladder and slept all night. He did not think of the question once. Early in the morning the boy woke; and he heard the large and the small bird talking on tile edge of the roof. The big bird said, 'It is a hard question because the boy did not see where the Chief's wife was buried. It was in the right-hand corner of this house under the foundation, and when the Chief wept, it was his right eye dropped the first tear.'

The boy got out of his blankets and climbed down the ladder. He washed and they ate breakfast. The council met in the council room. They said,

'Can you answer the second question: "Where was the Chief's wife buried and when the Chief wept, which eye dropped the first tear?" '

The boy answered, 'The Chief's wife was buried at the right-hand corner of this house under the foundation, and when the Chief wept it was his right eye dropped the first tear.'

So the second question was answered, and the Chief's daughter said, 'You have answered two questions. The third question is to find my youngest sister and to bring her home.'

The boy said, 'Let me have today and tonight, and in the morning I will answer.' He did not think once of the question and at night he took his blankets and went up onto the roof to sleep. He slept till morning, and when he woke he heard the birds talking on the edge of the roof. The large bird said, 'It is a hard thing to find the Chief's younger daughter. A giant stole her. He lives a long way off in the caves in the mountain. Anyone who brings her back will need a fast horse and a big horse. This boy has eleven horses but they are all small. It will take at least a year for them to grow large enough and to learn to run fast enough.'

The boy took his blankets and climbed down the ladder. He washed and they ate breakfast. The council met in the council room. They said, 'Can you answer the third question?'

He said, 'The youngest sister was carried off by a giant who keeps her in his den. Anyone who brings her back will need a fast horse and a big horse.'

The Chief said, 'Have you such a horse?'

'I don't know. I shall have to go home and see.'

The boy left the Chief's home. He travelled for a week and came to his own home. His father was dead and buried and his oldest brother had held the boy's share until he returned. The youngest son's share was eleven mares and one stallion. The boy went out to see them. All the mares had little colts. He called the stallion Demon.

He was very large. He came up to the boy and said to him, 'I am not large enough this year. Do what I tell you, and by next year I shall be large enough. Kill all the colts. Cut their heads off so that I can drink their blood. Then I shall grow large. On this very day come back again next year.' The boy did as he was told. He went back to his brothers and told them he would be back again in a year.

He returned to Chief Black Cloud's. The Chief said to him, 'Have you found your horse?'

The boy answered, 'Yes. I have found the horse but it is not large enough to fetch your daughter. In another year he will be full grown.' The boy worked for Chief Black Cloud for a year. At the end of that time he went back to his home. He said to his brothers, 'I am going to give each of you one of the mares but the stallion I will keep.' He went up to where they were pastured. Each mare had a new colt. The stallion told him to kill these colts also so that he could drink of the blood. He did so. Then the stallion told him to ask of his brothers a saddle and a bridle and a saddle blanket. His brothers were glad to give him these in exchange for the mares.

The youngest son went back to Chief Black Cloud's and worked for another year. When the time had passed he returned to his home. The stallion was now full grown. He was so large the boy could stand up under him. He had the blacksmith fit shoes for the horse and the saddle-maker fit a saddle and bridle for him. When he was furnished with everything he needed, he mounted the stallion and rode to Chief Black Cloud's. He stabled his horse. The Demon was so large and dangerous that he had to order the Chief's men to take all their horses out of the stable.

The boy said to the Chief, 'I am ready to go to get your daughter, Little Flower.' The Chief was glad and asked him to start at once. Next day the youngest son mounted his horse and went in search of Little Flower. The stallion knew where the giant's home was, and he galloped off. He shook the earth, and dust and rocks flew behind his heels. When they had gone half way, the Demon stopped and told the boy what he should do. He was to ride into the den as fast as he could. The stallion was to stop only long enough for the boy to pick Little Flower up and ride away again out of reach of the giant.

In the afternoon they reached the giant's cave. They rode in as fast as they could. Little Flower was among many other women who had been captured by the giant. The boy set her on the back of the Demon and they rode out of the cave like lightning. Behind the Demon's hoofs immense rocks fell and blocked the way of the giant.

That evening they arrived at Chief Black Cloud's. They welcomed the sister and had a great feast next day. People said it was the wedding feast, but Yellow Corn would not marry him until he had found a horse for her that would be the equal of his stallion. She wanted to ride a horse just like his.

There was no horse on earth like the Demon, but in the underworld was the Flaming Horse. The Demon told the boy to ask for two large boxes to place on either side of the saddle, two sacks of pitch, two bags of flint arrow points, half a deer's carcass, a bale of deers' hides, and a sack of oats, wheat and corn. 'Tell the Chief you must go far away to get the Flaming Horse and you need these for your food.'

The boy went to the Chief and told him what he needed. 'If you will give me these things, I will go at once and bring the other horse for your daughter.' The Chief gave him all that he needed. The next day the boy got ready. He saddled his horse and started on his trip. Everyone watched him as he started out.

He travelled a long way until he came to the entrance of the underworld. It was in the side of a mountain. His horse spoke to him and said, 'There are birds guarding this horse, and they bring him warning if anyone comes. When you see them, scatter the grain on each side so that the birds will be busy picking it up. They will forget to fly back with the message. Beyond that there are lions and bears and wolves that guard his den. When you come to them take the meat that you carry and throw off small pieces. Every now and then, throw off a deer's hide for the animals to feast on. When you have passed these animals, we shall be safe. I will give a loud whinny and the Flaming Horse will answer me.'

They heard a sound like a great wind. The boy saw that it was the birds that were coming. He scattered grain on either side and the birds stopped to eat the grain. They went on and came to the wild animals. The horse did not stop. The boy threw pieces of meat and deer's hide so that the wild beasts ate these and the boy and the horse passed through unharmed. They travelled all night. In the morning the horse whinnied but there was no answer except echo. They went on again. The Demon stopped and whinnied a second time. They heard a very faint answer. The Demon said to the boy, 'We will go on a little farther and I will tell you where to stop. At that place get off and take the bags of flint and the pitch. Spread the pitch around me in a large circle and scatter the flint thickly over it. Take off my bridle, and hide yourself, so that the Flaming Horse will not see you. When he comes, the battle will take place inside the circle of pitch. From my nostrils I will blow my flame twice toward the circle of pitch. If the second time the pitch does not ignite, the Flaming Horse will kill us both. If it catches fire he will call out. Then you will take this bridle and slip it over his head and he will be gentle enough to handle. He is as large as I am, and no one can tell us apart.'

The answers of the Flaming Horse came closer and closer. The Demon told the boy to make the circle of pitch and flint around him. He grazed inside of the circle. The Flaming Horse came like the wind, kicking and rearing on his hind legs. He dashed into the circle and the two horses fought there. The Demon blew fire from his nostrils but the pitch did not ignite. A second time he blew fire from his nostrils and the flame rose in a circle around the two horses. The Flaming Horse called out in sign that he was overcome. The boy came up and put the bridle upon him. The Flaming Horse said to him, 'I have a master now. I will do whatever you say and I will go with you gladly.'

The boy mounted the Flaming House and started back to Chief Black Cloud. The two stallions were exactly alike. No one could tell them apart. They travelled for a day and a night and they reached the house of the Chief. Everyone came out to look at the beautiful pair of horses. The Chief made another stable for the Flaming Horse, and he said to his daughter, 'Are you willing now to marry this boy?' Yellow Corn answered, 'No, not yet. I will play hide-and-seek with him and if I can't find him when he hides twice, I will marry him.'

They played hide-and-seek. Yellow Corn went to hide. They covered the boy's head and Yellow Corn made tracks all over the pasture and the corn fields and the gardens and in the orchards and then into the house. She called him. The boy followed her tracks but he could not find her. He went to his horses. He said to them, 'I am playing hide-and-seek to marry the Chief's daughter. Tell me where she is hidden.'

Flaming Horse said to him, 'Go and get a bow and arrow from one of the Chief's men. Take it to the shore of the lake and shoot at the beautiful swan that you see there.' The boy did what the horse told them.

He asked one of the Chief's men for his bow and arrows and went out to the lake. He called out, 'I am going to shoot that beautiful swan for my dinner.'

Immediately the Chief's daughter hopped out of the water and said, 'Don't shoot me!'

The boy said, 'All right, you may hide again.'

They covered the boy's head and the girl made her tracks all over the pasture and the corn fields and the orchards and then into the house. The second time the boy followed her trail but he could not find her. He went to his horses. The Demon said to him, 'Go into the kitchen. On the table you will see four loaves of bread. Pick up the second loaf from the south. Take a knife and sharpen it and while you are whetting it say, "I am going to have a slice of fine bread." ' The boy went into the house and into the kitchen.

He said, 'I wonder where that girl went. I'm getting hungry.' He picked up a knife and a stone to sharpen it on. When it was very sharp he picked up the second loaf of bread from the south end of the table, and he said, 'I am going to have a slice of fine bread.' Just then, the girl jumped out of the loaf of bread in his hands.

It was his turn to hide. He made his tracks in and out of the fields and went to the Demon. 'Can you hide me so that the Chief's daughter cannot find me?' The Demon turned the boy into a fly and the fly flew into the nostrils of the horse. He called the girl. The fly was so small that his voice sounded very far away. The girl hunted a long time and could not find him. At last she went to the stable where the horses were.

She said, 'I think that fellow is in here somewhere.' She was afraid to go near the horses because they were dangerous.

She gave up. The boy came out of the stable and said, 'All right. Once more.' They covered the girl's head and the boy made his tracks in and out of the field. He went to his horses, and the Flaming Horse hid the boy under his front hoof. He called to the girl. She hunted for him everywhere. At last she went to the stable. The horses were standing very quietly and she examined the stable and the horses. Because they were so gentle she thought the boy was not there and she named him Arrowhead Boy.

She called, 'I can't find you. Come out.' She was still standing by the horse.

The boy spoke and said, 'Here I am. Are you willing to marry me?'

She answered, 'Yes.' Yellow Corn chose the Flaming Horse, and Arrowhead Boy chose the Demon.

Next morning the council met in the council room. The Chief's daughter and Arrowhead Boy set the wedding day in four days. They had a great feast, and made a fine saddle and bridle for the Flaming Horse. The two married each other by riding their horses around the village.

Kaupata

In those days they invented all the games for gambling. They played at a kind of quoits. But they grew tired of gambling in this fashion and they invented the stick race. The good runners liked the stick race, but those who could not run wanted another game. They invented 'toss'.

But they grew tired of this game, and they invented hidden ball. They staked their lives on hidden ball. They sang all night and in the morning at the end of four days the winners took their great flint knives from around their necks and cut a slit in the earth. The losers fell into the cavity and were lost.

Every day the Sun watched them playing hidden ball. He was angry because so many people were losing their lives. He called his only son and he said to him, 'Make yourself ready and visit the earth.' He took him to a place where sharp thorns grew and he thrust his hands upon the thorns so that blood dripped from his hands. Everywhere his blood dripped it coloured the rocks and they are used as paint by the Indians. The Sun gave his son a bundle of one hundred straws cut evenly at the ends and four cylinders with which to play hidden ball. He gave him also the ball to hide. He said, 'Take these with you to the earth and show them how to gamble. Teach them not to gamble for human lives, but only for ornaments and valuable things. Do to these katcinas, the gamblers, what they have done to others. On the first four games that you play stake the lives that they have already won. Your cousin, the Moon, and I will help you.'

Tsutea started down and came to the earth. He travelled for many days and came to the far north. The gamblers were gathered in the kiva gambling. He sat at the hatchway and watched the game. He held carefully the gambling outfit the Sun had given him. From the hatchway he called down to them in which cylinder the ball was hidden. He was always right and the katcinas called him in, saying, 'Who are you who always guess the hidden ball? Come down and play with us.'

They hid the ball, but he said, 'Let us play a new game. Let us play four times and stake the lives that you have won.'

The gamblers whispered to each other and said, 'He is young. He will soon lose his life.' They started a new game.

They played four times. The gamblers gave the boy the ball to hide first and he sang his gambling song. They did not know any of the songs that he sang, and they laughed at him. He held the ball and sang his four songs while the men were holding the curtain to shield him. The fourth song was stranger than all the rest and the katcinas thought to themselves, 'Perhaps he has supernatural power?' He won that game. All the games that he played he won. He won back the lives of all the peoples that had been destroyed by earthquake and he brought them back to life. When they crawled out of the ground, they looked like rabbits. They became people.

In the morning just at sunrise he won the fourth game. He said to the katcinas, 'Hereafter do not gamble for lives. Gamble for valuable articles, and use a bundle of a hundred straws to keep track of your games.' So he laid down the rules of hidden ball.

The Sun's son set out to find the most dangerous of all the supernatural gamblers. His name was Kaupata. He travelled many days and he came to his house. Kaupata was gambling. He received him kindly, and gave him food. The gambler placed an herb in the food he gave to his visitors so that their minds grew weaker and weaker and they lost the game. Tsutea, however, had a secret belt around his waist and he slipped into it the gambler's food. After they had eaten Kaupata offered him cigarettes. The boy substituted his own cigarette and smoked it. Kaupata mixed this same herb in the cigarettes he offered to visitors, so that they could not win the game. Kaupata said, 'Why have you come here?'

'I have come to gamble with you.'

'Yes. Let us gamble.' Each of them wanted to use his own gambling outfit. At last they agreed to use the Sun's child's cylinders for the first games, and then to use Kaupata's. They gambled all night with the Sun's son's cylinders and Kaupata lost everything. First he staked the lives of people he had destroyed and he had to bring them back to life. He tried to win back what he had lost and he staked his whole country. He lost that and he tried to win it back by staking his house. He lost that and he tried to win it back by staking his clothing. He lost that and he tried to win it back by staking his household goods. He lost and he staked his moccasins, then his blankets, then one leg, then both legs, then one arm, then the other arm, and last of all, he staked his eyes.

He lost and the Sun's child said to Kaupata, 'I will not take your life away. I have won everything. And all that I will do is to dig out your eyes. You might be useful in some way without eyes.' He dug out the gambler's eyes and threw them up to the sky as stars and when the children look through a certain hole in the rock they look up to the sky and see his two eyes shining there. Sun's child told everyone who had been watching the game to take something out of Kautpata's house and he said to them, 'This game shall not be played for human lives. You will stake only ornaments and valuable things.' So the people took everything from Kaupata. All that was left was a powerful torch which was hidden in the ceiling between two rafters.

Kaupata was blind. He crept around his house trying to find his torch. He searched for it and found it where he had put it. He took his flint and struck fire. He sang his supernatural song and set fire to pitch from the piñon trees. He stirred the burning pitch and set his house on fire. He stirred it round and round and the lava flowed in both directions to the north and west.

The birds tried to put a stop to the burning earth. Crow was snow white. He tried to beat out the fire with his wings and he was changed by the heat till he became black. Eagle also was snow white, and the smoke changed his feathers to its own colour. Kowata went too close to the flames also, and the fire coloured his wings and tail red. Buzzard led the attack of the birds upon the fire and the heat burned off the feathers on his head and made the feathers on his body black. Hummingbird flew around the great waters to the north, west, south and east, to rouse the tides to put out the fire. He flew through the rainbow and for this reason the hummingbird wears the colours of the rainbow in the feathers around his neck. The clouds came from every direction. The hail fell on the burning lava rock, but it could not cool the terrible heat. Rain fell and the lava rock stopped flowing and the fire was put out.

There was a witch who was married to a husband who did not belong to the witches. Every night the witches met in their cave in the rocks and her companions scolded her saying, 'Every night you are late because you have to wait for your husband to fall asleep. How can we have our meeting?' The witch was in love with one of the handsome men who belonged to the witches.

That night her husband only pretended to sleep and he followed her to the meeting place. He listened and he heard them planning to kill him so that his wife could be more prompt to the meeting. The magic of the witches would not work and at last they were suspicious and they said, 'Someone is watching us.' They sent the witch woman out to look. She stepped on her husband.

'Who is that?'

'I am your husband.'

'Come with me!' She took her husband before the witches' council. They made him sleep and gave him to his wife to lead away. She took him to every cave in the mountains. She said, 'Is there a room for my husband so that I can put him to bed?' and she answered as if the answer came from inside the cliff, 'No, there is no room.' At last she came to a cave and she said, 'Is there a room for my husband?' And it answered, 'Yes, there is a room for your husband.' She left him there on the cliff in a cave from which he could not get down.

Next morning he woke. He was in great trouble. He called for help, and nearby the chipmunks heard him. They said to one another, 'I hear a call.'

The youngest chipmunk said, 'I see a man sitting on a cliff, crying for help.' All the chipmunks went out to see what they could do. They climbed up to the ledge where he was.

They said to him, 'What is it that you wish?'

'Is there any way to get down this precipice? I am thirsty and hungry and I cannot move.'

The chipmunks said, 'We will feed you and give you water. Do not fear; in some way we will help you down.' They went back to their home and brought an acorn cup. They filled it with water and carried it up the cliff. The man laughed when he saw the tiny cup. They said, 'You cannot drink all the water that we have brought you.' He put it to his lips and drank and drank. He could not drink all the water in the acorn cup. Every day the chipmunks brought him nuts and water. At the foot of the cliff they planted a cottonwood tree. They pulled and pulled it so that it would grow fast. On the fourth day it had grown as high as the ledge. He climbed down the cottonwood tree. The chipmunks said to him, 'Your wife is living with her witch sweetheart. Go to Spider Woman and she will tell you what you are to do.'

He went to Spider Woman. She said to him. 'On the fourth day your wife has planned to call the whirlwind. It would have blown you off the cliff and killed you. Take these two herbs. When you find your wife and her lover, take one of these herbs and paint the crowns of their heads and the centres of the soles of their feet and the middle of the palms of their hands. Do not be afraid that they will wake up. When you have finished, pull their arms away from each other and sprinkle the second herb over their bodies.'

He found his wife and her lover and did as Spider Woman had told him. In the morning when they woke they had been changed. They were both ugly. The witch woman seized hold of her sweetheart's hand, but she could not let go for the paint that her husband had used was a spell to hold them together. They tried to talk and they could not. They set off toward

Acoma. They met a man. They ran to him and begged him in dumb-show to pull them apart. As soon as he had touched them he stuck to them also. They went on toward Acoma. Whenever they met anyone, this man called out, 'Help! Pull me away!' But everyone who touched them was stuck fast. They went on toward Acoma in a long string. The people at Acoma came out and drove them away.

They wandered out across the desert. They came upon old blind Kaupata looking for a home. They laid hold of him and he was stuck to them. Wherever they went he had to follow along. When they lay down to sleep they had to lie in a row. They said, 'We will go to the village of the katcinas. Perhaps they can pull us apart.' When they had come there the katcinas laid hold of them and separated them.

The people asked to make their home there but the katcinas said, 'No, you are too ugly. Go back into the world. Wherever your voices come back to you (echo) that shall be your home.'

Kaupata directed them to his home. When they had come into the midst of the black lava there, one of the men shouted at the top of his voice. His voice came back to him and they said, 'This is our home.' The witch woman changed herself into a deer and all the men began to build homes for themselves. Their footprints are still to be seen in the lava beds.

The Kobictaiya Are Challenged to the Test of Lightning

Long ago when giants were still on the earth, a giant was walking among the red cliffs southeast of Acoma. Yellow Woman was hunting there, and he saw her. He followed her till she took refuge from him in a cave in the rocks. Patuchima saw the giant waiting for her to come out of the cave. He took his long flint knife and went down to save Yellow Woman. He threw his flint knife, and it struck the giant and cut off his head. Yellow Woman was terribly frightened, and Patuchima took her to his own house till she should recover from her fear.

Now when the masked dancers knew that Patuchima had had Yellow Woman in his houses they accused him and said that he had lost his power. Patuchima said no, he had not had intercourse with her. They agreed to put it to the test by Lightning. On the fourth day they went to call upon the Lightning to strike him, and if he had lost his power, Lightning would strike him dead.

Patuchima went out into the desert looking for a horned toad and a mud turtle. On the fourth day he took them with him to the contest. The clouds came from all directions and the Lightning flashed and the Thunder rolled. The clouds came nearer and nearer. Patuchima stood up waiting for the Lightning; his right foot was on the mud turtle, and his left upon the horned toad. Therefore the Lightning struck all about him but could not hit him.

Then Patuchima challenged the Kobictaiya to prove that his power was still his and that he had not slept with Yellow Woman.

When the fourth day came the Kobictaiya gathered in their kiva. They thought that they were hidden from the Lightning because they were underground, but Lightning wound itself around the ladder of their kiva and tore their bodies to bits and scattered them in every direction. After Lightning came a terrible Thunder; then a second Thunder which drew the scattered bits together. When they came to life, they were all pieced together wrong, a red body with a white arm, one green leg and one yellow one, one leg that was half one colour and half another. So Patuchima overcame the Kobictaiya.

This is why in the November ceremonies, the Kobictaiya, come painted pi-fashion. They do not dance, but come from the rocks to the east, and just about sunrise they climb to the top of the mesa up the south way by the stone steps. They bring gifts to their relatives, the people of Acoma.

The Windows of the Fox

In the beginning the trees touched each other in the forest and all the birds sang the same songs and the animals were all of one family. Each was appointed to separate over the earth and to each was given his own work. The birds were appointed to carry the seeds to drop over the earth, and to sing to make people happy in the morning and the evening. The rat and the bear and the squirrel were appointed to stow grain and nuts so that there would always be food. The woodchuck and gopher were appointed to make valleys to let air and sun into the earth. Butterflies were appointed to lead children home when they wandered away, and homes for the eagles were in the highest rocks that they might watch for enemies and warn of coming danger. But to the deer and the rabbit were given the hardest task: to furnish food for the animals by giving up their own lives.

One day the clouds gathered from all directions and met over the great plain. Lightning flashed and blinded the animals, and when the storm was over, in the middle of the plain, they saw a man standing. He was red like baked clay. The animals said to each other, 'What is that?' The man shook his fists at the clouds and they hurried away across the sky. The animals came close and formed a wall around him. They gave strange cries, but he did not move. They said, 'We will set a guard and watch him by turns.' They appointed the bear. When night came the snow began to fall. The bear looked at the man and saw that he had lain down to sleep. Bear went off to his winter cave and did not return until the spring. In the daytime the man walked about and studied the foot prints of the animals. He watched them kill a deer and eat it. He also killed a deer and grew fat. He followed the squirrels and stole their nuts so that the animals were often hungry. He put the skin of the deer on his back and made himself warm at night. The mountain lion screamed at him from the trees but Man laughed at him and scared him away.

At last Man wanted a wife. He took slabs of stone and set them up in a line so that the animals could not see him. He took yellow flowers and painted pictures on the stones. He took cactus flowers and painted purple pictures on them. He took green stone and ground it together. He made green paint and painted green faces on them. He took white clay, and black charcoal from the fire, and painted them black and white. He went to a tree that had been struck by lightning and got fire. He carried it to a hole that he had dug before his altar.

Eagle came to see what he was doing. The man choked him, took out his tail feathers and put them in his hair. He gathered pollen from the flowers. He filled his mouth with the pollen and spewed it out into the wind, to the north, to the west, to the south and to the east. A sweet odour filled the air. He fasted for four days. On the fourth day he took an ear of corn. He gathered up the feathers that were scattered on the plain and bound them around the corn ear with the fibre of the soap-weed leaf. When it was finished he wrapped the ear of corn in deer skin and set it up at the foot of his altar. He lay down and fell into a deep sleep.

When he awoke there was a woman at his side. She said, 'I have come from the north where the white lights rise straight up into the sky. I am White Light Woman.' They went together to his house in the cliffs.

White Light Woman used her power to call the animals. She called the wild turkeys and the man killed them for their food. She called the deer, and they came and were killed. Whenever she used her power she made the man cover his head with the blanket so that he could not see what she did. She made him dance after every rite, and she laughed at him because of his dancing.

The animals were afraid because she hung their skins on the man and on herself, and stuck the feathers of the birds in their hair. They tried to spy on her, to see her power, but whenever anyone came near she knew; she called him into her magic circle and killed him. The animals and birds called a council. They sent Owl to spy on her. Owl went, but the sun shone on his big eyes and blinded him and the woman choked him. They sent Prairie Dog, but when he peeped out of his hole the woman saw him, and she sent Rattlesnake to live with him and warn her of his approach. They sent Horned Toad. He hopped to the edge of the cliff and lay flat on a stone and spied on her. She used her power and he fell off and was killed.

At last Fox went. He saw a dead deer lying on the plain. He waited for a storm, and when all the animals were in their dens, Fox crept inside the ribs of the deer. He could look out plainly. He lived on the deer meat and the storm covered his tracks. On the fourth day of the storm, White Light Woman came from her home in the cliffs. She brought with her strips of fur from all the different animals, and feathers from all the different birds, and laid them in front of the altar. She took a flint arrowhead from her neck and drew it four times across the fur of the deer and the feathers of the eagle. The nearest deer felt her power and was drawn down closer and closer until the man shot him with his arrow. She drew her flint arrowhead over the eagle feathers, and the nearest eagle felt her power and circled nearer and nearer until Man shot him with his arrow. In this way Fox learned the secret of her power. He called the animals and the birds together and he told them White Light Woman's power. He said, 'When you feel her power, run with all your might in the opposite direction and eat the pollen of all the flowers nearby.' So they spoiled White Light Woman's magic. After that Man had to hunt animals by following their tracks through the woods and across the plains. This is why the ribs of the deer are called 'the windows of the fox'. And for this reason, when we dance, we hang a fox skin at our belts or put it on our war poles, to mean that we are wiser than the fox because we wear his skin.

The Travels of Salt Woman

The people were living at Cipap. They set out to separate over the world. Salt Woman said, 'I shall travel anticlockwise around the earth, circling inward (spiral fashion) to its centre. Follow after me. Tell your children and your children's children that they will meet me again at a place called Acoma at the middle of the world.'

Salt Woman travelled. In the west she camped at a great salt lake. Wherever she camped she made a great salt lake. She travelled all around the world and became dirty as a Navajo. She came to a small pueblo and stopped there to rest. She went into the kiva with the men. There was no other woman with them in the kiva and the men said to her, 'Parch corn for us.'

'Gladly.' She parched the corn that they put into her hands. When she had parched it she washed her hands in the wash water. With a corn cob she sprinkled the wash water over the corn. It was good. Up to that time people had seasoned their food with alkali.

As soon as the men had eaten they said, 'We have never tasted corn like this.' They said to Salt Woman, 'Prepare all the corn that we have!

'Gladly.'

Next day she parched their corn. Two of the men of that society said to each other, 'How is it that this corn tastes so good? What does she do to it?' They hid themselves in the corner of the house where she parched the corn, covering themselves with blankets. They saw her take wash water and wash her hands. With the corncob she sprinkled the dirty water over the corn. The men went back to the kiva secretly and lay down on their stomachs in a far corner.

Salt Woman brought the parched corn into the kiva. They called to one another to taste the corn. They called to the two men who were lying on the floor, but they made no move to come and eat. They said, 'That corn is dirty. We saw her sprinkle it with the wash water.'

The war chief also wished her to parch corn for his family. He went to ask her. He told her what the two men had said about her. Salt Woman answered, 'Let it be brought before the kiva.' When evening came Salt Woman went to the kiva. They sat together for a while. The chief rolled native tobacco and wrapped it in a corn husk. He lit it and offered it to Salt Woman to smoke. She took it. She blew the smoke to the north, west, south and east, and she said. 'Whatever you want to know, I will answer willingly.'

The war chief said to her, 'Who are you?'

She answered, 'I am Salt Woman.' They recognised her.

The war chief said, 'Two of the members of our society watched you secretly. They saw that you washed your hands in the wash water and sprinkled the corn with it.'

'Yes. I have salted the corn. From now on without salt you will not enjoy your food. Now that you have tasted it you will not please your bodies without it. These two men that spied on me I will take with me on my journey and they shall serve me.' There were two brothers who offered to go with her also. The four men accompanied her.

Next day she set out on her travels. They reached Mots (Hopi). They were having a great ceremony there. Salt Woman and her four companions went from house to house. Nobody offered them any food. They were dirty and poor. While they were travelling all over the village, a girl of the pueblo saw them. She returned to her home and told her grandparents. Her grandfather said, 'Bring them into our house. We are poor, but we are glad to feed them. It may be one of our relatives that we are expecting at this place. Invite them to eat with us.' The girl went out and waited for them patiently outside the house. Salt Woman and her companions came and the girl took them inside. They treated them like relatives and set food before them. When they had eaten they said, 'Who are you?'

Salt Woman answered, 'I am Salt.' The grandfather wept that they had almost forgotten her. Salt Woman said, 'My other relatives did not greet me nor offer me food. You are my friends, but the others I shall destroy.'

Salt Woman went out of the house with her four companions. They went to the south where they had left their games and bows and arrows. All the children in the village followed them out of the village. Salt Woman said to them, 'Go back and bring whatever paint is in your houses and I will paint you for a game.' So she painted their bodies and faces with all the different colours. She chose a large willow tree and held down the top branches for the children to catch hold of. When the branches were full of children she let go of the branch and it lifted the children up into the air. They were all the different kinds and colours of birds.

They flew off and the people in the village saw how many birds there were and said, 'Something has happened down there where the children went.'

Salt Woman told her servants to play the game of shooting a ball with arrows. She said, 'Roll the ball toward the village and circle the pueblo. Then roll it into the centre of the dancers. Pretend to shoot at the ball but hit the big drum they are using for the dance.' Salt Woman kicked the ball in the direction they were to go. They circled the village. Everyone was watching the dancers and no one realised what was happening. They kicked the ball into the middle of the dancers and one of the arrows hit the big drum. As the arrow went through the head of the drum the whole tribe became rock. In this way Salt Woman destroyed the village.

She started out again on her travels with her four companions. As they went on, every day she grew larger and heavier. Salty sores appeared upon her body. She said to them, 'In four days we shall reach our home.' They went on for two days. The two brothers who were with her asked Salt Woman that they might go on ahead to look for water at the next camp. She said, 'Yes, you will find water.' They left the other two to be a guard for her.

When the brothers were returning, the older brother said, 'When we get to the top of this mesa I am going to throw my flint knife at her. I will call out to her to catch it and hold it steady.' The younger brother did not like this. He knew Salt Woman was very powerful. When they got to the top of the hill they saw the other approaching them. The older brother called out to Salt Woman to catch the knife. She reached up her hand and caught it. It did not knock her head off. The brother asked her to throw the club back at him.

'All right.' He stood as if to catch the flint knife. It cut off the heads of both brothers.

She said, 'I am sorry I have killed them.' She went up to them and put their bodies and heads together. She covered them with their blankets. They danced in a circle around the two and sang. When the song was ended the two men jumped up from under the blanket.

They said, 'We went to sleep.'

'My dear children, you were not asleep. I cut your heads off.'

'Never mind, mother, we did this on purpose to make red paint from our blood. The Indians shall come here and gather the red rock and grind it for paint for their faces and bodies in the dance.'

They went on till they reached Kominatsi (the salt lake in the Apache country near Acoma). Salt Woman said, 'This is my home. I cannot travel farther. Whoever comes here can read his fortune in the water.' She was salt. That is why medicine men put water in a pottery dish before their altars and read their fortunes in the water. And that is why whoever goes to the Salt Lake to be healed is well again.

Paiyatyamo and Yellow Woman

The cliff dwellers were living in the north. Among them there were three beautiful sisters who refused every man who came to marry them. Each one brought them presents, but when he had presented them the girls refused, saying, 'You did not bring what we wanted.'

In the east lived the Paiyatyamos. The eldest Paiyatyamo was the most beautiful man in the world. His breath was sweet as flowers. He set out to find these three sisters. The other Paiyatyamos said, 'No. Do not go. They are powerful and they will harm you.'

He answered, 'Yes. I am going. If I do not return in four days look for me.' He set out towards the north. He sang his songs (to attract women). He ornamented himself with blossoms. He mixed the petals of all flowers and ground them to powder on a stone. He took the powder in his mouth and spewed it to the north, to the west, to the south, to the east, wherever the sisters might be. He rubbed the powder on the palms of his hands and on his cheeks. He sang a song:

> For all's sake I start out. For all's sake I start out.
> I start out this morning from my home looking for women.
> For the sake of any girl, I am travelling.

He sang song after song until he reached the home of the sisters. His songs travelled ahead of him, and as he came closer he saw the sisters climb the ladder to the top of their house, looking in every direction. He came towards their house pretending that he did not see them. The three sisters were glad when they saw Sun Blossom, for everyone all over the country knew him because of his beauty. They said, 'We are lonesome for you, Paiyatyamo. We have heard of you, but we never saw you before.'

The oldest sister was in love with Paiyatyamo. She said to him, 'Let us play hide-and-seek.' She covered his head with a blanket. She made her tracks everywhere through the cornfields and the garden. She came back and took the form of a little beetle on the ground behind him. She crept under his blanket on his back. She lay there as a heavy weight so as to tire him out. She called to him. Paiyatyamo threw off his blanket to look for her. He followed her tracks around the cornfield. The weight of the woman (in the beetle form) tired him out and he gave up. He called out to her to appear, and the beetle dropped off in her own form, close beside him. 'Why couldn't you find me?'

'I don't know. It's my turn to hide. If you don't find me I will win your heart.' He covered her head with the blanket. He made his tracks around the bushes, backwards and forwards. He went up to his father, the Sun, and hid behind the big disk.

His father said to him, 'This is very dangerous. You must sit without moving for if you move she will see you. At noon I shall stay still in the middle of the sky. You must sit quiet for an hour, for then she can see any move that you make.' Paiyatyamo called out to the girl. Kotcininak threw off the blanket and looked for Paiyatyamo. She looked everywhere. She drew milk from her breast into a little shell and sat down to look into the milk. She could not find him on earth so at last she looked for him in the sky. The Sun warned Paiyatyamo that she was watching, but at last he had to change his position, and he peeped out from one side of the Sun.

Kotcininak saw him and she called out, 'I've found you! Come down from the Sun.'

The Sun was sad and said, 'My son, you will have to go to meet Kotcininak.' He came down and as he reached the earth she drew out the flint knife which she always carried and cut off his head. She cut open his body and took out the heart. She took the fluff of the cattail and wrapped it in it and placed it in a pottery jar. This is why mothers to this day will not let their children shout into a pot, for if they do, they will lose their hearts.

As soon as Kotcininak had taken the heart Paiyatyamo fell dead. His blood ran out upon the ground, and from every blood drop a flower sprang up. His body lay there and was burned by the sun till it was as black as coal. Kotcininak took the jar that held Sun Blossom's heart and put it on the north wall of her house. On the west wall she hung the great flint arrowhead which he wore around his neck. On the south wall she hung his flute. On the east wall she hung his wrist guard.

In four days the other Paiyatyamos were troubled. They had a pottery jar full of water that showed the north and the south, and the east and the west. They took four hailstones and they sang. First they dropped a yellow hailstone to the north, then a blue hailstone to the west, a red hailstone to the south and a white hailstone to the east. So they called the clouds to look for their leader who had been killed. From very direction they came with heavy hail and thunder. When they had reached the country of the cliff dwellers, the clouds saw the dead body lying motionless. Flowers were growing all over it and were blossoming. The thunder tore down Kotcininak's house to take out all the belongings of Paiyatyamo that she had hung there. The yellow clouds from the north struck her house on the north wall and flashed the yellow lightning. It threw down the north wall and the three sisters started up, catching hold of the jar that held Paiyatyamo's heart. They screamed to one another to throw his heart away. The blue clouds struck with the blue lightning on the west wall. The sisters caught up the flint arrowhead and called to each other to throw it out. The red clouds struck with the red lightning and tore down the south wall. The girls called to each other to throw out the flute. The white clouds struck with the white lightning and tore down the east wall. The sisters called to each other to throw out the wrist guard. In this way the clouds gathered all those things that belonged to Sun Blossom. From all the directions the lightning struck and hit his dead body to bring him to life once more. Kotcininak sang a song to restore him:

> I am calling Paiyatyamo to get up,
> To sit up and look north, west, south and east,
> To see from what direction the women are calling
> him and mourning for him.

Paiyatyamo got up. He saw that he was changed. His body was black as coal. He called out 'Ha ha!' He took his flute in his hand and put his flint arrowhead around his neck. He put his wrist guard on his left wrist and started for home, full of shame for what had happened to him. He found the other Paiyatyamos very sad.

When they saw him they called him Queer Face. They said to him, 'We missed you. What happened?' They told him that they would help him. Paiyatyamo planned that he would go back and get some things that belonged to the girls and make a charm to overcome them. His companions said, 'We will make a little snowbird for you to take. You yourself will be an old man and you will walk with a stick.'

So Paiyatyamo went back with his snow bird to the home of the three girls. He sang his songs and the snow bird danced and hopped about. It was always picking up hair and string and anything that lay around loose. He sang:

> Over in the east at his home
> You think there are all kinds of blossoms.

Again he sang:

> It points toward Kotcininak.
> Her heart and breath I am aiming at,
> To get her heart.

The snow bird picked up all the things that were lying around and he took them back with him. When he had returned home Paiyatyamo took the hair and the pieces of thread. He laid them on hot coals and burned them to ashes. He made a magic charm.

He set out again to go to the home of Kotcininak. He took the form of a large butterfly. As he flew along he sang:

> Butterfly, fly west.
> The women are running wild after you.
> They call to one another and say, 'Let's catch him.'

The oldest sister suspected this was not a real butterfly and she cautioned her sisters not to run after him, but they said, 'The markings on his wings are beautiful. We want them for a pattern for our pottery.' They ran after him. They took off their shawls and threw them after him, but he escaped. They ran after and he led them around the world. They went through sand storms and the hot sun, through thorns and through swarms of bees. For four days they chased the butterfly. At last he flew into some bushes and they could not see him any more. When they got there, there was an old man sitting asleep on his coat. They called out to him but he pretended not to hear them. They shook him.

He said, 'What is it? Who is it? Who is there?'

The girls said, 'Did you see a butterfly coming this way?'

He said, 'No. I was fast asleep.'

'Oh!' the girls said, 'We are so thirsty. Where is water that we may drink?'

Just then they heard a turtledove a long way off, and it said, (in Acoma) 'Here's water.'

The old man answered, 'Where the turtledove is there is water.' The old man led them far away to the water hole and he left them there to die. He sang:

> It hurts my feelings and it hurts your feelings, too.
> In the east Paiyatyamo lives;
> You women look for me from the west,
> But you do not know where I live.
> It hurts my feelings and your feelings when you find me.

But at last Kotcininak found the home of her Paiyatyamo and married him. For this reason, to this day, men are told not to sleep in the houses of their sweethearts if they go to visit them. If they do the girls sing these songs. They cut the boy's hair when he is asleep. They burn it to ashes and make a love charm. In this way the girl gets power over the boy so that no matter how far away he goes he will always be lonesome for her and come back to her.

Greasy Boy Recovers His Wife

Once upon a time Greasy Boy lived north of Acoma with his mother. He was Rainbow's younger brother.

Greasy Boy was a great hunter. Every day before he ate the meal his mother had prepared for him, she climbed the ladder to the roof carrying the jar of food she had prepared. She offered the soup or the stew or whatever she had made to all the directions, to Mountain-Lion, and to Eagle, to the north, the west, the south, and the east. Then she offered it to all the protectors of the hunt. When she came down again, Greasy Boy sat down and ate his meal. Every day he went hunting, and every day he brought home a deer. He gave venison to all the people of Acoma so that all the people loved him.

One day he said to his mother, 'Mother, put up a lunch for me that I may go hunting.' His mother put up a lunch for him, and he started toward the west.

He had never taken lunch with him before. As he sat down to eat, a big rat peeped out of his hole nearby. Greasy Boy always shot everything he saw so he raised his bow to kill the rat. He was pulling on the bow string when the rat said, 'My man, don't kill me. I have come a long distance to bring you a message. This morning your brother stole your sweetheart and took her on the rainbow up to his own country.'

'Tell me again. If you don't I'll shoot you.'

'Rainbow, your brother, has stolen your bride and taken her on the rainbow up to his own country.' Greasy Boy believed what Rat had told him, and he was very sorrowful.

Immediately he started back to his home. He did not stop to eat his lunch, and he came to his house empty-handed. His mother said to him, 'My son, how is it that you come empty-handed? You never come without bringing venison.' He told her what Rat had said to him. She was sad, and said, 'Rainbow is always taking women to his own country.'

Greasy Boy said, 'I am going to his country to get my sweetheart.'

'Yes,' his mother said to him, 'you two brothers are equal in power. If you can reach his country you may succeed.'

Greasy Boy set out to get help. Everybody loved Greasy Boy for he had always given venison to everyone, and they gave him whatever power they had. He came to Spider Woman and asked for help. She said to him, 'My grandchild, go to Whirlwind, and ask him to come here on the fourth day. Be here at the same time, my grandchild, and I will help you.'

On the fourth day Greasy Boy went again to Spider's home. She said to him, 'Be ready, and when Whirlwind comes, jump into his very centre. Whirlwind will carry you along, and I will let down my basket from the sky.

I will carry you up to Rainbow's country in the very centre of the Whirlwind.' Whirlwind came, and Greasy Boy jumped into its very centre. Then Spider Woman lifted them up to heaven in her basket.

They reached the sky country. Spider said, 'My grandson, if you need help again, call me at any time, and I will help you.'

'Yes, grandmother, I shall not be able to get down again without you.'

'I will help you.'

'Grandmother, tell me in which direction my brother lives,'

'Straight ahead of you, to the south. You will reach his house before sunset. Take these two cigarettes. When Rainbow gives you his, and asks you to smoke, draw these out of your knee and use these instead. The cigarettes your brother will offer you are poison; throw them away and do not smoke them. Also he will challenge you to eat all the food he has set on the table. Gopher will be there to help you; right beside you he will dig a hole. Put all the food he offers you down that hole, but the last plate that is brought in, you may eat; that will be good food. I know everything that will happen to you, my grandson, and it will be better if I go with you.'

'All right.'

They went on together to his brother's house. Spider found a house for herself and Greasy Boy, and she explained to him everything he should do when he met his brother. She stayed at home making him a suit of clothes. It looked just like the suit of arrowheads that Rainbow wears but she made it all of pitch.

Greasy Boy came to his brother's house. 'How do you do, my brother?' he said to him. He greeted him as a friend.

But Rainbow said to him angrily, 'What is it you want?'

When Greasy Boy saw that his brother was angry, right away he told him why he had come. 'I have come to get my wife.'

'Have I got your wife?' Rainbow said. 'Come in and pick her out.' He had stolen so many women he did not know which one was his brother's sweetheart.

Rainbow called all his women together. 'Set the table for your husband,' he said to them, 'let me know when you are ready.' Greasy Boy and his brother sat and talked together till the wives had prepared the food. Then Rainbow said to his visitor, 'Sit down and eat. If you eat it all up, you can take your wife.' There was food enough on the table for twenty men.

'All right.' Greasy Boy sat down to eat, and Rainbow left him to finish his task. He shovelled all the food into the hole Gopher had dug just beside him. The women kept pushing the food toward him; they had a jolly tune with him, and Rainbow was jealous when he heard the women laughing and enjoying themselves. Just as Greasy Boy tipped the last plate of food into the gopher hole, Rainbow came back. Gopher had just closed up the hole.

'Eat more,' he said to his brother.

'Yes, if you'll bring me another plate of food,' Greasy Boy answered him.

'Bring this pig the best plate of food I've got,' Rainbow yelled. The women brought in another plate and Rainbow sat and watched his brother eat.

He finished, and Rainbow said to him, 'Let us smoke.' He gave him a cigarette. Immediately Greasy Boy drew out one of those he carried in his knee and exchanged it for the one Rainbow had given him. They smoked.

'Now may I take my wife?' Greasy Boy asked.

'No, not till you have hoed the whole patch of my corn.'

'All right,' said Greasy Boy, 'I'll be here in four days to hoe your corn.'

Greasy Boy went back to Spider Woman. She said to him, 'Well, grandson, did you come home?'

'Yes, grandmother.'

'What did your brother say to you? What did he do?'

'He gave me lots of food to eat. I found the gopher hole as you told me and I shovelled all the food into it. At last I got my supper. Four days from now he will make me hoe his corn patch. It is a great cornfield. I do not know how I shall finish it in one day.'

'Be easy about that, my grandson. We will call together the gophers and the field mice, and I will get all the spiders, and with their help you will finish hoeing his cornfield in one day.'

The fourth day came. Greasy Boy and his grandmother were up early. She said to him, 'The gophers, the field mice, and the spiders are working at the cornfield already. When you get there, pretend to be hard at work, and by the time Rainbow's wives bring you your dinner, it will be all done. They will bring just as much food as they did before. Do not eat any of it except the food in the jar that your own wife has brought. When they call you to eat, say to your brother, "Go and look over my field and see if any weeds are left." Then you will see a badger hole beside you; shovel all the food into the hole that Badger has dug, but set to one side the jar of good food that your wife has brought. When your brother returns, let him watch you eat that last jar of food.'

Greasy Boy made ready to go. Spider brought out the suit of pitch that she had made, and a stool of pitch that looked just like Rainbow's stool of ice. She said to him, 'Take these with you. Wear the suit of pitch and carry the stool, and when you get to Rainbow's house it will still be early, and he will not be up. Put this stool in place of his stool, and change the suit you have on for the one he has. He will challenge you to another contest but by this suit and this stool you will overcome him.' He embraced his grandmother and set out for the house of his brother.

'How do you do, my brother,' he said to him (a friendly greeting).

But his brother spoke angrily and said, 'Why did you come so early?' He was still in bed. 'Are you ready to go to work?'

'Yes, sir.'

'That's good. I suppose you think you can hoe fifty patches all by yourself in one day?'

'It sounds like a great deal,' said Greasy 'but it will seem easy to me if I can have my wife.' While they talking, Greasy Boy had exchanged the suit he had on for the of arrow heads that Rainbow always wore, the stool of pitch for stool of ice, and the weapons he had brought for the ones that belonged to Rainbow. He was very happy for he knew he would overcome Rainbow.

Greasy Boy went down to the corn fields. All the time he was working he was singing his strong songs. He sang at the top of his voice:

> 'Halaina, halaina, hala ma ina, ina,
> It used to be that we lived near Acoma, to the north.'

Then he sang too,

> 'You call me skinny boy,
> All the women call me that. A h i i i.'

All the time the gophers, the mice, and the wood rats were cutting up the weeds, and the spiders were dragging them away. At last there only one patch left. Just then he saw the line of women bringing dinner across the fields, his brother in the lead of them all. Rainbow called to him, 'Come eat.' It looked as if only half of the field had been hoed.

'Wait a minute,' Greasy Boy called back. 'Only a few more weeds I'll be through.'

'Oho,' called back Rainbow, 'you can never finish that.' Just then Greasy Boy gave a shout and threw the last weed a the air (a sign that he had finished). 'Ugh,' his brother said angrily, 'that fellow has finished already.'

Just as Greasy Boy came to the place where the women were they set down the jars of food they had brought. There were a great many women but it was easy for him to tell which his wife was for she was in the line. He had just time to notice which jar of food was the one which she had brought. 'Are you through then?' his brother said to him.

'Yes,' he said, 'Go and see if all the weeds are cleared away.'

'All right,' said Rainbow, 'while I look over the field, eat all the food that the women have brought or I will cut off your head for you.'

Rainbow and his wives went off to look over the field. They found all the weeds cleared away. As soon as they had gone Greasy Boy shovelled the food into the hole that Badger had dug close beside him. He had just tipped in the last plate, and was eating the food his own wife had brought when his brother came back. 'You greasy pig,' he said to him, 'did you eat all that food?'

'Of course,' Greasy Boy answered. 'If I slept all day the way you do, I wouldn't be hungry. I worked hard so I was hungry.' Greasy Boy finished his dinner. He got up and said to Rainbow, 'Now can I take my wife?'

'No,' his brother answered. 'Four days from you must dig a hole in the ground for the green-corn roasting pit. I want it big enough to hold a whole winter's supply. In one day you must gather corn enough to last me all winter, dig the roasting hole to hold it all, and fetch the wood for the roasting.'

'All right,' answered Greasy Boy, 'I'll be here in four days. Will you show me where I shall dig the hole?'

Rainbow took him to a rocky place and said, 'Right here where the ground is hard.' Greasy Boy went back to his grandmother. She was very glad to see him wearing the arrowhead suit of his brother's.

'Well, my grandson, what happened to you?'

'Everything went smoothly. It was just as you said. Nevertheless, I must go again. He ordered me to prepare the pit for his green corn, gather the corn and fetch the wood.'

'We will manage that, my grandson.' She called together all those who chop wood, all those who dig holes, and asked for their help. The badgers and the gophers worked digging a great pit in the place that Rainbow had chosen. They dug it out to a great depth and left only a thin crust of earth on top for Greasy Boy to clear away.

The fourth day Greasy Boy and his grandmother were up early. He went to his brother's house and greeted him pleasantly. 'What did you come so early for?' Rainbow called angrily.

This time Greasy Boy spoke angrily too. 'Are you still in bed? Get up. It's time to get to work.'

'All right. Go ahead and begin digging that hole. By evening have the corn ready to put in and I'll be there to help you put it in the pit.'

Greasy Boy took his digging stick and went off to the place where he was to dig the hole. He was happy for he knew he had on the suit that would cause him to overcome his brother. First of all he brought the wood together. Then he began clearing off the crust of earth over the hole. By noon he was taking the last dirt out of the hole. Just then he saw all the women bringing his dinner to him, with Rainbow at the head of the line. They came. They looked down into the hole. It was three men's height and one man's length across. 'Well, come out and eat.'

'Yes, it's very hot down here.' They pulled him up out of the hole.

Greasy Boy sat down to eat all the food the women had brought him. The women liked him. They laughed and joked with him, and he showed them how he wasn't greedy, how he put all the food down the gopher hole. They helped him pick out the poisonous food and get rid of it in the hole, and they selected the good food for him to eat. When Rainbow heard them laughing and joking he was more jealous than ever.

When Greasy Boy had finished, Rainbow said to him, 'I suppose you think you can finish today.'

'Oh yes.'

'What time will you be ready?'

'Just before sunset.' They all went back and left him to finish his work. Greasy Boy brought in the corn. All the afternoon he worked. The oven was red hot, and all the corn was heaped ready when he saw Rainbow coming with his wives. Greasy Boy was throwing in the corn. His brother stepped up to him crowding him to the mouth of the pit. He was hurrying him so that his brother would not see what he was up to. Just as he threw in the last handful, Rainbow pushed the boy into the oven to roast with the corn. Right away he closed the opening with a big stone. They could hear him singing his strong song in the pit. Rainbow said, 'We will go home. That's the end of his life. He'll stop singing after a while.' They left him to roast all night.

Early next morning they went down, the women in a line with Rainbow in the lead, to see if the corn was roasted and Greasy Boy brown on the top of the pile. But Badger had dug a hole for him in the side of the pit, and he had been safe all night. As soon as he heard them pounding at the stone that closed the mouth of the pit, he crept out from his refuge. Badger was with him to close up the hole before it could be discovered. As soon as Rainbow had pried up the stone, up jumped Greasy Boy. 'It's nice and warm in there,' he said. 'This time I'm going to take my wife.'

Rainbow Brother was very angry to find him still alive. 'No,' he said, 'we must show her our powers. In four days we will have a contest in this little Rainbow village. The war chief will have wood stacked in two separate piles and he will prepare them so that they will burn fiercely. I will stand on top of my pile and you on top of your pile, and we will fight with our long flint knives.'

'Very well. In four days I will come again.'

For four days the war chief had wood brought into the village and piled in two separate piles in the centre of the village. Greasy Boy went about saying goodbye to everybody who knew him. All the people loved him for he was always good-natured and generous, and they hoped that Rainbow would be killed for he was cruel and sulky.

The fourth day Greasy Boy was up early, running as if he were practising for a footrace, and singing his strong songs. But Rainbow Brother was gloomy. When everything was ready Greasy Boy got onto his pile and

Rainbow onto his. They set down their stools and sat down on the top of the wood. Then the girl they were fighting for set fire to the pyres; first she lit Greasy Boy's and then Rainbow's. They both began to burn fiercely. Greasy Boy's had been lit first so he began first to sing his strong songs that told his name and where he lived. Rainbow Brother was angry and jealous and he took his flint knife and threw it at his head. As soon as it was touched by the heat of the flames it broke in two (it was pitch) and fell useless. Greasy Boy raised his knife and threw it at his brother. It cut his head off, and, the pitch of his stool burning up around him, he was burned to ashes. But Greasy Boy's stool, as the fire touched it, melted, for it was made of ice, and the water pouring down put out the fire.

Then Greasy Boy dismissed all the women his brother had stolen and told them to go to their own homes. He took his own wife and started back to Acoma. Spider let them down in her basket from Rainbow Village.

But Rainbow, when his body was burned, had stirred up the Storm Clouds against Greasy Boy. He and his wife had no sooner reached the earth in Spider Woman's basket than they saw that the Storm Clouds had almost overtaken them. They ran as fast as they could, but the lightning was upon them. They came to the river and hail was falling all about them. All that were with Greasy Boy dug a hole in the floating hail of the river. Rainbow Brother struck with the yellow lightning of the north, and it almost hit Greasy Boy. He struck with the blue lightning of the west, and it just blinded the eyes of Greasy Boy. He struck with the red lightning of the south, and it was far enough away so that their eyes were not dazzled. He struck with the white lightning of the east, and it was so far away they hardly saw it at all. They knew they were safe, and they reached home.

If Greasy Boy hadn't killed his brother Rainbow, he'd be stealing your wife nowadays.

Careful Burden Carrier

In the north a man set out to travel across the country. He was looking for some way to earn his living. He carried his bedding on his back. As he was travelling he saw a man ahead of him running zigzag back and forth as if he were chasing something. He said to himself, 'What can he be doing there? I will go up and see if he is crazy.' He saw that the runner was following a jackrabbit. When he came up to where the man was, he said to him, 'What are you doing?'

'I'll show you what I can do. This is my power. I can run down the jackrabbit.' He let the jackrabbit go and chased him. He caught him and came back.

The other said to him, 'Where are you going?'

He said, 'I am looking for a living.'

'What shall I call you?'

'My name is Careful Burden Carrier.'

The other answered. 'My name is Careful Runner.' Careful Runner said to Careful Burden Carrier, 'I will go with you to look for a job.'

'All right. Crawl up onto my back and I will carry you.' Careful Runner climbed onto the pack of Careful Burden Carrier and they went on.

Late in the afternoon they saw a man on his hands and knees. They wondered what he was doing, and they said to one another, 'What is the matter with that fellow?' They came up to him and said, 'What are you doing on your hands and knees?'

He said, 'I am blowing to start the cyclone.'

'What is your name?'

'My name is Careful Blower.' He said to them, 'What is your name?'

'My name is Careful Runner.'

'My name is Careful Burden Carrier.' Careful Blower said to them, 'Where are you going?'

'We are on our way to look for a job.'

Careful Blower said, 'I will go with you.'

Careful Burden Carrier answered, 'All right. Crawl up onto my back and I will carry you.' Careful Blower crawled up onto his pack and they went on.

Next day they saw another man. He had a bow and arrow, and they said to him, 'What are you doing?'

He said, 'I am shooting at a deer.'

The three travellers said, 'We can't see any deer.'

'No, you can't see him. My bow and arrows are very powerful, and I can see a long distance. The deer is in the next canyon beyond us.'

'Let's see you shoot.' He pulled on his bow and told them that the next day they would eat their dinner of the deer he had shot. They said to him, 'What is your name?'

He said, 'Call me Careful Seer. What is your name?'

'My name is Careful Runner.'

'My name is Careful Burden Carrier.'

'My name is Careful Blower.'

Careful Seer said, 'I will go with you.'

'All right. Climb up onto my back and I will carry you.' He climbed up onto the pack of Careful Burden Carrier and they went on.

Next day they arrived at the place where the deer had been shot. They feasted there. When they went on they saw another man on his hands and knees. They said to him, 'What are you doing?'

He said, 'I am listening along the ground so that I can hear the news.'

'What is your name?'

'My name is Careful Listener. What is your name?'

'My name is Careful Seer.'

'My name is Careful Blower.'

'My name is Careful Runner.'

'My name is Careful Burden Carrier.'

Careful Listener said to them, 'Where are you going?'

'We are going to look for a job.'

'I will go with you.'

'All right, climb up onto my back and I will carry you.'

Careful Listener said, 'I know of a job about a day's travel from here.'

'What is it?'

'It is a footrace with the chief's daughter.'

They said to him, 'What chief?'

'Half Moon Chief.'

'All right. Before we get there we will camp and you shall listen there and find out all about the race.' Careful Listener climbed up on the back of Careful Burden Carrier and they went on their way to Half Moon Chief.

When they had come close to his home they camped for the night. Careful Listener put his ear to the ground and listened to learn about the race. Chief Half Moon had a daughter whose name was White Deer and all the men were to race with her. If they lost, they lost their heads. But if White Deer lost, the men won all her father's possessions that they could carry off in one load.

They went on to Half Moon Chief's. Half Moon Chief greeted them as strangers and appointed the race in four clays. The travellers chose Careful Runner to run with White Deer. The race course was six miles long, and it was a circle. At the far end there was a statue. The runners who challenged White Deer ran in advance until they came to the statue and after they had passed it they fell behind. The statue belonged to White Deer. It was carved from lava rock, and before she began to race, White Deer put corn and pollen in the hands of the statue.

On the day of the race the people gathered along the race course. Early in the morning Careful Listener put his ear to the ground. He heard the gophers talking. One gopher said to another, 'White Deer's statue will overcome Careful Runner. She puts cornmeal and pollen on its hands and it blows upon the pollen to choke the breath of Careful Runner.'

'Thank you,' said Careful Listener, and he went to the travellers and told them.

They began the race. White Deer ran fast but Careful Runner passed her and came to the statue. Just before he reached it, Careful Shooter drew his bow and shot at the heart of the statue. When the arrow stuck in the lava rock, White Deer fell down overcome, and Careful Runner won the race.

So the travellers won all the goods of Half Moon Chief that they could carry off in one load. The Chief brought a wagon load of goods, but Careful Burden Carrier rocked it with one hand and said it was too light. The Chief's men brought wagon after wagon and loaded them with sheep and cows and blankets and everything the Chief possessed except his land. His land they could not take away. When they had brought together all of Half Moon's property, the rest of the travellers climbed on top of the wagons and Careful Burden Carrier hauled off the whole load.

They had gone only a little way when White Deer died. The chief was angry and sent his men to attack the travellers. They took the war path after them. The travellers heard them coming behind them giving their war whoops. Careful Blower was the only one who had not helped to overcome Half Moon Chief. They appointed him. He went to a hill of sand and blew a cyclone against them. They were overcome, and that is the way the first traveller got rich.

CHAPTER 4

Arapaho

On the War Path

Five young men and two boys, all Arapahos, once went on the war path. They started from home about noon, and travelled about ten miles, when they stopped for the night. It was dark. The leader asked each one to get water. They all refused. At last the youngest one went. When coming near the water, he was all at once caught by the leg by a man who had no scalp. It was an Arapaho. This man said, 'Where do you come from?'

'Oh, we are just stopping here for the night,' the boy answered. The man then said that the Pawnee had been fighting them and had killed many. The boy said, 'Wait, I will just get some water, and then we will go to our camp together.' When he had gotten the water, he helped the wounded man up, took him close to the camp, and carried the water in. He then asked the leader of the party, 'Are you strong, and will you not become frightened at anything?'

He answered, 'I am strong and am not afraid of anything.' The boy then put this same question to each one of the party, and each one answered the same way.

Only the youngest of the party, the boy, said, 'I do not know, I might and might not. This is the first time that I am on the war path.' They were all wondering why they were asked these questions. The boy (who had gotten the water) then went out and got the wounded man, and took him into the tent. All five of the warriors became frightened and huddled together in a heap. Only the two boys proved to be strong. The wounded man then told them that the Pawnee had been fighting them, and that his friends were all lying around there dead.

They prepared a supper, and, when they were through eating, went to sleep. In the morning the boy who got that man said, 'Now, my friends, I thought you were strong and would not be frightened, but I see you are not strong. It would be bad if we should go and hunt up a war. Tomorrow we start back, because it would be too bad if other tribes should kill us all.'

The wounded man then said to them, 'My friends, you will have to leave me here. Make a strong hut for me to sleep in, and get me a good supply of drinking water.' So the young men went home, and the boy told his friends about them. The scalped man soon died.

The Woman and the Buffalo

A woman went to get water, and saw what she thought was a man standing near the water. She ran away with that man; and after they were gone away a short distance, the man turned into a buffalo. The woman then wanted to return, but the buffalo would not let her. She tried to hide away, but could not do it. When they came to the buffalo herd, the buffaloes were sleeping. The woman's mother by this time began to look for her daughter. Her other daughter told her that her sister had run away. The mother then told a mouse that she should go under the ground and hunt her lost daughter, and that if she should find her, she should put her head out of the ground and stick two arrows into the ground beside the woman, so as to mark the place where she was sitting. In the morning, when the buffaloes got up, the (man) buffalo saw that his wife did not get up, and went to hit her, but found only her shawl. Then they followed her, but could not find her. She had gone home.

The Man Who Gets Advice from the Skunk

There was once an Indian who had an old rifle which he had owned a long time. He had a wife and only one child. Once they were very hungry, but the man had no cartridges. No other Indians were near. The man then went eastward and saw a herd of reindeer. Not having any cartridges, he did not know what to do. So he prayed to the skunk, and the skunk told him to take some mud and mould it into bullets. He did so, put one into his gun, took aim at a reindeer, and shot and killed it. He then went back and told his wife that he had killed a reindeer. In the meanwhile some bears had taken the reindeer that he had killed. This made the man so angry that he took his knife and cut his own throat.

The Origin of the Pleiades

Once seven men went on the war path. A bear got after them, and they did not know how to escape. Then they took a little ball, kicked it upward, and a man ascended with it. This, they repeated several times, a man going up with every ball they kicked up. When the last one was about to go up, the bear was just about to take him; but he quickly kicked the ball and went up too, and those are the seven stars up in the sky.

Origin of the Buffalo

Once the Cheyenne lived at the head of a stream which emptied into a hole or cave. One time they were nearly starving, and they consulted with one another as to whether they ought not to explore the cave once. No one wanted to undertake it. At last one got ready, painted himself up, and when he came to the cave, he found two others there ready to descend. He first thought those two only wanted to fool him; but they said no, they wanted to go in. So they all three jumped in. Soon they came to a door. Upon their knocking, an old woman opened and asked what they wanted. They said they and their people were starving.

'Are you hungry too?' she asked.

'Yes!'

'See there!' and they beheld a wide prairie covered with buffaloes. She then handed them a pan with buffalo meat. They thought that was not enough to satisfy the great hunger of even one of them, but they ate and ate until they were 'just full'; and then the old woman said they should take what was left and give it to their people in camp, and she would soon send them the buffalo. They did so, and the whole camp had enough of what they brought. Everybody ate and was filled. And when they awoke the next morning, they beheld around them great herds of buffalo.

The Mother's Head

At a certain place there was once a single tent in which lived a man with his wife, daughter and little boy. The man always used to paint his wife's face; but every time when she would get water, the paint would disappear. So one time the man concluded that he would go and find out once why his wife always went after water so late, and why the paint was always gone. After he had painted her again, she went after water; and he followed her, and hid himself in the bushes. Soon she whistled, and he saw an alligator come out of the water and lick her face. He at once shot both, cut off the woman's head, took it, home, cooked it, and he and his children ate of it. The little boy always said it tasted like their mother. Afterwards the man told the other Indians that the children had eaten their mother. They at once all left the place, leaving the children alone. The children followed, but a head would always call after them; and when they came near to the other Indians, the latter would run away from them. All at once the children came to a river, laid a board across, and walked over. The head followed them; but when it was on the middle of the board (i.e., halfway across), they turned the board, the head fell into the water, and did not follow them any more.

The girl then covered her face and wished that she had a nice house, a lion and a tiger; and many other things. When she uncovered her face, the house and many nice things were there, and under the bed were also a lion and a tiger. They then had much meat to eat; and they called the Indians, and they came and ate. The father of the children also came, and they gave him meat to eat too. The girl told the two animals to kill their father when he went out of the house, because he had killed their mother and then given them her head to eat, and then had accused them of it. The animals did as they had been told. The Indians afterwards would always come to these children to eat.

Origin of the Medicine Arrows

A long time ago some Cheyenne were out to hunt buffaloes. When the chase was over; a number of young men went to the hunting ground to eat some of the meat, such as the kidneys, liver, etc. One young man, seeing a buffalo yearling which one of the chiefs had shot, said he wanted to have the hide of that yearling and skinned it.

Soon the chief, who had killed the yearling came and claimed the hide. A controversy arose. All at once the boy took the lower part of the buffalo's leg and clubbed the chief almost to death with it. He then ran to his grandmother's tent, she being the only relative he had. Here he lay down and slept. She put the kettle on the fire to cook a meal.

In the morning the men of the tribe came to the lodge where the young man was. His grandmother told him about it. He said he did not care and remained in bed. They called to him that he should come out, but he would not do it. They repeated the command, but in vain. At last they began to cut up the tent. He quickly upset the kettle, pouring the boiling water into the fire and going up into the air with the steam and ashes that arose. All at once they saw him way off, just going over a ridge. They followed him; but before they overtook him, they saw him farther off again; and so it continued. They could not get him.

The next morning some women going after water saw him under a river bank and went and told the men. They went and chased him again, but in vain. When they were upon his heels; they would all at once see him way off. Sometimes he would disappear, and then reappear again in a different costume. The last time he appeared dressed in a fine buffalo robe costume. He went over a ridge, and they saw him no more at that time.

With that young man the buffalo had disappeared, too, and the Indians soon began to starve. They finally had to live mostly on mushrooms. Once some young men wandered away from the camp; and all at once they saw a young man, nicely dressed in a buffalo robe, coming towards them. It was the young man who had so mysteriously disappeared. He asked them the condition of the Indians in their camps, and they told him that they were nearly starving and had to live on mushrooms. He told them to hunt a 'dry buffalo' (skeleton). They did so; and he hunted out of the decayed remains the 'book' of the stomach, and gave it to them to eat. He also broke some of the bones, and, behold! there was some marrow in them. This he also gave to them. He then sent them to camp, and told them to tell the medicine men to have a lodge ready for them in the centre of the camp. In the evening he came; bringing with him four arrows that he had brought along. He now made 'arrow medicine', and sang arrow songs with the chiefs all night; and in the morning the buffalo had reappeared, and the Cheyenne had plenty to eat again. Since that time the Cheyenne celebrate the 'medicine arrow medicine', which is one of the most sacred and most severe medicines. Later the Pawnees got two of the arrows in war, one, however, the Cheyenne recovered again.

The Frog and the Woman

A woman once went to a river to get water. When she dipped the water, a frog jumped into the pail; and when the woman got home, that frog all at once became a man. He was standing in the bucket, and then jumped out. Afterwards this man married that woman, and after a while they had two children. After this the man once got very hungry and ate up his wife, after which he turned into a frog again and lived with the other frogs in the river.

How a Bird and an Alligator Saved Two Children

Once there stood at one place a number of tents. Outside some children were playing. A white man who came along sat down not far away. The children saw it, and said, 'Look at that white man! He is making something.' When, the white man heard it, he got angry; and went to the tents and demanded of the Indians that they should move away, but leave the children, which they did. Soon some of the girls who had been playing outside told their sisters to go and get something from the camps. They went, but found no tents. An old dog was tied at the place where the tents had been standing. Then the children asked the dog where their friends were. He told them they had gone away, and then went with the children to hunt them. While they were going, they came to a little tent where an old woman lived, whom they asked whether she had seen their mothers.

The old woman said; 'My grandchildren, my grandchildren! You can sleep here during the night.'

So they slept there; all in one row.

While they were sleeping the old woman sharpened her knife and cut off all the children's heads. Only one large girl awoke and begged for her and her little sister's life, promising the old woman that they would love and help her. In the morning the old woman asked the children if they wanted to eat of the bodies of the children which she had just cooked. They refused, saying they were not hungry. During the next night the smaller girl wanted to go out. The old woman told the larger girl to just let her sister do it in the tent. But she said no, because it would get 'muddy' in the tent; and so they went out. In a little while the little girl again had to get up.

The old woman again protested against their going out; but the larger sister said, 'There will be a little hill in the tent,' and the woman again let them go out. When they were outside, a little bird told them they should run away, as the old woman would cut off their heads too. So they ran away.

Meanwhile the old woman kept calling from the tent that they should hurry up or else she would come out. The bird kept answering, 'Wait!'

The girls, in the meantime, had come to a river . On the shore lay an alligator, who told them to go around him four times. Then he asked them to sit down by him and see if they could find something on him. They did so, and found frogs, which the alligator told them to crack as they crack lice that they hunt on each other. Then the alligator told them to get on his back; and when they did so, he carried them across the river. When they were across, they ran, and saw a very nice tent at a distance, in which they lived.

The Cannibal and the Fox

A man once went into some tents and told the women there were many plums across the river, and they should go and pick them. He would stay and in the meantime watch their babies. So they went; and while they were gone, the man cut off the babies' heads, and left them in their cradle swings. The bodies he took away. Presently the women came back and told some of the girls to go in and see how the babies were. They came running out, and said that only the heads were in the swings. The women came crying; and when they looked, they saw the man at a distance. They pursued him; and when he saw them coming; he wished there were a big hole there. At once the hole was there. He ran into the hole; and when the women came there, they sat around the hole and cried. The man, finding some paint in the hole, painted his face, and then came out and asked them why they were crying. The women, not knowing him, said a man had killed their babies, and they thought he was in that hole. He came out; and said they should go in and see. They did so; and when whey were in the hole; the man threw fire in, and thus killed them. He then got out the bodies, built a large fire; laid the bodies around it, and roasted them in order to eat them. Just then a fox came there and said he was sick and wanted to get something to eat. The man proposed to the fox that they go on a hill and then run towards the fire. Whoever should get there first should eat first. To this the fox agreed; and he got there first, and ate up all the bodies. When the man got there, he found nothing, and went home.

Bad Robe Resurrecting a Buffalo

When the Arapaho still lived north in a village, an Arapaho named Bad Robe wanted to make medicine to see if he could not get the buffalo to come. He told Cedar Tree to go westward and see if he could not find a buffalo. Cedar Tree went; and when he had gone a short distance, he saw some black objects in the distance, but could not say whether they were buffaloes or not. He made up his mind that he would not tell the Indians a lie and say he saw buffaloes when he was not sure about it. All at once he saw those black things fly up, and noticed that they were ravens. He went back to camp and told the Indians about it. So Bad Robe would not make medicine, but scolded Cedar Tree for not believing that what he saw were buffaloes. If he had believed, they would not have changed into ravens. One man got so angry at Cedar Tree and his failure, that he killed his own wife. The camp was then broken up, and the Indians scattered.

The mother of the murdered woman, her two sisters, and an uncle, started in pursuit of the murderer. They pursued him a while, but got hungry, so that they had to return. When they came near their home, they put up their tent and stayed there. One of them was very hungry; and, as they had nothing else to eat, her folks cooked moccasin soles for her. Early in the morning her uncle went west to hunt, but had no bow or gun. He met Bad Robe, whom he asked to loan him his gun because his folks were very hungry. Bad Robe gave it to him, and said that in the morning he would be at their tent and try to find some dried buffalo. The man whose name was Trying Bear went northwest and found a dry buffalo. He went to his tent and told others about it. Bad Robe, who was already there, had a white pony. This he painted, put a buffalo robe around himself and a fine eagle feather on his head. This was in the morning. He now started off for that buffalo carcass, telling the uncle, Trying Bear, to follow him after awhile. But the man followed him right away, because he was curious to know what would be done. About noon Bad Robe got there. He got off from his pony, took his eagle-feather, threw it at the carcass, and all at once it became alive. Bad Robe then turned around and saw Trying Bear, whom he told to shoot that buffalo, skin it, and take everything eatable about it to the camp and eat.

The Bear Girl

At a certain place there was once an Indian village. At one time some children were playing some little distance from camp. One girl had a sister who was a bear. This Bear girl was playing with the children, and told her sister to take their little sister home, which was refused. The Bear girl then scratched the face of the one who refused to take the little sister home, and said, if she would tell their father and mother, the dogs would bark, and she would come and tear up all the tents and eat up all the people. The girl then went and hid in a dog tent. The Bear girl hunted, and at last found her and threatened to eat her up. But the girl begged for her life, and promised that she would live with the Bear girl, get water for her, and work for her; and so the Bear girl let her alone. The two then lived together in a big tent. One time, when the girl was getting water, she met three men, who gave her a rabbit, and told her to go and give it to the Bear girl, and say to her that she gave her that rabbit. The girl took it home, and, giving it to her Bear sister, said, 'Here, I killed this rabbit for you.' The Bear girl took it, and while she was cooking it, the three men came and placed themselves, one on the north, one on the south, and one on the west, side of the tent, and shot and killed the Bear girl. They then took one of the Bear girl's leg bones and put it on the girl's back, telling her if she should lose it, the Bear girl would come to life again and come after her. They then took the girl along, and while they were walking along, the girl lost the bone three times. Every time she would see the Bear girl coming at a distance, but every time she found the bone again before the Bear girl would overtake them. The last time they were just climbing up a high mountain when the Bear girl was near; and while the travellers got on the mountain all right, the Bear girl would always roll back, and finally asked the parties on the mountain to come down, as she would not hurt them. But they stayed on the mountain; and finally the Bear girl went away, and the party, including the girl, went to an Indian camp on the other side, where they remained.

Why the Bear Has a Short Tail

Once an old woman was walking by a river, and all at once she saw a red fox. She said to him, 'My grandson, come here! I want to tell you a story about my folks at home. I am walking along here to hunt my grandson, and I have been very lonesome for my grandson, and at last I see him. Now, come here and sit down by my side, and listen to me!' She then began to tell him a story, which never ended. She had already been talking quite a while, and the old fox began to sleep. She went on telling her story until the fox was fast asleep. The old woman then got up while the fox was sleeping, and took a knife and cut off his head. Then she made a fire and roasted the fox. After he was done, she took him off the fire and went to get some more wood. While she was gone, a bear came and carried the fox away. Soon the woman returned; and when she did not find the fox, she asked a tree, 'Who has taken away my fox?' The tree told her that a bear had taken it. The woman said, 'Now, this is bad, what the bear has done to me. Now, I will say this: 'Bears shall have bob tails.' And that is the reason why bears have short tails.

The Alligator Boy

Once upon a time some Indians moved to a new place. After having made their camp, two boys were riding out and got into the woods. Here one of them found two large eggs. They did not know what kind of eggs they were. They took them across the river, where they erected a small tent. The younger boy said he had once tasted big eggs, and then he cooked these. After he had cooked them, he offered one to the larger boy, who refused to eat it. The younger boy ate his, and in the night he took sick. He soon noticed that he began having green spots and small raised parts all over his body. He began to cry. His brother said, 'I told you not to eat that egg, but you would not listen.' By that time the boy had turned into an alligator, all but the head. He told the older brother, who by this time was crying too, to go and call his friends. This he did. All came to see the unfortunate boy. The alligator boy said, if they ever wanted to talk to him, they should whistle, and he would then come out from the water. The Indians then went back, and the boy, who now had entirely become an alligator, went into the water.

The Boy Who Was Carried off by the Wind

Once a man and a woman had two boys; they were twins. These boys often took their bows and arrows and went out to hunt. One time when they were hunting, they found an eagle's nest. The old eagles were not at home. The boys asked the young eagles what kind of clouds generally came when their mother was angry. The young eagles said black clouds. Then the boys cut off the heads of the young eagles; and when they were about to cut off the last one, the clouds got black, and it began to storm. The boys ran home. One got into the tent, but the other one was taken by the storm just as he was about to enter the lodge. The door of the tent, of which the boy had taken hold, was also carried along. When the boy, as the wind carried him along, would grasp at something – for instance, the branch of a tree – it would break off. So the wind carried him way off to some other camps.

Here the wind dropped him. He was all covered with dirt. An old woman, who came to cut grass, found him. She took him to her tent and took care of him, and he grew up to be a young man.

One time a little red bird was sitting on the poles of a tent. Some men, of whom this young man was one, tried to shoot it. One old man said, 'Whoever shoots that bird shall marry one of my daughters.' All tried hard, and this young man hit it. Then a raven came and took that bird away from him, and showed it to the father of those girls. When the young man heard of it, he told the people that it was he who shot the bird; and so he got the younger daughter, and the raven the older one.

One time the young man went to shoot buffalo, and once he drove a herd to the camp. Many came to take part in the hunt. The raven had nothing to do, but flew around and picked out the buffaloes' eyes.

When they had killed the buffaloes, the women took home some blood in their shawls on their backs. Those two young women were jealous of each other because one had a nice man, and the other a raven. When the raven's wife went home, that young man went and cut her shawl, so that the blood was spilled and the shawl spoiled.

The younger woman was nice looking, but her husband sometimes looked filthy. During the night, however, he would get handsome again. Once the couple wanted to go and get wood. The older sister wanted to go along, but the younger would not allow her to do so.

CHAPTER 5

Blackfoot

Legend of Red Coulee

There lies in a 'coulee' near the Marias River, on the road that leads from Macleod to Benton, a large 'medicine stone', venerated by the Indians belonging to the Blackfoot Confederacy. The 'coulee' is named by the Indians the 'Red Coulee'. When the Blackfeet came from the north, the Snake Indians, who at that time inhabited the country, told the Blackfeet that there was a large medicine stone on the top of a hill, close to a ravine.

Several years after they were told this, a Blackfoot chief with fifty men went southward, on the warpath. They all went to this stone, and the chief, being sceptical about the mysterious powers possessed by it, laughed at his men for exhibiting such childishness as to believe in it. In derision he hurled the stone down the mountainside into the ravine, and then departed. They engaged in a battle with some Indians in the South, and all of them were killed, only one man returning to tell the fate of his comrades.

Ever since that time the Indians have called the place the 'Red Coulee', and as they travel to and fro, they never forget to go there and present their offerings to insure safety in battle and protection by the way.

The Legend of Sheep Creek

Napioa, which means 'The Old Man', who is the Secondary Creator of the Blackfeet, was travelling one day with the Kit fox, near Sheep Creek, which is located about twenty-five miles south of Calgary, in the Provisional District of Alberta. As they travelled together they saw a large rock; and Napioa felt constrained to make an offering of his robe to it. He presented the robe and, with the Kit fox as his companion, departed. He had not proceeded far upon the way, when, perceiving that it was going to rain, he told his companion to return, and ask the rock to give him back his robe, as he was afraid of being drenched with the rain. The rock refused to give the robe to the Kit fox, and then Napioa, becoming angry, said, 'That old rock has been there for a long time and never had a robe. It has always been poor. I will go back myself and take away my robe.'

He returned and took the robe by force, and then the rock became very angry, and followed them, determined to punish them. Napioa fled southward toward High River, and the Kit fox, anxious for his own safety, hid in a hole in the ground. Napioa saw an old buffalo bull, and he called to him for help; but when the buffalo came to his rescue, the rock ran over him and crushed him to death. Then two bears came to help Napioa, and they too were killed by the rock. Two small birds, with very large strong bills, came to help him, and they attacked the rock, breaking off pieces from it, as they suddenly pounced upon it, and then flew upward. In a short time they killed the rock, and Napioa was saved. The Indians then named the stream 'Oqkotokseetuqta, the Rock Creek, or Stony Creek,' but it is called by the white people at the present day, 'Sheep Creek'.

Legend of Tongue Creek

Tongue Creek is situated between Sheep Creek and High River, about nine miles south of Sheep Creek. In the distant past Napioa was travelling in the vicinity of Tongue Creek, when he espied a band of elk sporting themselves on its banks. They came to a place where the bank was steep, and they all leaped down, seeking a sandy resting place in the bed of the stream.

Napioa reached the creek, and, lighting a piece of wood, he threw the firebrand over the bank. The elk heard him, and asked him what he wanted. 'Oh,' said he, 'I was laughing when you spoke to me, and I could not answer; but that is a very nice spot down there, and I want to go down, for there is abundance of beautiful clean sand.' When the elk saw the firebrand they became frightened, and, rushing headlong over each other, broke their necks. A single young elk escaped, but Napioa said, 'Never mind, there are many more elk in the country; that one can go.' Napioa pitched his lodge, and erected a pole with a flag upon it. He skinned the elk, filled his lodge with the meat, and made preparations to camp there and have a feast. While thus engaged, a coyote entered his lodge and asked him for something to eat, but he would not give any. He noticed that the coyote had on a necklace of shells, and said he, 'If you will give me that necklace, I will give you something to eat.'

The coyote replied, 'I cannot do that, for this is my medicine (amulet) and it is very strong.'

Napioa then said, 'Well, I will run a race with you, and if you beat me I will give you some of the meat.'

But the coyote refused, and as he did so he held up a bandaged foot, and said, 'I cannot run for I am lame!' and the two went off together, the coyote protesting that he had a sore foot, and could not run.

He managed to get Napioa a long distance from the lodge, and then quickly unloosing the bandage from his foot, he ran back to the lodge. Napioa followed, a long distance behind, shouting, 'Save me some of the meat!' When the coyote reached the lodge, he called aloud for his fellow coyotes, who speedily came and devoured all the meat. Napioa had placed the tongues upon the top of the pole, but a mouse ran up the pole and ate them all. When Napioa found that the meat was all gone he said, 'Then I will have the tongues, for the coyote could not get them.' But as he took down the remaining portions, he threw them away, saying, 'They are not good!'

The Indians call this creek 'Matsinawustam, The Tongue Flag,' but the white people call it 'Tongue Creek.'

CHAPTER 6

Carrier

The Giant's Grandson

A boy and his sister, with a boy cousin, went out into the woods one day to hunt squirrels. They found many squirrels playing in the branches of the big trees in the heart of the forest, and the boys, standing on opposite sides, shot at them with their arrows. One squirrel came racing down the tree towards the ground, causing the girl to laugh aloud. The squirrel ran up again, and her brother, who was on the point of shooting at it, scolded his sister for frightening it away. Again the squirrel ran down the tree. The girl was unable to control her laughter, however much her companions scolded her; she laughed and laughed until she died. The boys then became very frightened. They scooped out a hollow in a tree to serve as a coffin, placed the body inside, and covered it over with earth. Being afraid to return home, they wandered aimlessly about the woods.

After several days they came to a hole in a mountain near which lay a fir tree. One of the boys set fire to the tree, and the smoke from the fire tainted his body. Then they entered the cave, and in spite of the snakes, frogs and other creatures that lay in their path, pushed on until they emerged into the open air, in a country that looked the same as this earth. In front of them was a good road marked with the tracks of bare feet, men's, women's and children's, all leading south. The boys wandered down the road to a big river, on whose opposite shore was a town divided into two portions. On one side all the houses and canoes were red, on the other black. The black houses were the homes of the dead; the red, of the robins, which dwell on earth during the day and depart to the underworld at evening. Standing on the bank the boys shouted for some one to come and ferry them across, but no one heard them, though people were wandering as thick as mosquitoes to and fro among the houses.

For a long time then the boys remained on the bank, unable to make themselves heard. At last one of them became sleepy and yawned. Immediately a man on the far side shouted, 'Some one is calling to us from the other bank.' Two canoes came speeding across the river, one black, the other red. The black canoe arrived first and a black ferry man landed on the shore. The smoky boy embarked, but when the boy whose body bore no taint of smoke stepped into the canoe his foot went right through the bottom and he had to remain behind. But now as the canoe pushed out into the river its four paddlers began to sniff their passenger's body, and one of them said to his companions, 'It is strange that this boy has no taint of death.' They pushed him back and forth from one to the other, saying, 'No smell,' until he was reduced to skin and bones and fell dead. Then they threw his body overboard into the river, where a big sturgeon swallowed it.

Meanwhile the boy who had remained on shore was weeping at his cousin's fate. He longed to go back home, and searched for the cave from which he had emerged. At last he found it, but it was now so full of frogs that he had to crawl on hands and knees. At intervals he heard a voice, and the path was enveloped in darkness, for a giant at the far end of the cave kept placing his hand over the entrance. The boy groped his way for a long long time, although when he and his cousin had passed through before the path had seemed very short.

At last he reached the end of the cave and sprang out on to his feet. Confronting him was a huge giant as big as a tree. The boy was terrified, but the giant said, 'Come with me, my boy, I am your grandfather.' He tucked the boy under his arm inside his blanket and carried him to his home, which two animals, a wolf and a wolverine, were guarding after the manner of dogs. The boy remained there for many days with the giant, who gave him plenty to eat, though he ate nothing himself.

One day the giant said to the boy, 'Go and see where the rabbit are, so that I may set snares for them.' The boy searched all round the place, seeing no rabbit tracks, but many herds of caribou. On his return he said to the giant, 'I saw no rabbit tracks, grandfather, but there were plenty of caribou track and caribou.'

'Yes, yes,' the giant answered, 'they are rabbits. Make me some arrows before I go.' The boy made some arrows of the size an ordinary man would use, but the giant threw them outside saying, 'They are no good. They are too small.' The lad then cut down some big trees and sharpened their tops. These satisfied his grandfather.

In the morning they went out to capture the caribou. From one side of the mountain to the other the giant made a fence of tree trunks, leaving gaps here and there in which he set snares. He stationed the boy near the fence, telling him to shoot with small arrows any caribou that approached him. The giant himself went round behind the caribou and with his shouts drove them towards the fence. They came in countless numbers; many the boy shot, and many were caught in the snares. Afterwards the giant himself came up with many caribou, some strung like rabbits to his belt, others wrapped inside his blanket. He carried them all home and skinned them, stripping off their hides as an ordinary man strips the skin from a rabbit. Since he had eaten nothing for many days he cooked a score of caribou on stakes in front of the fire and ate them all at one meal. He even reproached the boy for eating only a small part of the one caribou set aside for him.

The next day the giant said to the boy, 'Over in that direction are many big wolves. Go and see if you can find them.' The boy went out and saw many shrews, but no wolves. He killed a shrew with his snowshoe, threw the body into the bushes and, returning to camp, told the giant what he had seen and done. 'It is my grandfather that you have killed,' said the giant. 'Did you not see any big wolves?'

'No,' answered the boy, 'there were none.'

'That is strange,' said the giant. 'There have always been wolves around here. Tomorrow I'll go and look myself.'

The next day they went out together and the boy showed him the backs of the shrews. The giant made camp on the spot, took a stick, and tried to lever over the shrew that the boy had killed. He could hardly roll it over, so the boy picked it up in his fingers and threw it into the camp. 'How strong you are,' said the giant, who proceeded to skin and cook it. The first day he ate one leg, the second day another leg; it was five days before he could consume the whole shrew. Meanwhile the boy ate the rest of his caribou.

They remained for some time in this place. Then the giant said, 'There are two big beaver living somewhere over yonder. Go and find out the place and I will kill them.'

The boy skirted a large lake without finding any trace of beaver or their houses, but on a big mountain nearby he saw many fallen trees scored as with an axe. He returned to the giant and said, 'Grandfather, I saw no big beaver, but there were many fallen trees covered with claw marks as though they had been chopped with an axe.'

'Those are beaver marks,' the giant replied. 'Tomorrow I will go and kill them.'

Next day they went to the big lake, the giant carrying a huge pole. He planted the pole in the ice and set the boy on top of it, saying, 'When the walking stick shakes to and fro call me, for a big beaver will be gnawing it;' then he went upon to the mountain and stamped around.

Soon the stick began to shake, and the boy shouted to the giant, 'Grandfather, come. A huge beaver is gnawing through the pole.' The giant rushed up and killed it.

'There is still another,' he said, and he stamped around on the mountain again. The pole shook a second time, and the giant, called by the boy, killed the second beaver. 'Now we will go home,' he said. 'There are never more than two beaver together.'

When they reached camp he chopped off the tails of the beaver and threw one to each of his watch dogs, saying, 'These are not good to eat.' But the boy caught one tail and cooked it for himself.

When it was ready he said to the giant, 'Grandfather, open your mouth. I want you to taste this.'

'Then tie yourself to that tree before you throw it,' answered the giant. The boy lashed himself securely to the tree and threw the beaver tail; only the lashings saved him from being engulfed with it in the giant's maw. 'What was that choice meat you gave me?' his grandfather asked.

'It was one of the beaver tails you cut off and threw to the dogs; the other one they have already eaten.' The giant seized his huge walking stick, smote his dogs on the back, cutting them in two, took out the beaver tail and swallowed it. Then he put the halves of the dogs together again and they sprang up alive. The bodies of the two beaver he ate at one meal.

One day the giant said to the boy, 'Go and see if there is a big man fishing through the ice of the lake.' The boy walked all over the lake but saw only a large island with one big tree standing up in the middle, a dry tree without limbs.

He went back and told the giant, 'I saw no man fishing on the lake, only a large island with one big limbless tree standing up in the centre.'

'That is the man,' answered his grandfather. 'You thought it was an island. It is a man and the tree is his fishing pole. Come with me tomorrow. I am going to kill him. While we are fighting go behind him and chop his legs with an axe.'

Next day they went together to the lake, and the giant and the fisherman fought against one another. The fisherman was the stronger, and would have killed the giant if the boy had not cut his enemy's legs and caused him to fall to the ground. The giant then killed him and pushed him through the hole in the ice. Up to this time the giant had drunk nothing, despite his enormous meals; but now he said, 'I want to drink,' and, stretching himself flat on the ice, he drank and drank all day, until the water in the lake was drained and the ice suddenly collapsed. Then they went home.

On the following day the giant said, 'Yesterday I killed that big man. Now go and see if you can find his wife.' The boy walked all around the lake, but saw only a long ravine in a mountain. He returned and told his grandfather, who said, 'That is a woman, not a mountain. Tomorrow I will go and fight her, but you must stay at home, and take my copper walking-stick. If tomorrow rain should fall in large drops like fish, one side white and one side red, you will know that the woman has killed me. Then flee to your own country, or she will come and kill you too. Before you start out hold up my copper walking-stick and let it fall. Your home will lie in the direction in which it points. If you are hungry on the journey let the stick fall again and it will point in the direction of game, which you will find not far from its tip. Finally, when you draw near your home, fasten the stick to the top of a big tree where no one can see it and leave it there.'

Early in the morning the giant went away to fight the woman, leaving the boy in camp. After a time rain began to fall, huge drops, half red and half white. The boy, instead of going straight home, went to find out what had happened to his grandfather. In the place where he had seen the ravine there was now a smokehouse inhabited by two women and two boys. His grandfather's body, cut in two at the waist, lay half on one side of the house, half on the other, and the boys were shooting their arrows into each half alternately. At this sight the giant's grandson became filled with anger. He killed the two boys, took their arrows and shot also the two women. He placed the bodies of the boys between those of the women, piled logs across them to form a funeral pyre, placed his grandfather's body on top and burnt them all. Then he went home, weeping. But to this day you can see the giant's body at a place known as Kwanchaz, south of Francois Lake. There stands a mountain, divided into two, that looks like a man, with two small lakes forming his eyes.

Now the boy remembered his grandfather's words, and, guided by the copper walking-stick, set out for his own country. When he was hungry he let the stick fall, and, circling round its point, found a big black bear in its den. He killed it, cut off a small portion of the meat for himself and threw the rest away. Other bears he killed in the same manner whenever he had need. After a long time he came to the place where his sister had died of laughter. There he climbed a tall tree, and fastened his stick to the top where no one could see it. Then he went on to the village.

Now his father and mother had become very poor since the loss of the three children, and spent nearly all their days in weeping. When the boy arrived and stood outside the house his younger sister, who was playing there, ran in to tell her mother. But the mother would not believe her, and beat her with a stick, saying, 'Why do you tell lies? Your brother has been dead for a long time.' The girl went outside to cry, but, seeing her brother still standing there, she ran in again and told her father.

'Are you sure it is your brother?' the father asked; and the little girl answered,

'Yes.' Then the mother went out and found the son, whom she had believed dead. Both she and his father wept for joy.

The boy remained for a time in his parent's house, going out only rarely. At last he began to notice that there were no young men in the village, only girls; and he asked his mother, 'What has become of all the young men? There is not a single one left in the village.'

His mother answered him, 'You were away so long that they all died.'

He knew, however, that she was concealing something, and one day he called to his little sister, 'I am going to shoot some ducks. Come with me.' They went out together, and the boy shot a swan. Then he asked the little girl, 'Where did all the young men go?'

'I don't know,' she answered. 'I have never seen any young men.'

'If you do not tell me I will kill you,' her brother said, and, stringing his arrow, he shot her in the little finger.

The girl was terrified and said, 'All the young men went, away to the sky to see Sa's two beautiful daughters and never returned.'

'Ah, now I know,' the boy answered. 'I'll depart at once and you can go home alone.' He handed his sister a small wisp of the swan's down and said, 'Lie down and blow this down into the air. As it ascends I will ascend with it.' The girl blew the down into the air, and the boy floated up into the sky, while his sister went home to tell her parents.

The boy discovered a small hole in the sky, and passing through it, found a good country like that he had left below on earth. He wandered about until he came to two houses, one small and one large. He entered the small one first, and discovered an old woman who seemed very angry at his appearance. 'Sa has killed the other young men,' she said, 'why, have you come?' Then she added more quietly, 'All the other young men chose to go to Sa's house first and passed me by. You have been wiser, so I will help you. Every time Sa bids you go and do something come and tell me before you leave.' She then gave him two hollow bones about a foot long and said, 'When you enter the big house, Sa will say to you, "My son-in-law, what are you going to eat in my house?" He will heat two big stones, one black and the other red, bid you open your mouth and will throw them in. That is the way he killed the other young men. But when you enter put one of these tubes in your mouth and let the first stone pass down the tube out of your body. Then go outside, remove the first tube, which will be greatly burnt, and put in the second tube to protect yourself from the other stone.'

The boy thanked the old woman and entered Sa's house. Everything happened as the old woman had said. Sa welcomed him and said, 'My son-in-law, what are you going to eat in my house?' He then placed two stones in the fire, one black, the other red; but while they were still heating the boy secretly placed one of the bone tubes in his mouth. Suddenly Sa said, 'Open your mouth;' and when the boy opened his mouth he threw into it one of the hot stones, which passed down the tube and out of the boy's body without harming him. Going outside, he removed the tube and replaced it with the second one that the old woman had given him. In the same manner he swallowed unharmed the second stone that Sa threw into his mouth.

Greatly puzzled, Sa now took his axe and walked out to the end of a tree that overhung a small lake near by. There he deliberately dropped his axe into the water, and returning inside, said to the boy, 'My son-in-law, I have dropped my axe into the water. Jump in and recover it.'

The boy went out and visited the old woman. 'My grandmother, Sa has thrown his axe into the lake and orders me to jump in and recover it.' She gave him a hair from her head and a tiny fish about half an inch long with big eyes.

'Take these,' she said. 'He will cause the lake to freeze after you have jumped in, and you will not be able to rise to the surface. But change yourself into this little fish I give you and search out a hole. Then change to the hair and you will be able to issue safely.'

The boy thanked her and with the hair and the fish jumped off the end of the tree that Sa had pretended to chop. Under the water he found a road, which led him to a smokehouse inhabited by sculpins. 'Where is Sa's axe?' he asked them; but their mouths were sealed and they could not answer.

There was one fish, however, whose mouth had not been entirely sealed, and it answered, 'I heard the axe drop there behind my mother.' After the boy had found the axe he removed his legging, rolled it between his hands and laid it on the ground. It became a stone, and all the fish went under it, which is the reason that the sculpin always lurks under stones. Only the fish that had directed him to the axe failed to get under in time; so the boy removed his other legging and changed that also into a stone to shelter his friend.

Now he tried to return to the surface, but found the lake solidly covered with ice. He changed himself into a loon and swam all around until he found a tiny hole. Then he changed himself into the small fish that the old woman had given him, but when his eye proved too big to pass through the hole he changed himself into the hair and emerged. Now that he was on the surface he changed into a boy again and took the axe to Sa's house. Seeing Sa asleep beside the fire with his shirt off, he threw the axe among the hot ashes, which scattered over the old man's back and burned him. Sa sprang to his feet, saw the boy and the axe, and said, 'Alas, my son-in-law, what am I going to do now?' But his daughters were glad, and married the boy.

Sa, however, still plotted to kill him. One day he said, 'I am going to split trees to make a salmon trap. Come and help me.' But the boy first visited the old woman's house and told her Sa's command.

'Yes,' said the old woman. 'He has killed many young men by that device. He will split a tree and place a wedge in the crack. Then he will tell you to leap through the crack to the other side, but just as you leap he will pull out the wedge and crush you. Take this file and keep it upright beside you when you pass through; and drop this lump of white mud. Then the tree will not nip you.'

The boy thanked the old woman, took the white mud and the file and returned to Sa. Sa cut down a huge tree in the woods and opened up a big crack in its trunk with his hammer and wedge. 'Jump through this crack,' he ordered the boy. The boy jumped, keeping the file upright and dropping the white mud in the crack as the old woman had told him, so that when Sa pulled out the wedge the file protected him and he passed through in safety.

When the mud oozed from the crack; however, Sa thought it was the boy's brains and tasted it. 'How sweet his brains are,' he exclaimed then he saw the boy on the other side of the trunk and cried, 'Oh, my son-in-law, you have conquered me again. What am I going to do now?' They went home together, and Sa's two daughters who were now the boy's wives, rejoiced greatly, for they loved their husband.

Sa made another attempt. He said to the boy, 'Make a fire for the copper sweat house and we will go inside together and sweat.'

The boy went to see the old woman. 'Sa told me to make a fire for his copper sweat house.'

'Yes, he has killed many men by that device. You will see their bones lying on the ground outside the sweat house. Twice he will attempt your life. The first time you will become so hot that you will be nearly dead. Then break a piece off this block of ice I am giving you. After that the sweat house will become very cold and you will be almost frozen; but if you open this bag a little a warm wind will fill the place and make it comfortable.'

The boy thanked her, and returned to Sa with his block of ice and the bag. Sa made a big fire and heated large stones. When they were very hot he said to the boy, 'Go inside the sweat house;' but when the boy entered the old man rolled a big stone against the door so that he could not go out again. The hot stones heated the copper sweat house so terribly that the boy nearly died; but he broke off a fragment of his ice and the place grew cold as in winter. He was now almost frozen, but he opened his bag a little and let out some warm wind, which made the temperature so pleasant that he fell asleep. Sa's voice awakened him; he was telling his daughters to open up the sweat house and throw out the boy's bones.

The girls came slowly, saying one to another, 'It is a shame that our father should kill all the young men. This one was such a fine-looking boy.' At these words the boy laughed softly. The girls kicked open the door of the sweat house, and when they saw him lying not dead, but apparently asleep, they went inside and played with him, closing the door behind them.

Presently Sa heard their laughing voices and called out only, 'Why are you laughing? Why don't you throw out all the bones and come home?'

But the girls answered, 'We have thrown out all his bones except his head, which we are going to throw out now.' They played with the boy all day inside the sweat house, and at evening they returned with him to their father's house.

Sa was troubled and said, 'Alas; my son-in-law. You have conquered me again. What am I going to do now?'

Sa tried again. He said, 'We will go and gather big eggs on an island in the sea where they abound.'

The boy went to ask the old woman's advice. 'He will maroon you there,' she said. 'But think of me and I will contrive something to help you.'

He returned to Sa, and together they crossed in a small canoe to a distant island. There the old man said, 'Go round that side while I go round this.' The boy gathered many eggs, but when he returned to the place where they had disembarked he saw his father-in-law far out on the water, returning home. Then the boy thought of the old woman, and immediately a fine canoe with a paddle appeared on the beach. The boy placed all his eggs on board and paddled home; even his leggings he filled with eggs. After he had landed and put his eggs on the beach he pushed the canoe and paddle out into the water, where the vessel changed into an otter and the paddle into a mink. Then he carried his eggs up to the house, where the old man was sleeping with his back to the fire again. The boy flung his eggs into the hot embers and burned his back.

Sa made another attempt. He said to the boy, 'Tomorrow I am going up the mountain to discover where there are mountain goats. You will come with me.'

The boy went to the old woman. 'Sa has ordered me to accompany him up the mountain to find out where there are mountain goats.'

'Yes,' she answered, 'there is a very dangerous precipice on top of the mountain. He will tell you to look at some mountain goats down below and will push you over the edge. But take this swan's down and change yourself into that. Then you will light gently and unharmed at the bottom.'

The boy thanked her, took the swan's down and returned to Sa. Next day they ascended a mountain and stood together on the summit, where a very steep precipice fell away on one side. 'See if there are any mountain goats on that side,' said Sa. The boy looked over, and Sa pushed, him over the edge. As he fell he changed into the swan's down and lit gently at the bottom; there he changed into a squirrel and raced up the mountain again to the summit. Sa was looking over the edge, saying, 'I can't see where the boy has gone.' Then the squirrel came up behind him, changed to the boy again and pushed him headlong. His body was broken into fragments and his blood wept. As it wept darkness descended and Sa's mouth said to it, 'My son-in-law has killed me. Make me alive again.'

The boy now descended the mountain on the other side and came to

Sa's body. He gathered up all the fragments and the blood, laid them in a pile, and commanded the sun to circle round them. The sun circled round the pile, and Sa came to life again.

The boy would not return home with Sa after this, because the old woman had told him that she could help him no further; Sa would try to kill him in other ways, but he must rely on himself. So they wandered about to different places.

They saw a grizzly bear. 'Kill it,' said Sa. The boy killed it. 'Now skin it for me,' the old man ordered. 'I want to make a blanket for myself.' The boy skinned it, but allowed the fat to remain on the hide. Sa took it for a blanket, wearing it with the fur inside. He then said, 'I am going to burn up the countryside.'

'Very well,' answered the boy. He set all the countryside ablaze, hoping to burn the boy in it; but the latter went round behind the fire, spat and extinguished it. He now took out of his bag the skin of a red-headed woodpecker, and, swinging it around his head, himself set fire to the country all around. Wherever the boy walked the fire went out, but Sa's bear skin blanket began to scorch, and the melting fat that dropped on to his legs burnt him so severely that he wept with pain. He followed behind the boy where the fire was extinguished, and entreated him to stop the blaze.

'Stop the fire,' he cried. 'I'll let you return home with my two daughters.' The boy extinguished the fire, and they went on.

Again Sa said, 'Let us compete once more. I'll make rain.' He spat into the air, and hailstones as big as a man's fist rained down on them. The boy took shelter under a large tree with long leaves, so that the hail could not strike him.

When the storm ended he said, 'I'll make rain too,' and taking a flint from his bag he threw it into the air. Now it rained flint stones. Sa too tried to find shelter under a tree, but the flint severed all the branches and cut his face and body until the blood streamed all over him.

'Stop the rain, boy,' he cried. 'I'll give you my two daughters to take home with you.' The boy stopped the rain, and they went back to Sa's house.

The boy remained in Sa's house, having his two daughters as wives. One day a red-headed woodpecker began to peck a hole in the house post. 'Shoot that woodpecker for me,' said Sa. 'I want the bird. You have married my daughters, and must obey me.' The boy shot his arrow over the head of the bird and it fell to the ground. Sa picked it up, rejoicing, and fondled it.

The boy thought to himself, 'Let the bird peck out his eyes and escape.' It pecked out Sa's eyes and blinded him. Then darkness fell over everything, the bird escaped, and Sa wept. 'Come here and heal my eyes,' he begged the boy. 'You may take my daughters home with you.' The boy moistened his finger on his tongue and touched Sa's eyes. Immediately his sight was restored.

'No more will I try to kill you,' said Sa. 'You are too clever for me.' So they remained there quietly for a long time. But at last Sa said to his daughters, 'My daughters, your husband lingers here too long and is grieving for his old home. Return with him.' So the boy started out with his two wives. Scarcely had they left Sa's house when he called, 'My elder daughter, return; my house is burning.' The girl returned, and Sa gave her a ball containing cold. They started out again, and again Sa called, 'My younger daughter, come back. My house is burning.' He gave his second daughter a ball containing heat. Then they descended to earth down a big tree the top of which reached to the sky, while the bottom rested on a hilltop south of Fraser Lake.

When they drew near the village the boy said to his wives, 'Remain here while I go to see my parents. Later I will send my brother and sister to bring you.' He went on to his home and said to his parents, 'My two wives are just outside the village. Go, mother, and call them in.' His mother went out to bring them in, but as she drew near them, the elder girl opened her ball of cold. Immediately the air became exceedingly cold, although it was the middle of summer. The mother, unable to endure it, stood and shivered a moment, then returned to the house to get her blanket.

She said to her son, 'I tried to approach the girls, but it became so cold I could not reach near enough even to speak to them.'

'Try once more,' he answered. The old woman put on two blankets, moccasins, mittens and a cap, and went off again; but as she drew near a second time the younger girl opened her ball of heat, and the air became scorching. The old woman struggled close, so close that she was already stretching out her hand to grasp one of the girls when the heat overwhelmed her and forced her to return.

She said to her son, 'I had already extended my hand to take hold of one of the girls when the heat overwhelmed me, and I was unable to touch her.'

'Never mind,' her son answered. 'Let them return home. I don't want them any more.' So the two girls returned to their father.

The boy remained in his father's house all summer, rarely going outside. When autumn came, and the ice began to form on the lakes and rivers, many young men from Fraser Lake went down to where the Nattle river joins the Nechako to hook in to shore the big ice cakes that floated by. The boy said to his mother, 'I am going to watch the young men playing in the canyon.' His mother begged him not to go, but he answered, 'I shall only watch them, not play myself.' So she gave her consent, and the boy went down to the river. He had neither pole nor hook.

One of the young men said to him, 'Play with us.'

'I have no hook,' he answered.

'I will lend you a pole and hook.'

'Very well.' He fastened the hook to the pole with his dentalium headband, and, when a large ice cake came floating by, hooked it with his pole. But the hook fell off, and his dentalium headband was left on the ice. Seizing his blanket, he leaped on to the floating cake, and shouted goodbye. Day and night he stood on the ice cake as it travelled downstream. Whenever he reached a canyon he changed the ice into a canoe and passed through safely; then he changed it into an ice cake again.

At last he came to a big, level space without trees near the salt water, where many little people were playing games close to their village. He was very hungry, and landing from his ice cake, he walked around the village until he reached a small house. He sat down outside the door, and an old woman bade him enter. When he went inside she said to him, 'You thought all those people who play there in the open glade every day, never working, were human beings, but they are not. This is the village of the salmon. Some of them have roe inside them. Whenever you are hungry take a little girl aside, and smite her with a stick. As she falls dead she will change to a salmon, and the roe will fall out of her body. But be sure after you have cooked and eaten the salmon to burn all the skin and bones.'

The boy was very hungry. He thanked the old woman and, going outside, approached a little girl and said, 'Come and play with me over yonder.' He led her out of sight of the village and killed her with a stick.

She changed to a salmon, which he cooked and ate, burning the skin and bones. It was full of roe, which he also ate. Then he thought to himself, 'I wonder why the old woman told me to burn all the skin and bones. I'll try to find out.' So he left one eye beside the fire, unburnt, and returned to the village. Soon he noticed a little girl weeping because her eye pained her.

The old woman called the boy inside and said to him, 'How is it this girl's eye pains her?'

He answered, 'I burned all the skin and bones as you bade me. But one eye was not fully cooked, so I laid it on one side.'

'Run quickly,' she ordered. 'Cook it a little more and eat it.' The boy cooked and ate it, and at once the little girl's eye was healed.

When he returned to the old woman she said to him, 'Remain here and play with the children. You will be sorry if you do not. Whenever you are hungry kill a boy, or, if you want roe, a girl.' So the boy remained there all winter, playing with the salmon people.

One day he ate a salmon and burned all the bones except a rib. When he returned to the old woman she asked him, 'What have a done? One of the boys has a pain in his side.'

'I buried a rib,' the boy answered ; and she commanded, 'Dig it up and burn it.' He dug it but and burned it; at once the boy was healed.

(That is why Indians never throw away any part of a salmon, but burn it in the fire whatever they or their dogs fail to eat. It is like other fish. When it is killed the Indian may eat its body, but its soul or essence returns to the water and becomes a fish again.)

Spring came, and all the salmon prepared to depart, making hooks and adzes for themselves. By March everything was ready, and they said to one another, 'Let us depart.'

The old woman now called the boy and said, 'The time has come for the salmon to return to your country and lay their eggs. You will return with them. Take your hook and adze and follow them. Whenever you reach a canyon pull yourself up it with your hook; and when you reach a dam cut your way through it with your adze.'

One morning the salmon people leaped in a body into the water and became salmon. The old woman rubbed the boy's face and body and said, 'Leap in and follow them.' He leaped, and changed into a salmon. He followed the school up the Fraser river, sporting with them and joining in all their games. Whenever they reached a canyon they pulled themselves up with their hooks, (a salmon has a little bone hook on its shoulder); and whenever they came to a salmon dam one of them would cut a small hole with his adze through the bottom of it and call on the rest to follow him. In some places, where many berries overhung the banks, they changed to human beings, left the water, and feasted on the berries until they were satisfied; then, leaping into the water again, they reverted to salmon and continued up the river.

Finally they came to an Indian village at the entrance of Fraser Lake. A man who was watching at the salmon traps heard the salmon coming up the river, playing and shouting, and he thought to himself, 'Salmon don't usually act like this. Surely that boy who went away with them is returning.' Now the boy knew that his father had made a pen for salmon and set a trap in it, just below the entrance of the lake, so he searched around until he found it, and entered the trap. As he lay there he prayed, 'May my father not strike me with a stick, but carry me up to the village and lay me outside his house.'

His father went down to inspect his trap. Finding a salmon in it he carried it up to his house and laid it down outside, without striking it with a stick. When no one was near the salmon changed to the boy, who went inside, wrapped himself in his father's blanket, and fell fast asleep.

Early next morning everyone went out to get salmon, not noticing the boy sleeping in one corner. After a time his little brother entered the house and recognised him. He ran and told his mother, saying, 'Mother, my brother has returned and is sleeping inside the house.' But his mother, not believing him, was angry that he should renew their grief, and beat him with a stick, saying, 'Why do you lie? Your brother was drowned last autumn.' The little boy cried, but persisted in his story.

Soon afterwards he entered the house again, and his brother, who, was now awake, said to him, 'Go and tell your mother that I am lying here inside the house.'

The boy ran out again to his mother and said, 'It is my brother who is lying there. He spoke to me.'

Still the mother thought it was some other boy, and said as she entered, 'Why are you sleeping here? This is not your home.'

But her son opened up his blanket and answered, 'It is really I, your son. I have come home.' Then his parents rejoiced exceedingly.

All the time the people were trapping the salmon the boy remained in the house, eating and sleeping. But when the salmon season ended, the young men and girls began to play each day in an open space near the village; and the boy would sometimes watch them, although he never joined in their games.

Now before he had gone down to the salt water he had courted a certain girl, intending to marry her later. He played with her and no other. She was the daughter of a chief, and during his absence she allowed many young men to visit her at her home and play with her. After the salmon season was over the boy visited her in her house one day, and, finding several young men courting her, was so angry that he return home without speaking to her. A few nights later he visited her again. The young men who were there all rose at his entrance, and one of them said to him, 'Before you went away you used to court this girl, intending to make her your wife. Now you have come to visit her again. We will all go out and leave you alone with her.' So they all went out, and he was left alone with the girl.

Now was his opportunity to punish her for her infidelity. He took from his side a piece of salmon skin that he had retained when he reverted from a salmon to a man, and unknown to the girl, he laid it against her side. Then he rose up and said, 'Now I will return home. You may play with anyone you wish.' Hardly had he left when the girl's side began to irritate her so much that she could not resist scratching it. But the irritation became more intense, and she scratched and scratched until she killed herself. So she was punished for her misconduct.

The boy now wanted to play with the other children, who were bathing in the Nattle river. His parents protested, but he said that he would simply go and watch them. As he lay watching them, the children called to him to join in their sport, but he said, 'I may not touch the water, for I lived in it so long.' They still called to him until at last he undressed and entered the water. Taking care not to wet his head, he swam a little way towards a stick they had set up as a mark and returned, saying, 'I can't reach it.'

But when they laughed at him and said, 'You were a salmon, and yet you can't swim as far as we can,' he leaped angrily into the water again, touched the stick, and changing into a loon, swam up the river into the lake. The villagers launched their canoes and, tried to capture him, but without success. Thus loons came into existence.

With the approach of winter the lake froze over, but the boy loon still remained at its outlet. The villagers tried to capture it, and at the end of winter a lame girl succeeded by placing pitch round its water hole. It changed into a boy again and married her.

After his wife had borne him a son the youth went out hunting. Every day he went out, and every day he returned carrying on his shoulder the intestinal fat of a black bear wrapped around a stick. He never carried home any meat, and his bear fat he placed in a small birchbark basket which he kept hung up behind his sleeping place. Small as the basket was it never became full, however much fat he placed in it.

One day while he was away hunting one of the villagers said, 'This basket is very small, yet he puts bear fat in it every day and it never seems to get fuller. Let us take it down and count the number of pieces of fat inside it.' So they lifted down the basket and laid it on the ground. Piece by piece, they took out the fat until the pile on the ground was enormous; still the basket remained as full as before. They grew tired of counting, and began to put the fat back again, but the first piece they put in filled the basket and the pile still remained on the floor. Terrified, they concealed the fat in different places and hung the basket up again.

When the salmon boy returned towards evening, his wife was sitting beside the fire, and in front of her was her little son, who, though just born, was able to walk and talk. The child said to his father, 'Father, the people have taken some bear fat from this basket.' The salmon boy stopped immediately, while his wife and the people around the sides of the smoke house sat silent and terror stricken. He stood there without moving all evening, and all through the night. The people watched him until they fell asleep; only his wife tried to remain awake. From time to time her head would nod, and when she looked up she would see her husband rising into the air; but the moment she looked at him he would resume his position beside the fire. Finally he spoke to her and said, 'Next year at this time I will come again, perhaps as a mosquito, perhaps as a wasp. If some one captures me and holds me I will become a man again.' His wife kept on watching him, but at last, overcome with drowsiness, she closed her eyes for a moment in sleep. When she reopened them her husband had disappeared.

That winter the salmon boy's younger brother found the den of a black bear and killed the animal; but when he skinned it and cut it up there was no fat inside its body. The next day he killed another bear; it too lacked fat. So it happened again and again; every bear killed that winter lacked intestinal fat, for the salmon boy had taken it all.

The following autumn, exactly twelve months after the salmon boy had disappeared, a yellow-jacket flew into his wife's house. His mother tried to catch it in a blanket, but it escaped. His father, his brother, his wife, all tried to catch it in their blankets, but it always managed to fly away. At last his wife remembered his words, and, folding her blanket, she threw it over the wasp and caught it. Then she tied it with her hair, but it buzzed so fiercely that it broke the hair and flew out of the house.

When winter came the salmon boy's brother went hunting again. He killed a black bear and camped beside the carcass for the night. Hardly had he made his camp when he saw his brother approach the farther side of the fire, his skin black and cracked all over. For a long time he did not speak, but pulled out a small piece of miserable black meat from under his blanket and warmed it over the fire on the end of a stick. Water, not grease, came out of the meat, yet he rubbed it over his body. Then at last he spoke, 'My brother, it is an evil place in which I live. I stand on the moon where the wind blows fiercely all the time. That is why my skin is blackened and cracked. This meat I am eating is from a big crow, for there is a crow that lives in the sky. You will never see me again, but do not weep. Soon you, your mother, your sister, my own wife and all the rest of the people will die and be forgotten. But I shall live forever, standing in the moon. Say goodbye to them all for me.' With these words he vanished like the wind and was never seen again. Only at night the Indians still see him, standing in the moon.

A Big Frog

A big frog near Moricetown squawked day and night: 'Kwa Kwa.'

At last the people called to it, 'What is the matter with that frog that it squawks all the time?'

The frog answered, 'I am only talking to my sister's son, Luskwatak.'

The Trickster

At Moricetown there is a rock whose smooth face slopes steeply down to the water. It is known as Estes' Slide, because Estes, Trickster, once slid down its face and left his traces on it. At Beamont station, again, just west of Moricetown, there is a long trench across a stone on top of the hill. It was Estes who made this trench as he walked along.

Estes was the son of a nobleman. When he was a young man, he refused to eat anything. Even though his mother offered him the best of food he hardly tasted it. Then an old woman gave him some berries with which she had mixed rotten flesh from her leg. He ate it greedily, but it made him so hungry that he went round among the houses eating up all the food like a dog. The people were so angry with him, and his father so ashamed, that at last he ran away. This was the beginning of his career as a trickster.

At the salt water he came to a village, which, hungry as he was, he feared to enter. He changed himself into a raven, flew into a tree and called: 'The raven has the rump of a small whale.' Then he flew away, changed into a man, and entering the village, asked its inhabitants, 'Did you hear anything today?'

Someone said, 'Yes. I heard a raven call. The raven has the rump of a small whale."'

'That is unfortunate,' answered Estes. 'Raven uttered the same words at my place and all the people died except myself. That is why I have to wander. Now I am afraid that all you people will die also. There is only one way in which you can escape. Close up your houses, take your blankets and canoes and leave the village for several sleeps.'

The people took his advice and departed in their canoes, leaving most of their food behind. As they put off from the shore, Estes said to them, 'I am going away over yonder,' but when they were out of sight, he re-entered their village and ate all their food. One of the inhabitants returned after several weeks to see if their property was safe, but by that time Estes had disappeared.

Estes had two daughters with whom he fished for a month until their smoke house was full. They dried the meat, the eggs and the heads of the fish separately, the heads in order to make oil; and they stored the meat in boxes of spruce bark, the eggs and the oil in boxes of birch bark, intending to make holes in the ground and keep them for the winter. Before they had actually stored them away, however, Estes wandered off for four days in succession, and his daughters did not know where he went. Then on the fourth evening he said to them, 'My heart feels queer, my body is shaking all over as though someone is about to attack me. You had better go into the woods and hide while I wait and see if there are enemies around.' The girls were frightened and hid. At daylight they heard shouts in the camp as of men fighting, and concluded that enemies were attacking their father.

But when the shouting lasted the whole day the elder girl said, 'I don't believe father is fighting at all; for he could not resist a whole party all day long. I am going back to see.'

As she drew near the camp she saw her father surrounded on all sides by birds and animals to whom he was giving all the eggs and oil. She chased them away, and declared she would kill her father. Her younger sister said, 'Let our poor father go. Don't kill him.'

But she answered, 'Why has he given away all my food? Now we shall starve to death.' Then she shoved him into an empty box, covered it tightly with a lid and kicked it into the river.

Estes went floating downstream. As he floated along he waved his hand outside the box and caught a ling. Cutting open its belly, he inserted a little bear fat, and more fat inside its head. The fish said, 'I have a headache;' so he replaced the fat in its head with two stones. The fish then said, 'I feel all right now;' and he threw it into the water again. So now this fish has two little white stones in its head and a thick layer of fat on its belly.

Estes continued to float down the river in his box. His brother, who was living with his daughters far below beside a salmon dam that he had constructed, heard a drumming against the piles and said to one of his daughters, 'Go and see what is making that noise. I think Estes must be interfering with my dam.' The girl lit a birch bark torch and went down to the water. When she pulled the box out onto the shore and opened it, out stepped Estes, his head entirely bald owing to the tightness of the lid. After sleeping that night in his brother's house, he asked his niece to comb his head as though his hair were still long. Then, as she combed, his hair grew again until it fell to his thighs.

Estes now wanted to return up the river. As he walked along, he saw a number of little ducks cooking their eggs over a fire. He said to them, 'Bsa. Sleep, little ducks;' and when the ducks fell asleep, he ate all their eggs and changed into a stump. After a time they awoke and wanted to eat their eggs, but found them gone.

One of them saw the stump and said, 'Here is a stump to put on the fire.'

But the others said, 'Be careful. We did not see that stump there before.' They gathered round to examine it, but Estes changed into a man again and ran away laughing.

As he continued up the river he became hungry again and wanted to eat a ling that he saw in the water near the opposite bank. He called to it, 'My mother lived as a ling for a long time. She had a big lip. I wonder if you resemble her.'

The fish allowed him to approach until he was almost able to seize it, but then it recognised him and swam away, saying, 'I know you. You are Estes. You want to kill me.'

Estes walked on. Seeing many steel head salmon, he sat on the bank of the river and said to them, 'Jump up and hit my heart.' A steel head hit him on the heart and knocked him unconscious. After a time he rose and tried to catch it, but it had regained the water. He invited them again and again to strike his heart, but each time he fail to catch them. At last he said, 'I am very foolish. If I make a hole in the ground for them to fall into I can catch them easily.' So he made a hole in the ground and invited the salmon to strike his heart again. One of them knocked him down, but itself fell into the hole, whereupon Estes rose and killed it with a stick. He lit a fire, spitted his fish on a stick and set it up to roast. When it was almost done some ducks came along and said to him, 'Estes, go to sleep.' Instantly he fell asleep. Then they ate his salmon, rubbed a little grease on his hand and lips, placed a tiny fish between his teeth and hid.

After a time Estes awoke and said, 'Estes, wake up. Your salmon is cooked.' He rose and went to the fire, but his salmon was gone. Then he felt grease on his lips and hand and said, 'Estes, did you eat the salmon yourself? No, you couldn't have eaten it, for you are still hungry. I'll cut open my stomach and see if I ate it.' Suddenly the ducks laughed aloud, and Estes knew it was they who had eaten it. He caught them and tried to twist their necks, but could not kill them. Then he tried to hammer their heads on his knee, but he could only flatten them. Finally he said to them, 'Wait here while I get a stick to kill you.' But when he went to find a stick, the ducks swam away down the river. As they were going he cried, 'You ducks are no good. Hereafter people shall call you flat heads because I flattened your heads.'

Estes walked on up the river until he reached a place about twelve miles west of Fort George. There he camped beside a dam which had an opening for the passage of the salmon and a fall below. He wanted to catch some of the salmon, but had no weapon. 'What shall I use to kill them?' he said.

A voice answered, 'Make a spear.' He made a spear, and caught so many that he completely filled a smokehouse; so he stayed there for a month to dry them and extract their fat. To pass the time he tried to make himself a medicine man, and since there were no singers to help him, gathered some stumps and set them around like men inside his smoke house, placing at the back two large stumps to represent his wives. Each day he sang and danced around the house, pouring grease on the stumps to pay them for their imaginary singing. But once as he was dancing, his hair caught in a salmon that hung over the door. It made him so angry that he pulled it down and threw it outside. Then all the dried fish came to life again and returned to the water; not one remained, not even an egg. As they disappeared, too, they caused snow to fall and cover his house so that he could not go out. He placed a stump, one of his two wives, on the fire, lay down beside it and wept for several days, while the smoke curled upward and issued through a tiny hole in the roof. A berry fell through this hole onto his back, and Guzi, the blue jay, called down to him, 'Estes, why are you weeping? There are many berries out here.' Then Estes shovelled away the snow and went out. Outside there was no snow at all, the weather had the warmth of midsummer, and all the berries were ripe. One may still see near Fort George the little hill where the snow covered his house, and the hole through which he emerged. Near by is Natsankas where he caught the salmon.

Estes gathered many berries and wandered away, no longer ascending the river. He had only one miserable blanket and a bow with small arrows. One day he encountered a black bear and her three cubs, which fled up a tree. He threw away his blanket, saying, 'Now I shall have some good blankets' and was about to shoot the bears when he checked himself, thinking, 'You are foolish, Estes. If you shoot them in the body you will make holes in their skins and spoil your blankets. Don't shoot them in the body, but in the feet.' He shot at the bears' feet until he had used up all his arrows. Then he said to himself, 'Climb the tree and kill them with your hands.' He climbed up and seized a cub, which scratched him so fiercely that he had to let it go. While it fled, he climbed after the second bear and was scratched again. He suffered the same fate with the third and fourth bears; all four animals escaped. Greatly chagrined, he returned to recover his blanket, but a bird had carried it away. He called to the bird, 'What are you doing with my blanket?'

'You abandoned it for me,' the bird replied, and flew away. So now Estes had neither arrows nor blanket.

He went on and approached two girls who sang as they gathered the ripe berries. They were daughters of a chief, and beautifully dressed in long coats of caribou fur decorated with pendants of dentalia shells. Estes envied their clothes and said to them, 'Why are you wearing such warm coats when the sun is so hot? They will spoil with the heat. Lay them in a cool place while you pick your berries. See, I have laid my coat aside.' The girls took his advice and laid aside their coats. Then he said again, 'Why don't you eat these raspberries?'

They answered, 'At our age we are not permitted to eat raspberries, only blueberries.'

'Well, I saw many blueberries over yonder. Come with me and I will show you them.' After leading them away a short distance, he added, 'Keep straight on. The berries are just a little way ahead. I will overtake you presently.' Then as soon as they were out of sight, he ran back, stole their coats and fled.

He came to a place where the people had baited their fish hooks with caribou fat. To plague them he left his coats on the bank, changed to a fish, broke all their lines and ate the bait. The people made a strong line that he could not break and a stouter hook, which caught in his mouth and jerked him out of the water. Several men seized the line to drag him to shore, but his jaw broke off and he ran away. They placed the jaw on a moose skin blanket and danced around it, men and women together. Estes, however, was very angry, and going to the woods, made himself a new jaw of soft maple. On his return he asked an old woman who lived in a small hut on the outskirts of the village why the people were dancing. As soon as she told him he killed her, put on her skin and hobbled with the aid of two walking sticks towards the moose skin. The people saw him coming, and mistaking him for the old woman, said, 'Let the old woman see the jaw; let her sit down near it.' Estes hobbled up and sat down beside his jaw. Presently he rose to dance also, and the people said, 'Make room for the old woman to dance.' But while he was dancing he suddenly threw away his maple jaw, snatched up the proper jaw, stripped off the old woman's skin and ran away.

He came to an open field where some young men were tossing to each other balls of beaver and caribou fat. Estes joined in the game, but as fast as he caught the balls he swallowed them. 'Where do you get them?' he asked,

They answered, 'You must climb one of these tall trees and jump down. At first you will lie as if dead, but when you waken you will find the balls all around you.' Estes had climbed half way up a tall tree when he became frightened and called down, 'Isn't this far enough?'

'No,' they answered. 'Go right up to the top.'

He climbed a little higher and called again, 'Is not this far enough?' and they said,

'No, higher yet.' So he climbed to the top.

'Now jump,' they called. The fall nearly killed him, and while he lay unconscious the youths laid beside him a ball of mingled caribou fat and filth. Estes was so greedy that as soon as he recovered he ate it.

He went on, following a trail littered with swan's down that became thicker and thicker until it covered the ground like snow. At last he came to a small lake and a smoke house in which were two or three girls, but no man. The girls set swan's meat before him, and he sat down and ate. Hanging from the rafters to dry were the bodies of numerous swans. He asked one of the girls, 'How do you catch so many swans?'

She answered, 'My father catches them, using a hat of swan's skin. When the swans settle on the lake he puts on his hat, swims out, ties their legs with a rope and fastens the other end of the rope to a stake on the shore. Then as soon as he takes off his hat the swans fly up and are caught in the noose. The birds are so strong that he can tie only three of them together at one time.'

'Your father is really not very strong,' said Estes. 'When I was young he and I used to have contests of strength. I could carry a heavy stone all round the house while your father could carry it only part of the distance.'

While they were talking many swans settled on the water, and the girl said to him, 'Take the rope and hat and catch them.' Estes swam out with the hat on his head, imitating the cry of the swans, kro, kro, kr.

He tied the legs of the birds, fastened the end of the rope to his waist and swam back to shore; but he forgot to tie the rope to the stake before removing his hat. The swans flew up, carrying him away with them. They carried him down to the salt water, where they kept him all winter.

In the spring the swans flew back again and circled over Fraser Lake round a hole in the ice. Estes cut the rope that bound him to them and fell upon a large rock, into which he sank as though it were mud (you can see the outline of his form to this day, white seams of quartz in a rock of granite). He called to Lynx, 'Lynx, help me to get out of this rock.' Lynx licked away the stone until one of his eyes became visible; but then Raven flew down and pecked it out. Lynx extricated the other eye, and Raven carried that off also. Lynx kept licking the rock until Estes was free, but eyeless. He groped his way along until he found a spruce tree, when he filled his empty eye sockets with balls of gum.

Travelling on, he heard the laughter of girls inside a smoke house and groped for the door. The girls laughed at him and said, 'Ho, Estes is blind.'

He answered, 'No, I am not blind. I was merely searching for some small hole through which to peer at you.' Two girls were playing and laughing inside.

He asked them why they were laughing and they said, 'A little while ago Raven gave us two human eyes that he had carried off. We are making something with them.'

'Show them to me,' said Estes. They gave him one of them. 'This eye is no good,' he said, laughing; 'show me the other.' They gave him the other, whereupon he pulled out his spruce gum eyes, inserted the true ones and ran away.

Estes had other adventures. One winter's day he said to his wife, 'I am going to visit my brother-in-law Dedinye.'

When he reached Dedinye's house, the bird invited him in, then flew up to a small box that was hanging from the ceiling and sang, 'Ho biyo biyo biyo.' Immediately the box filled with ripe huckleberries. The bird flew down, changed to a man and offered the berries to Estses.

He ate half of them and said; 'I will take the rest home to my wife, and return you the box when you come to visit me.' So Estes returned home with the huckleberries. After a time Dedinye went to recover his box. Then Estes too sat on top of it and sang, as the bird had done, 'Ho biyo biyo biyo;' but at his song the box overflowed with dirt, not huckleberries.

Estes said to his wife on another occasion, 'I am going to visit my brother-in-law Rat.' Rat hospitably invited him to enter, then took up his blanket and axe and went outside. Presently he returned with the blanket full of ice, made a hole in the sand of the fire place, put the ice in the hole and covered it. When he removed the covering after a few minutes, the ice had changed to a cooked bird. Estes ate half of it and said, 'I will take the rest home to my wife, and return you the blanket when you come to visit me.' Some time later Rat visited him to regain the blanket, whereupon Estes in his turn covered some ice in the fireplace; but when he removed the covering, the ice had melted and extinguished the fire. Rat was so angry that he snatched up his blanket and went home.

Estes said again, 'I am going to visit my brother-in-law Skunk.' Outside Skunk's house were the carcasses and skins of many caribou. Skunk invited Estes inside, fed him some of the dried meat, and gave him more to take home. Estes said to him, 'How do you manage to kill all these caribou?'

'I strew nuts around my house and go to sleep,' said Skunk. 'In the morning many caribou come to eat the nuts and I shoot them with my poison.' Estes asked him for some of his poison and Skunk gave him three doses. On his way home Estes shot his first dose of poison at a big cottonwood tree, which fell shattered to the ground.

Farther on he shot his second dose at a big stone, saying, 'The tree was not very strong. I'll test the poison on this stone.' He shattered the stone, and finding a still larger one, shattered that also with his third dose. On reaching home he strewed many nuts around his house and lay down to sleep. In the morning when he tried to shoot the caribou that came to eat the nuts, the animals ran away, for he had exhausted all his ammunition.

He returned to Skunk, who asked him, 'Did you kill many deer?'

'No,' said Estes. 'You gave me three doses. With one I shot a cottonwood tree, with the two others stones. Then when I tried to shoot the caribou they fled.' Skunk was very angry, but at Estes' entreaties gave him one more dose, cautioning him not to waste it. So Estes was able to kill an entire herd of caribou. While his wife was drying all the meat, he returned to Skunk to rearm himself, but Skunk had moved away. Estes himself then wandered off, and did not return to his wife.

He came to a lake covered with ducks, swans, geese and other water fowl. Plotting to capture them he gathered a quantity of moss in his blanket and carried it on his back to the water. The ducks called to each other, 'Look at that pack.' One after another asked him, 'What are you carrying?' but he pretended not to hear them.

At last he stopped and said, 'It is only a blanket full of songs.'

'Let us hear them,' they begged. 'We will go with you wherever you wish if we may listen to them.'

Estes answered, 'Very well. I will arrange a place at my house and will call you to hear them when everything is ready.'

He built a large house without any holes and with only one narrow door, and invited the ducks to hear his songs. They came in such numbers that they filled both sides of the house. Estes then began to sing and dance, but presently he stopped and said, 'This song is so strong that unless you close your eyes you will all die.' When the ducks closed their eyes, he went singing all along one side of the house and killed them.

But a fish duck on the opposite side stealthily opened one eye and saw what he was doing. It called out, 'Estes is killing us.' All the surviving ducks rushed outside, leaving only the fish duck in its seat. Estes was so angry with it that he kicked it out of the house, which explains why the fish duck is flattened behind.

To cook the ducks that he had killed Estes now built a large fire, and as soon as the ground was warm, dug a number of holes, put the ducks inside and covered them over. His eyes closed in sleep before they were cooked, and as he slept, many other ducks came along, ate the ones that he had cooked, leaving only their feet in the ashes, and went away again. When Estes awoke he said to himself, 'My ducks must all be cooked. I had better stir away the ashes, not spoil the birds by pulling at their feet.' He prodded in the ashes with a stick, but could find nothing but the feet of the ducks.

Estes once visited a village whose inhabitants had nothing to drink except grease; for the chief kept all the water hidden inside a ball, and would not sell it except at a price so high that the people could seldom buy any. Now his daughter, Eski, was living in seclusion at the back of his house, and when the villagers begged Estes to get them water, the trickster stole into her room during the night, and threatened to expose her if she did not give him some water. The terrified girl offered him some water from her father's ball, but he said, 'I must hold the ball in my own hands.' No sooner had she handed it to him than he ran away. The girl told her father, who gathered his relatives and pursued him. Estes ran all over the country, spilling here and there drops of water which turned into lakes and rivers. When the ball was nearly empty he hurled it to the ground, and the water that flowed from it became the sea.

Grizzly, Black Bear, Wolf, Wolverine and many other animals contended, tugging against one another with interlocked middle fingers. Grizzly was the strongest and out pulled them all. Marten said, 'I'll try to beat him;' but Grizzly pulled off his arm, wrapped it carefully inside a beaver net, and hung it behind his sleeping place. All the other animals wanted to restore Marten's arm, but were afraid to enter Grizzly's house. One night Estes changed himself into an old man and hobbled on two sticks to the door.

Grizzly said, 'Poor old man, where do you come from?'

'I came to visit you,' said Estes.

'Sit on the other side of the fire,' said Grizzly. When his guest sat down, he offered him a bowl of mingled bear grease and fat, which Estes ate greedily. Just before it grew dark Estes shaded his eyes and looked around to see where Grizzly slept and where he had hung the beaver net.

'What is that hanging over your sleeping place?' he asked.

'Oh, that is Marten's arm. I pulled it off when we were wrestling.'

'You should not hang it there,' said Estes. 'I once pulled off a man's arm and hung it in a beaver net over my sleeping place; but my parents and all my relatives died soon afterwards and I became very poor. Don't hang it there, but outside the house over the door.'

'Thank you,' said Grizzly, as he took down the net and hung it outside . During the night Estes stole out, slashed away part of the net and went inside again. He kept at his task all night until, shortly before daylight, he managed to destroy the net and extricate Marten's arm. Then he ran away to Wolf, Wolverine, Fox, Black Bear and the other animals, with Grizzly pursuing hard at his heels. Growing tired, he handed the arm to Wolf, Wolf in turn to Wolverine, and Wolverine to Fox. So the chase continued all day until it reached Muskrat's home in a small lake. Muskrat then took the arm and dived under the water just as Grizzly was leaping on him. Grizzly followed, but Muskrat eluded him by his repeated diving until they reached the far side of the lake, where Marten was running along the shore. As Muskrat threw the arm, Marten caught it on his shoulder, but could not fit it properly. That is why Marten now has a crooked arm.

Estes wanted to visit a certain town. Meeting Raven he said, 'Come with me to this town.' Raven consented. As they travelled along together, Estes said, 'I shall be the chief and you my slave. When we reach the town and a chief invites me to his house you must keep near me, for I shall be too lofty a chief to speak and you must interpret and answer for me.'

When they entered the town a chief invited Estes to his house, seated him and Raven on a blanket and set before them a large pan filled with bear meat and bear fat. The chief then said to Raven, 'Perhaps our guest does not eat this kind of food.'

Estes nudged his slave and said, 'Tell him that I will eat it gladly.'

Raven interpreted, 'No, my chief does not care for this food.' So Raven ate all the bear meat and bear fat, because Estes was too lofty a chief to refute his words.

The same mishap befell Estes at the house of another chief, where they were offered mountain goat meat and berries. Raven was now so satiated that he could eat no more, but Estes was famishing. So when a third chief set before them meat that was rotten, Raven said to him, 'My chief is very fond of this food,' and Estes was so hungry that he was glad to devour it. He then left the village with Raven, and on its outskirts began to beat him for his treachery; but Raven flew away.

Estes now lives on an island far away across the sea. He is so big that if he put his foot in a boat it would sink, so he has to remain there.

Coming of the White Man

The first white man who visited Fraser Lake (Simon Fraser and his party in 1806), wishing to impress the Indians with the power of his musket, primed it, rammed a bullet down its muzzle, and fired. The Indians ran away and hid, the majority in underground houses. He fired a second time, knocking down a lot of things that the Indians had hung up. Then he cut up some tobacco, lit his pipe, and offered each Indian a small plug. The Carrier, however, were not acquainted with tobacco at this time, and after sniffing it, threw it away. They thought that this man who could blow smoke from his mouth was a cremated Indian who had returned from the land of the dead.

Caribou Man and the Sekani

Once a number of Sekani visited the Babine Indians, and two young men, who were neither Sekani nor Babine, returned with them towards the Sekani country in order to marry Sekani girls. In those days the Indians had no tents, but piled brush together and covered it with skins. As the two youths slept in their shelter, a heavy snowstorm broke over them, and one youth said, 'I don't like the snow to fall in my face when I sleep. I am going back home.'

'I like to feel the snow,' the other answered. Next morning the first youth, who was really a black bear, turned back, but the other, who was a caribou, remained with the Sekani and married one of their maidens. That is the reason black bears now den themselves up during the winter, while caribou remain out in the snow.

The Sekani, having no permanent villages, moved continually from place to place, the men carrying only their weapons and small hunting bags while the women carried all the baggage. They lived on caribou, moose, rabbits, porcupines, squirrels and other game. One day when the caribou man was hunting, a big fool hen flew across a swamp in front of him. He said to his wife that evening, 'I saw a big fool hen today, but it flew across a swamp and I could not overtake it.'

His wife went outside and shouted, 'E–e–ha, e–e–ha. My husband says he has seen many fool hens.'

Her kinsmen gathered around them and said, 'Brother-in-law, where did you see all the fool hens? Tell us and we will kill them tomorrow.'

The caribou man answered, 'My wife is deceiving you. I saw only one fool hen, which disappeared across a swamp.'

'We will go there tomorrow,' replied the Sekani. 'There are sure to be a lot of fool hens there.' So the next morning he guided them to the swamp, where they found the fool hens as thick as mosquitoes. They killed them for two or three days until they could find no more. Then they moved on, and while the men hunted, the women carried the meat to the next camping place.

They came to a swampy place that was not fully frozen over, and the caribou man, falling short in his leap, got his snowshoe plastered with what he thought was black mud. He was cleaning it off in his camp when his wife examined it and shouted, 'E–e–ha, e–e–ha. My husband has found a tsaniltsa.'

The hunters gathered around him and asked, 'Tell us where you found the tsaniltsa and we will look for it tomorrow.

'I didn't find one,' he answered. 'My wife is deceiving you. I simple got my snowshoe plastered with black mud.'

Then they too examined his snowshoe and exclaimed, 'O, yes. You did discover a tsaniltsa, one that has several cubs.' The caribou man was frightened, for the tsaniltsa is a monstrous bear living in the ground that kills every Indian who catches sight of it.

'We had better not go near them, or they will kill us,' he said.

The Sekani answered, 'No. If you will show us the place in the morning we will kill them all.'

After guiding them to the swamp the next morning the caribou man fled back to his camp; but the Sekani attacked the animals, killed a mother and its three cubs, and carried the meat home. They ate it without harm, although the caribou man was afraid to linger in the camp, lest the mere smell of the monsters should kill him. Afterwards he said to his companions, 'My people are afraid of tsaniltsa, although we kill and eat black bears and grizzlies.'

'We are afraid to kill those animals.' the Sekani answered, 'but we are not afraid of tsaniltsa.' They agreed then that the caribou man would inform them whenever he discovered traces of tsaniltsa, and they would let him know when they came upon the tracks of either black bears or grizzlies.

He continued to travel with the Sekani for three or four years, and his wife bore him a son. Sometimes when they ate together, the woman placed tsaniltsa meat on one side of the dish for herself and bear meat on the other side for her husband. But one day their two-year-old child changed the places of the food. The caribou-man ate tsaniltsa meat, and his wife ate bear meat. Both fell dead immediately.

Origin of the Crest Sleepy

A boy and a girl who went out to hunt squirrels found one running up and down a tree. The boy would have shot it, but every time the animal ran down the tree the girl laughed and frightened it up again. Finally she became hysterical; and scratched her stomach until she died. Her companion laid her body beside the tree and wandered away, for he was afraid to return home.

As he wandered. He came to a big stone under which there was a large opening. He entered and followed a trail to a river, where three houses stood in a row on the opposite bank. At his shout someone put off in a canoe and ferried him over.

The boy approached the smallest of the three houses and stood outside the door. An old woman invited him inside. She said to him, 'You see all the bones lying outside the next house? A blind woman, Klestaste, Seated-in-the-dirt, lives there with her daughter and both are very evil. They have killed all my sons, and many other young men who went to woo the daughter.'

'I think I will visit the daughter myself,' said the boy; and he persisted in his resolution in spite of the old woman's warning.

He visited the house the next evening and received a friendly welcome. In the middle of the night, however, while the two women were sleeping, he quietly changed places with the daughter, placed her ear pendants on his own ears and her labret in his own lip, bound her two braids into one and separated his own braid into two, and lay down again. Soon afterwards the blind woman rose, stirred up the fire, and rubbed her arm bones against each other to whet their edges. After testing their keenness on a stick she crept to her daughter's usual sleeping place, felt the boy's head and face, and convinced that he was her daughter, moved along to discover her guest. She then passed her hand over the girl's face, which lacked all its distinguishing marks, and sure of her victim, chopped her in two with her arm. Then she lay down again.

Before daylight the boy slipped out of the house and returned to the old woman next door. The blind woman soon followed him, weeping. 'Where is that boy?' she asked. 'I have killed my own daughter.'

But the old woman answered, 'You laughed when you killed my sons. Now you have paid the penalty.' The boy then killed the blind woman also.

In the third house lived a man named Guhwok, Sleepy, because he slept all day and all night. His wife was so beautiful that the boy made up his mind to steal her. He confided his intentions to the old woman, who warned him that the man was very dangerous, but promised to help him. She made him a copper canoe with many paddles, and told him to tie the paddles in a bundle and drill a hole through them all. 'Now seize the woman,' she said, 'and paddle away as fast as you can.'

The boy entered Sleepy's house and said to his wife, 'Come with me.' She followed and embarked with him in the canoe, which began to speed over the lake. Just as it left the shore, however, a great beam fell from the roof of the house and struck Sleepy on the head, saying, 'Wake up, Sleepy. Someone is stealing your wife.' Still he slept on. Nor did he wake when a wedge struck him on the head and repeated the warning. But when a large red stone struck him he leaped to his feet and pursued the fleeing couple in his own canoe.

As he followed close in the wake of their copper canoe, he shouted; 'Labret, give me back my wife, or I will make the rain fall on you.' Presently rain fell on them, but the boy rubbed himself and the woman with his hands and the rain passed by them. 'Restore my wife,' shouted Sleepy again, 'or I will send more rain on you.' Then a rain of stones fell on the fleeting canoe, but the stones passed through the holes in the paddles and left them unbroken. 'Restore my wife,' shouted Sleepy a third time, 'or I will raise a mountain across your course.' A mountain suddenly confronted them, but the boy hurled the woman's labret at it and opened up a hole through which he passed in his canoe unharmed. Then he rubbed his hand across the woman's mouth and waved it back towards the mountain. The hole closed over, and Sleepy could follow them no farther.

The woman then said to the boy, 'I have never seen human beings before. Make some wooden images of whales and place them in the water. They will go to your home and I will follow them.' The boy made some images, which changed to real whales as soon as they touched the water and guided the boy to his home.

The woman said again, 'Invite all the people to your house.' When all the people had gathered, she took out of her bag a little grease and a tiny bunch of berries, which she mixed in a large box with water. The food swelled so much that it overflowed the box, and more than satisfied the desires of the villagers. After they had feasted, she rose up and said, 'My former husband was named Sleepy because he slept all the time, so now my new husband shall have Sleepy for his crest, and it shall remain in his family forever.'

Today Sleepy is the crest of a woman in the Gidamdanyu phratry.

The Revenge of the Mountain Goats

Many people from different places once gathered at Mosquito Flat and gambled with the inhabitants, using gambling sticks. A certain man won a pair of leggings so short that they reached only to his knees; and he ridiculed them, saying that their owner's legs must have been as short as a mountain goat's. After a time the gathering broke up, and the man who had lost the leggings in gambling departed, no one knew whither.

The following year the winner went into the mountains on the west side of the Saskwa (Bear) river to hunt mountain goats, and killed several. But one day when he was on top of a mountain, about to return home, a thick fog enveloped him. He waited until it dispersed, when, to his amazement, he found himself an a narrow ledge half way down the face of a great precipice. The mountain goats, whom he had ridiculed the year before, had brought him into this perilous position.

When the people down in the valley saw a man on the face of the precipice, they returned to their homes and made a long rope of cedar bark. They lowered this rope down from the top of the cliff until he was able to grasp it, but every time, he strained on it the sharp rocks above and severed it in two. His friends then lowered blankets and food, and sent messengers to summon help from Moricetown, Temlaham, and other places. Many people gathered on the Saskwa river to aid in the rescue. From a number of moose hides they made a strong, long rope, which they tested in a tug of war. Sure that this rope would not break, they lowered it down the cliff; but once again, as soon as the man pulled, it snapped in two. Now at last they realised that some supernatural agency was working against them; and all scattered to their homes except the man's brother, who kept watch at the bottom of the cliff. In his despair the man threw his blankets down the precipice, saying to himself, 'Let me die;' and to this day the mountain is called The Mountain Where the Blankets Were Thrown Down.

Worn out with weeping, he fell asleep. A noise, boom boom, awoke him, and he saw, standing at his side, a man clad in mountain goat skin. 'Why are you weeping?' the stranger asked.

He answered, 'Last year, gambling at Mosquito Flat, I won a pair of mountain goat leggings and ridiculed them because they were so short. Now the goats have brought this punishment on me; they have isolated me on this ledge from which I cannot escape. My kinsmen and friends tried in vain to rescue me. Now only my brother remains there below at the bottom of the cliff.'

The stranger said to him,' You were too haughty last year and mocked someone. Now I will give you the very things you ridiculed.' He produced a pair of goat skin leggings, and inserting his finger in his mouth, waved it in front of him. At once a narrow path opened up down the face of the cliff. When the man had put on the leggings the stranger said, 'Jump down along this path. When you reach the bottom remove your leggings and leave them there. Hereafter don't be so haughty, or you will certainly die.'

'I have been very foolish and ignorant,' the man answered. 'Now I have learned my lesson and will never mock at anything again. You have saved my life. Some day I will repay you.'

He leaped from rock to rock down the face of the cliff. Wherever his feet landed they sank into the hard rock as though it were soft mud, giving him firm foothold. So he reached the bottom safely and rejoined his brother. But before they departed to their home he removed his goat skin leggings and deposited them at the bottom of the cliff. They saw the stranger, who had been watching them from above, change to a mountain goat, descend the cliff to recover the leggings, and disappear up the cliff again.

Soon afterwards the man left Mosquito Flat and went to Temlaham. There he saw some young men playing with the skin and head of a mountain goat. He took the objects away from them, telling them that the mountain goats might be offended and relating his own adventure. A year later messengers came to Temlaham making a loud noise as though with a horn, and wearing blankets of mountain goat skin and bonnets of goat skin and goat horn. The first household they entered offered them salmon and berries, but they declined to eat. In the second house they were offered another kind of food and again declined. Soon afterwards they went outside to watch the young men playing, and lay down over to one side. There a young boy saw them nibbling grass and told his people, who gathered for them large quantities of grass which they ate without hesitation. Then they invited all the inhabitants of Temlaham and Mosquito Flat to a great potlatch that was to be given at a certain village.

Guided by these messengers, all the people travelled together for two or three days until they reached a big village where many totem poles stood in front of the large and imposing houses. Meat of different kinds was provided for them in abundance, and they were assigned one of the big houses in which to pass the night; but the man who had been rescued by a mountain goat received an invitation to stay with a certain young man in a house far over to one side.

During the evening the visitors were invited into a large house to behold an entertainment. As each chief entered someone said to him, 'Sit down and you will see something.' But when all the visitors had taken their seats round the sides of the house, it seemed to split in two, and in what had been the middle of the floor there appeared a precipice with two mountain goats wandering far below along its face. The scene vanished and the house resumed its normal appearance. 'Look again,' said a voice. Again the house divided, and the blue waters of a lake appeared, the same lake that lies at the foot of the cliff where the man had been isolated and later rescued by the goats. Then the lake vanished, the entertainment closed and the visitors, returning to the big house that had been assigned to them, slept.

In the house far over to one side the young host cooked food for his guest. After he had eaten, and was preparing for bed, his host said, 'If you hear a noise in the night don't get up. All your companions are about to die, but I will save your life.' They lay down together, his host sleeping in front of him. In the middle of the night came a great wind accompanied by the bleating wak wak of young goats. The man was frightened and would have arisen, but a young mountain goat stood directly in front of him and hemmed him in. There he lay till morning, unable to move on account of the goat. When daylight came he found himself on a narrow ledge overlooking a precipice; far below were the mangled remains of his companions who had fallen down in the night.

The goat now permitted him to rise to his feet. It rubbed his feet and hands and said to him, 'I will descend in front of you. Place your feet exactly in my tracks and grip the rock with your hands.' They began their descent. Wherever he touched the rock it seemed like soft mud, offering him sure footing. So they reached the bottom in safety.

Now the man pulled out his paint bag and rubbed red paint on the young goat's shoulders, saying, 'Next year many people will come here to hunt goats. I am marking you with this paint so that no one will harm you, as a reward for saving my life again.'

The mountain goat answered, 'Search among the corpses here for your family and kinsmen, the people of Mosquito Flat, not the people of Temlaham. For the Temlaham people mocked us last year and deserve their punishment. Rub the corpses with your hands and they will be restored to life. Next year I will gather all the goats on this mountain for you and your people to kill. I myself will be here also.'

The man restored his kinsfolk to life and they all returned home, but the next year they gathered at the same mountain to hunt goats. Above them were the goats, so thick on the mountain slopes that they looked like snow. Round the mountain the people went and killed them every one; save one young goat which was painted red on both shoulders. This one the man who had been rescued held in his hands and forbade the people to kill. The goat said to him, 'Let them kill me if they wish.'

But he answered, 'No. Twice you saved my life. If they kill you they must kill me also.' So the young goat was given its liberty.

Ever since that time the goat with red shoulders has remained high up on top of this mountain. Two Carrier hunters saw it a few years ago.

The Flood

A man down at the coast was spearing seals. He would paddle out in his canoe at evening and return home in the morning. One day he took home with him a second wife, whom his first wife greeted with a terrible scowl as they landed on the beach. However, she pretended to be glad of a companion and invited the girl into the house. There she cooked some food and they all ate together.

Two or three evenings later the man prepared to go hunting again. Before leaving he said to his new wife, 'If you hear anything in the night while I am away don't look, but cover yourself with your blanket. Then you will come to no harm.'

That night the young woman heard a noise as of dogs eating in the house. She thought to herself, 'We have no dogs. Where can they come from, these dogs that are pulling down and eating the seal meat that is hung up to dry?' Forgetting her husband's instructions she looked up, and saw, in the light of the fire, a great wolverine that was tearing down and devouring the seal meat.

The wolverine sighted her at the same moment and sprang at her, saying, 'I kill every woman who sees me.' Then it bit her in two and threw her body, outside, for it was really the man's first wife, who had already killed many other women her husband had brought home.

Meanwhile the man had speared at several seals, but without success. He thought to himself, 'It must be because my first wife has killed my new wife again.'

He turned back, and reached his home at sunrise. There he saw one half of his new wife's body lying bare and white on one side of the house, the other half on the other; but his wolverine wife was going down to meet him just as if nothing had happened. He made up his mind to kill her, but merely said, 'Cook me some seals.' She dug a pit, lined the bottom with stones and built a fire over it. Then as soon as the fire died down she raked aside the embers and laid some seals on top. Her husband sat down beside the pit to fashion a long, two pronged spear. As she halted for a moment beside him he pushed her headlong into the pit. She changed to a wolverine and clawed at him, but he held her down with his spear until she burned to death. Then he gathered up the two halves of his other wife's body and laid them on a moose skin so that the sun might circle around them; and as the sun completed its circuit she rose up healed.

After this the man had great success in his sealing, and accumulated a great store of dried meat, for his new wife, unlike the wolverine woman, ate very little. But one night he caught, not a black seal as usual, but a white one. When he reached home in the morning he said to his wife, 'Wash the toes of this seal, for they have a little blood on them.' She sat on a stone in the water and washed them; but as she rose up to go home the stone suddenly moved out into deep water. She called to her husband, who ran to his canoe and tried to paddle out to her; but his canoe would not move. Not until the stone had slowly sunk under the water with the woman still sitting on it did something release his canoe and allow it to go forward.

Stricken with grief, the man gathered up some clothes, paddled out to the spot where his wife had sunk, anchored his canoe with stones, and leaped into the water. As his feet touched the surface he seemed to be in a country not unlike this earth. He followed a path to a village of sculpins, who told him that a man had carried his wife farther on.

After giving the sculpins a lot of stones (because they are fond of living under stones) and entreating their help when he returned, he went on to a village of blind geese, who gave him the same information. He paid them by drawing off the skin from their eyes (whence these geese have round white eyes) and restoring their sight; and as he left them he said, 'Help me when I return.'

Farther on he heard someone splitting a tree with a wedge and hammer, and thought to himself, 'Let the wedge break.' The wedge broke instantly. Its slave owner, whose name was Satsan, wept aloud, 'My wedge has broken; and now my master will beat me again;' and seeing no one near, he added, 'The man whose wife was stolen must have made the wedge break. If he comes here I will tell him how to recover her.'

The man revealed himself, and when the slave promised to help him recover his wife if he mended the wedge, he rubbed the two halves of the tool together and reunited them. Then Satsan said, 'You killed so many seals and fish that they became angry with you and stole your wife to turn her into a fish. They sent me to make fins for her from this tree. But I will help you. After I finish my day's work, I always carry two large baskets of water to the chief's house, where your wife is sitting on a box. Tonight you sit down outside the door. When I carry the water into the house, I will spill it over the fire and throw the place into darkness. Then seize your wife and flee home.'

The man sat down beside the door, and when Satsan extinguished the fire, seized his wife and fled. The inmates pursued him, but Satsan swelled out his body in the doorway and blocked their exit. Someone punctured him and made him collapse, but he followed behind, shouting, 'Wait for me, I want to go ahead;' and when they let him go in front he again swelled out his body and blocked them. Thus the man and his wife succeeded in reaching Goose town, where the friendly geese laid sharp stones over his track so that his pursuers had to make a wide detour. With sharp stones, similarly, the sculpins checked his pursuers, enabling him to reach his boat in safety. But just as he embarked with his wife, the sea began to rise. It rose and rose until it covered all the mountains; it rose until his boat nearly knocked the sky. Then at last the man killed his wife with an axe and threw her body overboard. The water subsided immediately, while he wailed, 'Alas, I killed my wife just as the water began to subside.'

In his boat were two animals, a muskrat and a small beaver. Muskrat dived, caught up some mud from the bottom and brought it to the surface. Then beaver dived and also brought the man a little earth. So day after day they brought more earth until the man was able to knead it together and make an island. He kneaded more and more earth until the world became as it is today, but with two animals only, muskrat and beaver.

The Dead Woman's Son

The son of a chief married a girl of his own village. They lived happily together for many months, and the woman was about to bear a child. One morning she awoke very ill; by evening she was worse, and at midnight she died, the child being still unborn. The people mourned over her body for two days, and buried her on the morning of the third day.

The husband, stricken with grief, slept each night on his wife's grave. The people carried presents of food to him, but he declined to eat. At last his mother went and begged him to eat; and he entered her house and ate whatever she offered him. But at night he returned to his wife's grave and slept there.

The weather grew colder, and snow began to cover the ground. At first he cleared it away from the grave and slept on the bare ground; but when the snow grew deeper and the cold more rigorous he slept in his hut.

Spring came, and he went to visit his wife's grave again. As he drew near it he saw a little boy gathering firewood; very quietly it entered the grave with a bunch of flowers, then came out again and began to pick more. The man concealed himself and watched. Sometimes the boy gathered flowers and took them inside the grave, sometimes he gathered other things. And all the time the man watched from his hiding place.

Now as he pondered over this, he determined to try and catch the child. He returned to his house, speaking to no one, took down his tools, and made four tiny bows, which he covered with red paint. Next he cut some branches of the saskatoon tree and made four tiny arrows, which he feathered with great care. The villagers were glad to see him working again, although they did not know what he was doing; for they grieved that he should weep each day at his wife's grave.

Three days after he had first seen the boy the man returned to the grave, carrying his bows and arrows in a bag upon his back. Again he saw the boy, who was now a little bigger. When he entered the grave the man ran forward and planted a bow and arrow in the ground near by. He planted the second bow and arrow a little farther down the trail toward the village, and the third and fourth a little farther still. Then he hid and waited.

Soon the boy came out of the grave again. He laughed softly when he saw the first bow and arrow, and ran to examine them. At first he seemed afraid to touch them with his hands; but presently he pulled out the arrow and looked at it. It was very beautiful, and a low laugh escaped him as he strung it on the bow and began to play with it. Looking around, he saw the second bow and arrow, and ran to get them likewise. Now he noticed the third, and dropping the first two sets, which were rather heavy for him, he ran to gather them also. Both the third and fourth he gathered up and carried inside the grave, then returned a few moments later for the first and second. The man waited for some time longer, but when the boy did not reappear, he returned home pondering.

Now he made six more bows and arrows and set them out in the same way as before; and the boy came out of the grave and gathered them. Many more he made and also told his parents what he had seen. Twelve of the most noted medicine men gathered in his father's house while he went out and planted them about six feet apart in a long line that led from the grave to the village. Then he rejoined the people in the house and they waited.

The boy was growing bigger now. He came out of the grave, gathered the bows and arrows three at a time, and returned for more. All day he worked, carrying his burdens into the grave; and nearer and nearer he approached the village, while the medicine men watched him in silence through the part open door. The last bow and arrow had been planted in the ground just behind the house. Thither the boy came, timidly, to draw it out; but just as he turned to go back the chief medicine man ran swiftly and silently behind him, in a kind of trance, and caught him in his hands. The boy gave one frightened cry and shrivelled almost to nothing, while the other medicine men inside the house shook their rattles and sang their songs. They approached the child, one by one, and breathed on him; trying to restore him to life. Then they carried him inside the house, and sang over him for three days and three nights. On the fourth day the boy became truly alive. He was the man's own son, who had been buried in the grave with his mother but had been granted the semblance of life because of the father's constant weeping.

The boy was now alive, but he was not happy. He would not eat, but cried night and day. The villagers, unable to rest, called in a wise woman from another village and promised to pay her bountifully if she would cure the child. She came and listened to his weeping and to his constant cry, 'Dihl he Dihl he,' and she laughed as she heard the words.

'I thought it was something big and great that the child wanted,' she said. 'What he wants is only a little thing. He craves for the full free life of man, not the half life he enjoyed in the grave. He wants his cousin to accompany him halfway up yonder mountain where the giant spruce trees grow, and the people to set fire to the spruce trees so that the hot gum may fall on the bodies of them both as they stand underneath. Then the people must wash him and his cousin beneath a waterfall.'

As the old woman instructed they did. The hot gum that fell on the children's bodies they washed off beneath a tumbling waterfall. Thus the boy gained the full free life for which he craved, and cried no more. The people named him Dead Woman's Son. And the heart of his father was glad as he watched him hunting and playing with his cousin, both growing up to manhood together.

Now there dwelt in a far away country two beautiful girls, Iksmandamlkut and Tsabol, each the daughter of a chief. Many young men had travelled long distances to woo them, but none had ever returned. The fame of the girls' beauty reached Dead Woman's Son and his cousin, who determined to visit them. Their parents entreated them not to go lest they also should perish; but one day when the lads were alone Dead Woman's Son said to his cousin, 'Let us start out tomorrow. But first let us capture two birds, a chickadee and a woodpecker.' They captured the two birds, and Dead Woman's Son kept the dried skin of the chickadee, his cousin the skin of the woodpecker. Then, without the knowledge of their parents, they left the village early in the morning, donned their bird skins and flew away through the air.

In their flight they passed over many villages, whose inhabitants, warned by their medicine men, called up to them, 'Ha. It is not likely that Dead Woman's Son will ever reach Iksmandamlkut.' But the boys flew steadily on, paying no attention to their cries. They flew for two days, resting each night on the ground, and on the third day reached a rocky mountain which no previous suitor had been able to pass. Here at intervals the cliffs parted asunder and opened up a passage, but whenever a suitor had pressed eagerly through it flames had swept up from below and burnt him.

The two boys, tired and hungry, alighted in front of the mountain and rested. As they lay on the ground a small mouse touched Dead Woman's Son with its hind legs and said, 'My grandmother wants you.'

Then it ran under a pile of brush. The boy moved the brush aside, and saw the old lady mouse sitting inside a tiny house. She said to him, 'Come in, come in. I have something to tell you. This is skyland that you have reached. Whenever people try to pass through this mountain the lightning strikes them and they fall dead. Look at their bodies down below.'

The boys looked down, and saw, far below; a great pile of bodies, of clothing, and of bows and arrows.

'When the cliffs first open do not stir,' the old lady continued. 'First will come a blaze of lightning, then a second blaze. Wait until the second blaze has died down, then fly fast. The cliffs will still remain open a little while.'

The lads donned their bird skins as the cliffs began to open. A great cloud of smoke issued from the passage, followed by a burst of flame. Then came a second burst, not quite as great. As it died down they rose in the air and flew with all their strength. Dead Woman's Son with his chickadee's wings passed through unscathed, but the woodpecker's wings carried his cousin more slowly and a little fire dropped on his feathers before he reached safety. Hence today the woodpecker has black spots on its breast and wings where the fire burned it.

After escaping this peril they rested, but soon flew on again over a beautiful land dissected by many trails. They descended near a large village, doffed their bird skin clothing and became ordinary youths again. Outside this village was a spring from which the women drew their water, and as the boys watched there from behind a bush, Dead Woman's Son prayed, 'May Iksmandamlkut and Tsabol come hither to the spring.' At evening his prayer was answered; two beautiful maidens approached the spring. Dead Woman's Son whispered to his cousin, 'They are coming. Put on your bird skin again as quickly as you can.'

The girls had stopped at the spring to fill their wooden buckets when two little birds, a chickadee and a woodpecker, hopped along the ground towards them. 'Look at those two little birds,' exclaimed Iksmandamlkut. 'How tame they are. I wish I could catch them and keep them as pets.' Her cousin suggested that they should snare them, and she answered, 'We have no string, and our moccasin laces are too large. You, perhaps, have some long hairs; mine are all too short.'

'I have one long hair,' said Tsabol.

'Pull it out,' answered her cousin. 'Another will grow in its place.' From this one hair they made two snares which they set beside the spring. One caught the fluttering chickadee, the other the woodpecker. Gladly the girls released them, and lodged them in their bosoms; then, taking up their buckets, they returned to the village.

Dead Woman's Son prayed a second time, 'May they forget that we are nestling on their bosoms.' As they approached the village shouts of laughter arose, and children began to run in play among the houses.

The girls forgot the birds in their bosoms, dropped their buckets inside their home and joined the other children.

As evening drew on the girls retired to their room at the back of the house and lay down to sleep, still forgetful of their bird pets; but at midnight, when all was quiet, the youths removed their bird-skin clothing and resumed their human forms. When the girls' parents awoke in the morning they wondered why there was so much whispering and laughing in the inner room, and said to one another, 'How could any men have made their way in without our knowledge?' Iksmandamlkut's mother then picked up a stick and went in to attack the intruders. The four young people rose to their feet when she entered, and Dead Woman's Son prayed silently, 'May the people so admire our beauty that instead of harming us, they will gladly accept us as husbands for these two girls.' Iksmandamlkut's mother looked at them fiercely; their faces were fresh and handsome, their hair a glorious red . Without a word she dropped her stick and went out again. Then the chief, her husband, went in, and he too went out again without saying a word. One after another all the girls' kinsmen inspected the two youths and offered them no harm. Then Iksmandamlkut's father, scornfully disregarding the furious suitors who wished to kill the two youths, invited the people of all the neighbouring villages to attend the marriage feast of his daughter and niece; and they came in hundreds until the great house overflowed with the multitude.

After the feast had ended the two youths went away to hunt for their parents-in-law, as was customary among the Carrier. They brought in so many goats, beaver, fish and other game that their parents-in-law were able to feast the villagers every few days.

The youths spent a year in that village, very happy. Then they began to think of their own parents far away, and their hearts became so filled with loneliness that they could hardly talk. Their brides, filled with dismay, said to their parents, 'Our husbands are unwell, for they will not speak to us. What is the matter with them?'

But the old people understood only too well, and they said to the youths, 'You are longing for your old homes. Return if you wish, and take our daughters with you. If one day you wish to come back to us, we shall welcome you.'

The youths were filled with gladness at these words and immediately made preparations for their departure. They left the village three days later, each bride carrying food in four small bags. Straight through the fiery pass they walked, but this time no flames shot up to bar their path. 'It was my father who caused the fire,' Iksmandamlkut said. 'He wished no suitors from earth to reach his home. But you were too clever, and now we ourselves are following you to earth.'

While she was speaking they came to the high hill on which the old lady mouse had built her home, and the girls, looking down to earth, saw all the corpses that were strewn below. Their hearts were sad that so many youths should have perished in trying to reach them, but they rewarded the old lady and her grandchild for their help and continued on their way. After passing many camps and villages whose inhabitants gathered beside the road to admire them they arrived at last at the young men's homes.

The boys' people had long since given them up for dead and had draped their houses with blackened skins. Great was their rejoicing, therefore, when the two youths walked into their homes again. After the tumult had subsided a little the youths said, 'We have left our brides outside. Will you not bring them in?' Then the two chiefs, their fathers, hastily laid robes of moose and bear skins around the three sides of the house, seated the girls beside their husbands in the place of honour at the back, and placed before them the choicest foods that they could gather. Each chief then took his wand of office and went from house to house to invite all the people to a feast of welcome. From every house they came rejoicing, and gladdened the hearts of the youths and their wives by their feasting. Not until the feast had ended did Dead Woman's Son rise up and narrate their adventures.

Two days later Iksmandamlkut said to her husband, 'Tell your father that I also will feed the people. I shall give them sky food, that they do not know; and this will be our real marriage feast.' The chief summoned the people again, and each bride produced the four little bags that she had brought with her from above. One bag she laid aside, but from the other three she poured out an immense pile of meat that filled the whole house. The people feasted to their hearts' content.

The Man Who Ate His Wives

One summer a man travelled down a river in a spruce bark canoe loaded with the dried meat of beaver and groundhog, and landed at a village, seeking a wife. He chose a girl, gave all the meat to her mother in payment and returned to his home with his bride.

The following year he came again, but without his wife. 'My wife died,' he told the people. 'I have come for another.' They sold him another girl and he departed.

The following year he came a third time. 'My second wife died also,' he said. He handed over all his dried meat, and departed with his third wife.

The fourth summer also he returned. 'My wife died like the others. I have come to purchase another.'

The people were sure now that he had killed them, so they sold him a lame woman and cautioned her before she left, 'Keep watch. We believe he killed all his other wives.'

So the man departed with his lame bride.

They travelled a long way in their canoe until they reached the mouth of a small creek. There the husband landed, cached his canoe, and took a trail up the mountain side. On top was a smoke house that belonged to his unmarried brother. When they entered the brother-in-law cooked ten groundhogs in a box and laid them before the woman, saying as he laid his antler club on the ground beside her, 'If you do not eat all I will kill you.' The terrified woman ate all ten. Soon afterwards her husband cooked ten more groundhogs, sat down beside her with his club, and forced her to eat them all. She slept that night on one side of the hut, and the two men on the other, for her husband never came near her.

The two men went out hunting each day, and brought home great numbers of groundhogs which they forced her to eat as before. She did nothing but stay at home and eat, and within a month became so fat that she could neither walk nor work, but had to lie down all the time.

Early one morning her husband rose from his bed, sharpened his knife, and looked over to where his wife was lying. As she seemed to be asleep, he crept silently over to her and made a small cut in the sole of her foot. She heard him mutter as he examined the cut, 'No, she is not fat enough yet.' So they continued to fatten her still more.

One day her husband said to her, 'I have too many lice in my hair. Pick them out, but don't touch my head around the inion.' His wife, however, stealthily lifted the hair a little around the inion, and saw, just below it, a huge mouth.

She was sure now that the two men intended to eat her as soon as she was fat enough. She searched the house while they were away hunting, and discovered, beneath a pile of hay in one corner, the bones of all the other women they had eaten. As soon as they went hunting again, she opened up one side of the house and crawled out, for she was too fat to crawl through the door. A little way down the creek she made a small camp as though she were overtaken by menstruation, and when her husband came in the evening to order her back she cut her leg a little and frightened him away with the blood. During the night she stripped off her clothes and soaked her body in the water until all the fat was washed away from her, then dressed again and fled in the direction of her home.

She followed down the creek to the river. A little ice had formed along the banks, but the middle of the river was still open. At its edge she leaped up, caught the branch of an overhanging tree, and concealed herself in the topmost branches. Soon her husband came after her, carrying a big knife. He saw his wife's tracks leading out to the edge of the water, and stooped over to look in. The woman was leaning out from the tree, watching him, and he saw her reflection in the water. Thinking she was at the bottom he dropped his knife on the ice and leaped in; but his wife jumped down from the tree, seized the knife, and cut off his head when he re-emerged. His body went floating down the river, and she threw the head in after it. Then she climbed the tree again and hid.

Soon her brother-in-law came running down the trail. She killed him in the same manner. Now that she was safe from pursuit she started walking in search of her home, which she knew lay somewhere far down the river.

In the evening she reached a tiny house and seated herself on a pile of wood outside the door. Some one called to her, 'Come in.' Inside was a tiny woman who placed in front of her what looked like sawdust; but the lame woman refused to eat it and gave it back. 'That is the only food I eat myself,' apologised the little woman, who was really Chickadee. The lame woman stayed there that night.

Next morning she continued her journey and in the evening sat down on the wood pile in front of a larger house. A voice called to her, 'Come in.' It was Blue Jay who lived inside. Blue Jay placed a dish of dried berries in front of her, and she ate until she was satisfied. Then they went to sleep.

The next evening she reached a still larger house and sat down on the wood pile. A woman's voice called to her, 'Come in.' Inside dwelt a big woman loon, who gave her dried trout to eat. Before they lay down to sleep Loon gave her more dried fish, and said, 'Your home is very far away and you can never reach it without help. But I will help you, provided you will remain with me for a little while. Tonight I will catch fish. You remain in the house and sleep, taking no notice of any noise you may hear.'

Loon went out, and the lame woman lay down and slept. She was wakened by the cries of many loons. So loudly did they cry, and in such numbers, that she went outside to look. In a neighbouring lake were moored two canoes, one at each end, with torches burning in their bows, and between them, in the middle of the lake, was a multitude of loons, screaming and diving, and carrying all the fish they caught to the canoes. The lame woman watched them for a moment, then went inside again. Immediately the noise ceased, and soon the big loon woman entered and scolded her for her disobedience. Then they both went to sleep.

In the morning Loon ordered the lame woman to carry all the fish up to the house and hang them up to dry. The canoes were only about half full, for she had disturbed the birds in their fishing. But that night, when loon went out again, the lame woman slept and did not rise until daylight. The noise of the loons on the water ceased shortly before it grew light, and Loon woman returned to the house. The canoes were filled to their gunwales, and Loon woman gave all the fish to the lame woman to dry for her own use. All day the woman carried them from the beach and hung them up to dry.

Night after night the loons fished, and day after day the woman carried their catch up to the house and dried them. When they had collected an enormous number, Loon woman said to her, 'Make a bag of salmon skin.' When the lame woman had finished the bag, Loon woman placed all the fish inside it, and though they numbered many thousands they neither filled the bag nor made it heavy. Loon woman now said to her, 'Your home is so far away that not in one year could you reach it, though you walked day after day from morning till night. But I will shorten the trail for you so that you may reach it in three days. When you get home feed your father and mother, your sister and brother, from the fish in this bag throughout the winter. But when summer comes, and you hear the loons crying out on the water, you will think, "Those loons have caught no fish." Then sew up all the holes to your bag and throw it, fish and all, into the water.'

The woman started out in the morning and reached her home in three days. She told her people all that had happened to her and they rejoiced at her escape. All that winter she fed them from the fish in her salmon skin bag, and the bag never became empty.

Summer came, and one evening she heard the loons crying out in the lake. She thought to herself, 'The loons have caught no fish;' so she sewed up the holes in the salmon skin bag, and threw it into the lake. Immediately there was a great splash as all the loons dived simultaneously. Each one came up with a fish.

The Origin of the Tribes

In the first times people multiplied and scattered. Some went in one direction, some in another. Thus arose white men, the Stikine, Carrier and other Indians. Each race received a different blessing from the sky god Utakke. The Hagwilgate people are descended from a grizzly that once married a woman; hence they are always killing people.

The Babine people came from a loon; hence they are very foolish.

The Sekani came from a wolf, so they, like the Hagwilgate Indians, are always killing people.

The Fraser Lake Indians came from a mink; hence it is easy for them to catch fish.

The Kiskargas people came from a mountain bird, tsildulte, that once married a woman.

There is another people who came from a wolverine, and who therefore steal continually.

Long ago there were two villages only, Dizkle or Mosquito Flat, twelve miles above Hagwilgate on the Bulkley river, inhabited by Carrier Indians, and Temlaham, four miles below Hazelton on the Skeena river, inhabited by Gitksan Indians. Hagwilgate was the boundary between the two tribes. Something caused the Mosquito Flat people to scatter; they went to

Moricetown, Fraser Lake, Babine, and even to the island of the Sekani. Similarly the Gitksan Indians of Temlaham scattered and established themselves anew at Kispaiox, Kitwanga, Kitselas, and Kitsiyukla.

Long ago there were Carrier, Gitksan, and Sekani (Itateni) Indians all living together at Mosquito Flat, which was then a very large village. They decided to build a big weir across the river to catch the ascending salmon, and with their stone axes cut timber on the hillside and dragged it to the water's edge with ropes of cedar bark, moose hide and caribou hide. You can see the slide today, 40 feet wide, down which they rolled their logs. Strong men then drove in the piles with large stones, and they laid their logs in place, forming a bridge across the river with gaps in which to set their fish-traps. They divided the weir into three sections, one for each of the three tribes.

One midsummer's day, during the salmon run, when many people were standing on the weir, two squirrels wandered over it, quite fearless, and examined the structure above and below. The people were terrified, believing that their visit portended a great sickness or other calamity at the hands of the sky-god Utakke. So they abandoned the village and scattered in all directions. The Gitksan moved down the river to Hazelton, the Carriers to Babine Lake, Moricetown and other places, and the Sekani fled northward. But even today there are many places between the Bulkley river and Babine Lake that bear Sekani names, proving that the Sekani once inhabited this area.

The Monstrous Bear

Three young men who visited an old man's beautiful daughter failed to return to their village. Two other young men visited her and they also did not return. Nor did four others after them, so that people were convinced that the old man had killed them all.

Two cousins went to try their luck. As they walked along they came to a big fir tree under which lay the bones of many people. The cousins merely looked at them and passed on to the old man's house, where they met his beautiful daughter.

As the sun was setting, one boy said to his cousin, 'If we both stay here we shall be killed. I'll go back and sleep under the big tree where all the bones are lying.' He returned to the tree, lit a fire, and rested there without sleeping. In the middle of the night he heard a low call that came from the top the fir tree, and dimly espied something descending. Quietly stretching his blanket over two bags as though he himself was asleep under it he took up his bow and hid in the bushes a few yards away. Presently a little bird descended the tree and hopped under the blanket. He shot it, and as the arrow pierced its body it cried out like a child. When he pulled off the covering he found that it actually was a little child he had shot through the heart; so he made a big fire and burnt its body.

Meanwhile the other boy was sleeping with the girl. In the middle of the night the old man rose, stirred up the fire, took some paint from a bag and marked a moose skin with human faces. Then he warmed the skin in front of the fire and shook it in the direction of the boy under the tree. After looking around to make sure no one was watching, he put away the skin and the box and lay down to sleep again. The boy had noticed him, however, and after a while he got up and said to the girl, 'What is the matter with your father?' She went over to examine him. He was dead.

The boy then left the girl and went to find his cousin. He asked him, 'Did you see anything during the night?'

And his cousin answered, 'Yes, I killed something and burnt its body.'

'Oh, that is why he old man is dead. You killed his charm.'

They started back for their home, and as they were crossing a meadow came upon a tsaniltse, which is a monstrous bear that kills people with its glance. The boy who had slain the old man shot the monster. His cousin, thinking it was just an ordinary bear, said, 'I am hungry, so I will take a piece of its meat to camp.'

But the other boy said, 'Don't touch it. It is not an ordinary black bear but a tsaniltse.'

In spite of his warning, however, his cousin cut off some of the meat, cooked it in their camp and ate it. But in the middle of the night he woke and said; 'Look at my body. Hair is beginning to grow all over it.'

His cousin answered, 'It is your own fault. You insisted on eating a tsaniltse. Now you can't stay here any longer. Go down into the water of that lake back there.'

As the boy entered the lake the water rose high around his head. His cousin called to him, 'Your father will say that I killed you, so when the people come here tell them what has happened.'

The lake trembled in answer, the water rose higher and higher over the land, and the evil face of a tsaniltse, rising above it, said, 'Yes, it was my own fault. You warned me.' Then it sank into the water and the flood receded.

The surviving boy returned to his home and told his father's brother what had happened. When his uncle would not believe him, and accused him of killing his cousin, he led the people to the lake and called upon the water to attest his innocence. The lake trembled, and a face that rose above its surface called, 'Yes, it was my own fault. My cousin warned me.'

His father called to it, 'Come ashore and sleep near us.'

'I am too evil now,' replied the tsaniltse.

Then his cousin called, 'When the rest of us move far back from the lake come ashore and sleep with your kinsfolk.' So the tsaniltse went ashore and slept with his kinsmen; but when his cousin visited them the next morning the monster had disappeared and all his people were dead.

The Bear Wife

A man and his wife went hunting, accompanied by their two sons, the elder of whom was married. The younger son searched all the time for black bears, but was invariably unsuccessful. While he was hunting one day he saw a woman in front of him, and feeling sure that it was his sister-in-law, he returned to camp in order to avoid meeting her. To his amazement he found that his sister-in-law had never left the camp. He pondered a good deal over the incident, but said nothing.

The same thing happened the next day. He saw the same woman, whose hair was cut at the shoulders like his sister-in-law's; yet his sister-in-law had never left the camp. He then determined to accost the stranger the next time, and when he saw her the day following, hastened forward to speak to her. The woman, however, spoke first and said, 'Why did you turn back yesterday and the day before? Am I not good to look at?'

And he answered, 'I thought that you were my sister-in-law.'

'Will you not marry me?' she said; and he replied, 'I don't know.' She led him to the top of a hill, seated him at her side on the edge of a cliff and covered him with her blanket for a moment.

'Do you see anything?' she asked; and he answered, 'No.' She covered him again and repeated the question. Looking out over the landscape he dimly descried a column of smoke rising in the distance, and after she had covered him a third time saw clearly several small columns and one large one.

Then the woman, who was really a black bear, said to him, 'That big column of smoke comes from the camp of a grizzly that has killed all my people. You must kill it for me. The other columns of smoke come from the camps of other animals.'

The young man went to the woman's camp, and the next day sought out and killed the grizzly. He lived happily with his wife until the salmon began to return up the rivers, when he took her to live with his people at Nattle, at the east end of Fraser Lake. But although his people gathered and dried many fish, his wife, whenever he emptied his baskets on the ground, merely bit the heads off the fish and threw them into the water. After the fishing had ended, too, and the people were gathering berries, his wife refused to gather any.

In the autumn the entire family built a large underground house, glezkan, in which to spend the winter. There they lived together, eating the salmon and berries they had stored away during the summer. When they had consumed all their salmon, the bear woman said to them, 'Now let someone come with me and bring in my salmon.' She led her sister-in-law to a big hole in the ground, from which she drew out an enormous quantity of dried salmon. In the same way she supplied the people with berries when their own stocks were exhausted. Thus they were never short of food during the winter.

In the early summer they joined other families at a fishing place. There the young man met an old sweetheart one evening when he went down to the river for water, and he stopped to flirt with her. His bear wife knew immediately, and wept so bitterly most of the night that her remorseful husband could not sleep. Towards morning, however, he did fall asleep, but when he awoke his wife and her child had changed to bears and disappeared. He followed their tracks to Grizzly Bear Mountain about twenty-five miles north of Fraser Lake, but there he lost them, for the animals had entered the ground.

Late in the summer, when the Indians were picking berries, he encountered a strange woman and boy who were also picking berries in the neighbourhood. It was his own wife. He said to her, 'Come home with me.'

But she answered, 'I cannot return to you now, for my mind is evil.'

In the fall again, while he was hunting near Stuart Lake, his dog discovered his son in a hole in the ground. The boy called, 'Father, it is I, your son. Mother became so big and wicked that I had to hide in this hole lest she should kill me.' His father left him there, for he had the body of a bear, though his face was human. The bear child then went west towards Hazelton and killed many Gitksan Indians.

Porcupine

Invitations had gone out for a potlatch and people from all parts began to travel towards the village where it was to be held. Two or three days after all the others had left, Porcupine started out alone, and travelled along the trail day after day until he reached a river which the people had crossed in canoes and on rafts. Porcupine had no axe to make a raft and was unable to cross. He waited on the bank until a caribou appeared, to whom he said, 'My nephew, come and help me cross the river. Carry, me over.'

Caribou agreed, and said, 'Stand on my back.'

Porcupine said, 'I shall stand facing backwards.' So Caribou started to swim across the river with Porcupine. But Porcupine twisted his tail around and drove it farther and farther into Caribou's belly. When they were approaching the other bank, Caribou said, 'Something is sticking into me.'

But Porcupine answered, 'It is only the babiche string of my belt that is tickling you.' They had almost landed when Porcupine jabbed the tail right into Caribou's belly, who shivered and threw Porcupine into the river. After being carried far down he managed to land, when he followed Caribou's tracks until he came upon his dead body. He sat down beside him, wondering what to do, for he had no knife to remove the hide. As he sat thinking, a flock of ducks flew over him. Porcupine called out to them, 'Ducks, lend me a knife.' They threw him down a small flint knife, and he began to skin Caribou.

Then Wolverine came along and said, 'My nephew, you are a good hunter. I see you have killed a big caribou.'

Porcupine said, 'Yes, I have killed it.'

'I'll help you to skin it,' said Wolverine. 'You don't know how to do it. You are cutting it wrong. Sit down and let me skin it for you.'

Porcupine sat down and Wolverine skinned the caribou. He cut off the legs, then took out the entrails and placed them before Porcupine, saying, 'Wash these down at the river for me.' Porcupine took them down to the river, ate nearly all the fat from them, and returned with the remainder. Wolverine said, 'How is it there is no fat left on them?'

Porcupine answered, 'A little fish in the river ate it.'

But the little fish heard him and called out, 'Porcupine lies. He ate it himself.' Wolverine then took his antler club and struck Porcupine on the head. Porcupine bristled, and the club, striking his nose, made the blood pour out. He fell down and pretended to be dead. Wolverine exulted, saying, 'I am a good hunter. I killed a caribou and now I have killed a porcupine.' He piled up all the caribou meat, covered it with the skin and packed on his back just enough meat for a load. Then he placed Porcupine on top of his pack and started out. As he walked Porcupine caught at the brush, and when Wolverine tried to jerk free let go suddenly and made Wolverine fall, while he himself was flung in front. After this had happened several times Wolverine became angry and said, 'I'll bring my wife and children here.' He cached his pack and Porcupine and started for his home; but as soon as he had gone, Porcupine jumped up, took the pack and returned to where the rest of the caribou lay.

Near the caribou were some large trees. Porcupine carried all the meat up one of them, stripped the bark from the trunk so that Wolverine could not climb up and rubbed caribou grease on it. Then he went to the top of the tree and ate. Soon Wolverine returned with his wife and family, and was astonished to find the meat gone. One of his children said, 'Father, there is someone up that tree.' Wolverine looked up and seeing Porcupine, tried to climb the tree, but it was too slippery and he fell again and again.

Porcupine called down, 'Camp alongside the tree and I will drop some meat down for you.' Wolverine and his family camped under the tree; and Porcupine dropped down some meat for them to eat. There they stayed for a time. Then Porcupine said, 'Sleep together and cover yourselves with a blanket. I will throw you down some large pieces of meat.' But he sharpened all the ribs and back bone of the caribou and hurled them down on top of them. Wolverine was peeping through a tiny hole in the blanket and leaped away; but his wife and children were killed.

Wolverine wept and said, 'My nephew, I am in trouble now and hungry. Help me. My wife and children are dead.' Porcupine descended the tree, took Wolverine on his back and packed him up the tree. There he cooked some meat and gave it to Wolverine, who tried to seize him, but Porcupine leaped from tree to tree. Wolverine tried to follow him, but the distance was so great that he fell to the ground and was killed. Porcupine then ate him and all his family.

Porcupine then made a club of the caribou antler and went on towards the village where the potlatch was being held. As he approached a large village, someone saw him and said, 'Here comes Porcupine.'

He entered a house full of gamblers and was offered a seat, but he planted himself beside the door, and presently asked, 'Let someone tell me my name.'

One man said, 'I know. Your name is Porcupine.' Porcupine hit him on the head with his club and killed him, then ran away to another village, where he sat down inside the door of another house filled with gamblers and asked the same question.

This time a man said, 'I know, it is Chief of the foot hills.' Then Porcupine was satisfied and sat down in the place assigned him.

CHAPTER 7

Cheyenne

Falling-Star

Once, a long time ago, two girls were lying outside the lodge at night. They were looking up at the sky; and one said to the other, 'That star is pretty, I like that one.'

The other answered, 'I like that other one better.'

One of them pointed to a very bright star, and said, 'I like that one best of all; I would marry that star.'

That night as they lay down in the lodge, going to bed, they said, 'Tomorrow we will go out and gather wood.'

Next day they went out together for wood; and as they were going along in the timber, they saw a porcupine in a tree; and the girl who had chosen the bright star said, 'I will climb up and pull him down.' She climbed up into the tree toward the porcupine, but could not quite reach him. Just as she would stretch out her hand to seize his foot, he would move up a little, so that she could not reach him. Meantime the tree seemed to be growing taller. The girl below called to her friend, 'You had better come down, this tree is growing taller!'

'No,' said the other, 'I can almost reach him now,' and she kept on climbing. When the girl below saw the tree growing so high, and the other girl so far above her that she could hardly see her, she ran back to the camp and told the people. They rushed out to the tree; but the girl had gone, she could not be seen.

The tree grew and grew; and at last the girl reached another land, and there she stepped off the branches of the tree and walked away from it. Before she had gone far, she met there a middle-aged man, who spoke to her, and she began to cry. He said to her, 'Why, what is the matter with you? Only last night you were wishing to marry me.' He was the bright star.

He married the girl, and they lived together. He told her that she could go out and dig roots and *pommes blanches* with the other women, but that there was a certain kind of *pommes blanche* with a great green top that she must not dig; to dig this was against the medicine. Every day the girl used to go out to dig roots; and one day, after she had been out some time, she began to wonder why it was against the medicine to dig one of these strange *pommes blanches*, and made up her mind that she would dig one and find out about it. Next day she dug one up. It took her a long time; and when she pulled up the root, she saw that it made a hole through the ground on which she was standing. She could look down through this hole, and see, far below, the great camp from which she had come.

When she looked down and saw the lodges, and the people walking about, very small, she was homesick; she felt that she wanted to get back to her people, and she wondered how she could get down. Nearby there grew great long grass; and after she had thought for a time about getting away, she wondered if she could not make a rope of this grass. She began to do so; and for many days she worked, braiding a great long rope. Her husband used to wonder why she was out of doors so much, and what she was doing; and one day he asked her. 'Oh,' she said, 'I walk about a great deal, and that makes me tired; and then I sit down and rest.' He did not understand it.

At last the woman had finished her rope, and let it down through the hole in the ground till she thought she could see it touch the earth below. She got a strong stick and laid it across the hole, and tied the rope to it, and began to let herself down. For a long time she went down safely; but when she got to the end of the rope, she found it was not long enough, and that she was still far above the earth. For a long time she held on there, crying. At last, however, she had to let go; and she fell, and the fall broke her all to pieces. Although the fall killed her, her unborn child did not die; he was made of stone, and the fall did not kill him.

A meadow lark, flying about, found him, and took pity on him, and took him to its nest. The lark kept him there like one of its young ones; and when the boy got big enough, he used to creep out of the nest with the young birds. The stronger the birds grew, the stronger he became. He got so, after a time, that he could crawl about very fast. After the birds had grown big enough to fly a little way, the boy was able to run about. When the birds became strong, and could fly about anywhere, he could follow them. He was growing to be a big boy.

When the time came for the birds to go south, the meadow lark said to the boy, 'Son, you would better go home now; before long it is going to be very hard weather here; we are all going to the south country.'

The boy said, 'Father, why do you want me to go home? I want to go with you.'

'No,' said his father, 'it will be too hard; you would better go home. Your people live down the stream; go home to them.'

'Well, father,' said the boy, 'I will go home if you will make me a bow and arrows.' The meadow lark did so, and pulled out some of his own quills to feather the arrows. He made him four arrows and a bow; and after they were finished, the meadow lark pointed out to him which way to go, and the boy started in that direction.

He travelled along for some time; and when he reached the camp, he went into the nearest lodge, where an old woman lived. The boy said to her, 'Grandmother, I want a drink of water.'

She said, 'Grandson, water is very hard to get. Only those who can run the fastest can have water.'

'Why is it hard to get water, grandmother?' he asked.

'Why, grandson,' said she, 'only the young men go for water, the fastest runners. There is a fearful animal there, a minhi that draws in (to itself) people who go near it.'

The boy said, 'Grandmother, give me your buffalo paunch bucket and your buffalo horn ladle. I will go for water.'

'Grandson,' she said, 'many young men have been killed by going there for water. I fear you will be killed, too.' Nevertheless she gave him the things he asked for, and he went to the stream and began to dip up water. While he was doing this, he kept looking about for this animal.

When his bucket was full, the minhi raised its head above the water. It had a great mouth; and as it drew in its breath, the suction from the mouth drew in the boy, and the water and the bucket and the spoon. Now, when he was sucked in, the boy had his knife; and when he found himself inside the minhi, he saw there all the people that had ever been swallowed by it. With his knife he cut a hole in the animal's side, and let out all the people. Then he brought the water to his grandmother.

'Why,' said his grandmother, 'my son, who are you? What are you?'

'Grandmother,' said he, 'I am Falling-Star; I have killed the great thing that has been starving you of water.' The woman told an old man of this, and he cried it through the camp that Falling-Star had killed the great animal that had so long deprived them of water.

After he had saved that camp, he said to his grandmother, 'Grandmother, are there any other camps of people near here?'

The old woman said, 'Yes, there is one down below, on this stream.' Then Falling-Star left the camp, taking with him his bow and arrows.

It was now the fall of the year. The boy travelled and travelled, and at length he reached the camp below. When he got there, he went into an old woman's lodge. She was sitting there alone, with her head hanging down, and only one stick of wood [on the fire] . He said to her, 'Grandmother, I am very cold; why don't you have a larger fire?'

'Why, grandson,' she said, 'we cannot get any wood; there is a great owl in the timber, that kills people when they go for wood.'

'Give me your rope and axe,' said Falling-Star; 'I will go and get wood.'

'Ah, no, grandson! Do not go! He is a great and terrible owl. He takes people up and sticks them into his ears,' said the old woman.

Falling-Star took the rope and axe, and started out for wood. As he was chopping wood in the timber, he kept looking all about him for the owl. After his wood was cut and tied up, suddenly this great owl appeared, and took the boy up and put him into his ear. After the boy had been put in the ear, he took his bow and one of his arrows shot the thing in the brain, and it fell down dead.

The boy crept out of the ear, and took up his wood and carried it to his grandmother's lodge. 'Now,' he said, 'grandmother, we will have a big fire and get warm. I have killed this great thing that kept you from getting wood.' The grandmother told of this; and old man called it through the camp, that Falling-Star had killed the great owl that lived in the timber.

Some time after this, Falling-Star asked his grandmother if there were any other camps nearby, and she told him that on beyond there were others. So he left that camp. By this time it was winter, and snow lay on the ground. Falling-Star came to the camp, and went into an old woman's lodge and sat down. The old woman did not set food before him; and at length he said to her, 'Grandmother, I am very hungry.'

'O my son!' said she, 'we have no food. We cannot get any buffalo. Whenever we go for buffalo, a great white crow comes about and drives them away.'

Falling-Star said, 'That is bad, that is very bad, I will see what I can do. Do you go out and look about the camp for an old worn-out robe, with but little hair on it; and tell the old chief to choose two of the swiftest runners in the camp, and send them to me.'

The old woman went out to look for such a robe, and found one; and then she went to the chief's lodge, and told him that she wanted him to choose two of the swiftest men on foot in the camp; and that when he had found them, he should bring them to Falling-Star at her lodge. She took the robe back to the lodge.

The two swift young men were sent to Falling-Star; and he told them that when any buffalo came near the camp, he would go out to a certain place; and that when the buffalo ran, he would follow them; and that these young men must chase the buffalo, following him far, and not giving up; and that when they overtook him, they must shoot at and kill him; and that after they had killed him, they must cut him open and leave him lying there.

Not long after this, buffalo were seen, and came close to the camp; and the men started out to try and kill some. When they started, the white crow flew over the buffalo, and called out, 'They are coming! They are after you! Run, run!' The buffalo started and ran; and behind them ran an old scabby bull, with little hair on its body, which could not catch up with the herd.

The two swift young men chased this bull, and did not give up; and at last they caught him and shot him, and killed him, and then opened him and left him there, and returned to the camp, as Falling-Star had told them.

After they had cut him open and left him, as they were going back to the camp, the young men looked back, and saw birds of all kinds, and wolves and coyotes, gathering about the carcass. Among the birds was the white crow. He would fly over the carcass and alight, and say, 'I wonder if this is not Falling-Star!' Then he would fly over the bull again, and alight, and say, 'I wonder if this is not Falling-Star!' He kept getting closer and closer to the carcass, and called out to the other birds, 'Leave the eyes for me! Do not touch the eyes! I wonder if this is Falling-Star!' He kept getting still closer; and just as he was about to peck at the eyes, Falling-Star reached out and caught him by the legs. As soon as he did so, all the birds flew away, and the coyotes and wolves scattered all over the hills. Falling-Star brought the crow to his grandmother's lodge, and sent for one of the soldier bands and the chief, to decide what should be done with the crow.

The chief said, 'I will take him to my lodge and tie him in the smoke hole, and smoke him to death.' He took him to his lodge, and tied him over the fire in the smoke hole; but one day the crow twisted loose and got away.

Falling-Star sent some of his young men out to gather flax weeds; and from the bark he made a long string, and to the end of the string he tied a slender thread, and to the thread he tied a small feather. He blew this feather out of the top of the lodge, and told the people to watch the string; and whenever it stopped going out, to pull it back quickly; and at the end of it they would find the crow. When the string stopped, they drew it in, and soon the crow came fluttering down through the smoke hole. Then they killed it. After this they caught many, many buffalo. The people said, 'Now we are saved. Now we can have plenty to eat.'

Falling-Star left that camp, and travelled on to another. He went into an old woman's lodge, and said, 'Grandmother, I am hungry, I want something to eat.'

'Son,' she said, 'it is bad here, we have nothing to eat. When we go to chase buffalo, Winter Man sends a big snowstorm, and we can get nothing.'

Falling-Star said to his grandmother, 'The next time that buffalo come, you and I will go out and get some meat. So fix up your dog-travois.' When the buffalo came, he said to her, 'Get ready now! We will go.' They all went out and killed some buffalo. There was one nice fat cow; and Falling-Star said, 'Come, grandmother, we will cut up this one.'

As they were butchering, Winter Man appeared on the hill, with a great club in his hand. He started down toward them, and the grandmother wanted to run. Falling-Star said, 'Do not run away, grandmother!' and as he said this, he cut out the kidney from the cow, and handed it to his grandmother. By this time Winter Man was close to them.

He said to Falling-Star, 'Why do you give the kidney to that old woman?' Winter Man lifted his foot and kicked the old woman, and his leg flew off. He raised his hand and struck at her, and his arm flew off. He opened his mouth to speak to her, and his head flew off, and he fell down. They butchered the cow quickly, and went away and left Winter Man lying there.

After they got to the lodge with the meat, they had something to eat; and Falling-Star said, 'I think I will go over and see Winter Man.'

'No,' said his grandmother, 'do not go! You have treated him badly, and he may kill you.'

'I think I will go,' said Falling-Star. 'Where does he live?'

His grandmother said, 'He lives over there in that cut bank.'

Falling-Star went to the cut bank, and went in; and Winter Man, who had been brought in and cured by his wife, said, 'Why do you come here after the way you have treated me?'

'Why, uncle,' said Falling-Star, 'I only wanted to talk to you, and to see your bow.' He took up the bow, which was made of a great tree, and bent and broke it.

Winter Man said, 'Why do you do this? Get out of my lodge! Why do you stay here when I order you out? Have you no feeling? Have you no shame?'

'Oh,' said Falling-Star, 'I want to see your club.' He picked up the club and struck Winter Man over the head with it, and killed him with his own club. Then he killed his wife and children, all except one little one who got away and crept into a crevice in the ground. After he had done this, he went back to the lodge and told his grandmother that he had killed Winter Man and all his family except one.

He said to her, 'Tell everyone in the camp to heat water and pour it into that crevice, and try to scald that child to death.' The people did this for a long time; but whenever they stopped, they could see frost rising out of the crack, and at last they stopped. If he had killed that one, we should have had no more snow.

Falling-Star left that camp and travelled on. It was now the middle of winter. The days were short, and it became dark early. One night he came to a stream, and saw a light on it. When he had come close to this light, he saw near him a man, who wore a necklace made of many ears of people strung together, standing looking at the camp. Falling-Star said to himself, 'That is Double Eyes.' He crept back, and went to where some box elders grew; and from the fungus which grew on them he cut out many pieces shaped like ears, and strung them about his neck.

He walked back, and went up to Double Eyes, who said to him, 'Hallo, friend! Where do you come from? Why, you look just like me!'

'Yes,' said Falling-star, 'I am the same kind of a medicine man. Suppose, now, the people wanted to kill you, how could they do it?'

'Why,' said Double-Eyes, 'if the people knew it, and caught me and threw some grease into the fire, and rattled on a medicine rattle, I should fall down dead. I go around biting peoples' ears off, and making necklaces of them. There is one lodge here that I have not been into. After it is quiet, and these people all get to sleep, I am going into that lodge.'

Falling-Star said, 'We are just alike; that is the only way I can be killed.'

Of the lodge he was talking about, Falling-Star said, 'I will go in and see if all are asleep, and will come back and tell you.'

'It is well,' said Double Eyes.

Falling-Star went to the lodge; and when he got there, he said, 'Are all here asleep?'

Someone answered, 'No.'

Falling-Star said, 'That person who goes about biting off ears is coming here. You must all pretend to be asleep, and snore, and then you can kill him. The only way he can be killed is to build a big fire and throw some grease into the fire, and shake a medicine rattle. If you do that, he will fall down and die.'

The people in the lodge were glad when they heard this, and they said they would do as Falling-Star had told them. Then Falling-Star went back to Double Eyes, and said to him, 'All are asleep and snoring. Let us go! I will go in first.'

'No,' said Double Eyes, 'I will go in first.'

'Very well,' said Falling-Star.

They went to the lodge; and when they got close to it, they listened, and all were snoring. Falling-Star said again to Double Eyes, 'I will go in first.'

'No,' said Double Eyes, 'I will go in first.'

He entered; and when he was inside, Falling-Star closed the door and put his weight against it, and called out, 'He has gone in!' The people arose quickly and built up a big fire. Double Eyes was trying to get out everywhere, but Falling-Star was like a rock against the door. The people threw some grease into the fire, and shook a medicine rattle, and Double Eyes fell down dead. Next morning the people threw Double Eyes out of doors. All those in the camp came about him, and recognised their own ears and took them. Falling-Star made a big sweat house, and told the people to get into it and take a sweat, and to hold their ears against the sides of their heads. They did so; and when they came out, all had their ears on as natural as ever.

While he was in this camp, he was told that they needed him at the next camp; that a lodge had been built for him, and a girl was waiting to marry him. Those people were worse off than any. An old woman lived there who scalped people. Falling-Star reached the place, and found it just as he had been told. His lodge was up, and the girl he was to marry was waiting for him. All the people had been scalped, and had their heads tied up.

The old woman heard of his coming, and went over to see him. She said, 'Why, grandson! I heard that you had arrived, and have come over to see you. I need two scalps to use on the robe I am fixing.'

'Yes, grandmother,' said Falling-Star, 'we heard you needed scalps, and that is why we came.' The girl had not been scalped; she had long hair and so had Falling-Star. After a while he went over to the old woman's lodge, taking his wife with him. She did not want to go into the lodge, she was afraid; but he coaxed her to go, yet it was a long time before she would go in.

When they entered, the old woman said, 'I am glad to see you. You have nice hair.'

'Yes,' said Falling-Star, 'we came here for that reason, because we heard you needed good scalps.' He told his wife to sit on the side away from the old woman, saying, 'I will let her take my hair first.' The old woman made ready her knife, and walked over to Falling-Star to cut off his hair. As she came close to him, he struck her; and because he was made of stone, he knocked her down and killed her at the first blow.

When the people heard that Falling-Star had killed this old woman, they all rushed into the lodge; and after they had seen that she was really dead, when they looked about the lodge, each man knew his own scalp hanging there. Now Falling-Star made a big sweat house; and he told all the people to get in and take a sweat, and while they were sweating to hold their scalps on their heads. They did this; and when they came out of the sweat house, their heads were perfect.

Falling-Star married the girl, and lived always with these people.

CHAPTER 8

Chipewyan

Naba-Cha

In the great Northwest of Canada there flows one of the mightiest rivers of the earth, known to the whites as the Mackenzie, and to the Northern Indians as the Too-cha-Tes or Big Water. On the very border of the Arctic Circle another great river joins the Big Water from the southwest. This river the Dog-Ribs still know as 'the river that flows from the country of the Big Man'.

Naba-Cha, or the Big Man, was one of the most enormous men who ever lived. His wigwam was made of three hundred skins of the largest caribou that could be killed on the vast, plains far to the northward. It had taken the bark of six huge birch trees to make the onogan from which he daily ate his meals. And it took one whole moose, or two caribou, or fifty partridges to feed him each day. Famous indeed was Naba-Cha throughout the whole North Country; and many were the expeditions of war he had made into distant lands to the north, east, south, and west. He had travelled northward to the mouth of the Big Water to fight the Snow Men or Eskimo, eastward across the Great Lake of Many Slaves to the country of the Yellow Knives, where he had seen the pure copper shining in the sands of mighty rivers, southward away on to the great plains to the country of the Crees, where there were so many large animals – but westward he had never ventured far, because in that direction it was said that a bigger man than Naba-Cha dwelt. Now Naba-Cha was not only big, but he was also cruel and wicked, especially to a young Wood Cree boy whom he had brought back from the south once when on the warpath, and who had neither father nor mother not sister nor brother to help fight. Ithenhiela, the Caribou-Footed, as the boy was called, had, however, one great friend at the wigwam of Naba-Cha. This was Hottah, the two-year-old moose, the cleverest of all the northern animals. Truly he was clever, for he had travelled all the distance from the mouth of the Too-Cha-Tes to the wigwam of Naba-Cha in three days, and this was very far indeed. Now Hottah had long thought of a plan by which he might help Ithenhiela. He knew that far to the westward, much beyond where Naba-Cha had ever gone, flowed another river almost as great as Too-Cha-Tes, and that safety for a hunted man or beast lay on its farther side, because there dwelt Nesnabi, the Good Man.

One day Hottah came to Ithenhiela, and said to him, 'We will go away. You get a stone, a clod of earth, a piece of moss, and a branch of a tree, and we shall escape from the cruel Naba-Cha.' Ithenhiela got what he was told to get, and soon they were ready to be off. Hottah took Ithenhiela upon his back, and before long they were out on the great plains which lie many days beyond the Too-Cha-Tes. Hardly, had they started when they saw coming behind them Naba-Cha on his great caribou. Then said Hottah, 'Fling out behind you your clod of earth.' Hottah did so, and immediately there rose up behind them, and between them and Naba-Cha, great hills of earth so wide and so high that it was many days before NabaCha again came in sight. And during this time Ithenhiela ate the ripened berries, while Hottah chewed the sweet grass which grew beyond the hills.

When Naba-Cha once more appeared in sight, Ithenhiela flung out behind him the piece of moss, and a great muskeg swamp lay behind them. And for days the great man and his caribou floundered in the thick sphagnum. Meanwhile, on and on towards the country of the Setting Sun passed Hottah and Ithenhiela. And when once more Naba-Cha appeared, Ithenhiela dropped the stone, and great indeed were the high rocky hills which intervened between them and Naba-Cha. Up to the very clouds rose the hills, white with snow, and magnificent, such as had never been seen before. Long was it before the fugitives again saw Naba-Cha and the great caribou, and far had they gone towards the west before Ithenhiela had to throw the branch of the tree from him. Then arose a great and mighty forest of which the trees were so thick that Naba-Cha could not pass between them, and had to cut his way through, while the caribou was left behind because his horns had stuck in the branches, and he could not pass on. All this delay helped Ithenhiela; and when he once more saw the cruel Naba-Cha, he and his moose friend had already crossed the Great Western River which they had tried so hard to reach. Away into the northwest wound Tes-Yukon, through the high rocky hills to the northward, foaming as it flowed. Soon came Naba-Cha to the other side the Tes-Yukon, and called, 'Help me, Hottah, across this mighty river. Help me to reach the country that lies beyond, and I shall do no harm to Ithenhiela.' Then across for him went Hottah; and as he brought him back across the great Tes-Yukon, he overturned him, and down he swept through the swirling rapids of the river, and was lost. This was the last of the wicked Naba-Cha.

Then came Hottah to Ithenhiela standing upon the bank, and, turning to him, he said, 'Ithenhiela, I must leave you now; and return whence I came. Go you and follow this great river, and soon you will come to a great tepee.

This is the home of Nesnabi, the Good Man. Great indeed is he, and far has he travelled, into our country to the eastward, among the golden rivers lost in mountains to the southward, to the great water which has no ending to the westward and to the silent plains, all snow covered, to the northward, where live the Snow-Men. He, like Naba-Cha, is big; but he is not cruel, and harms no one. He will aid you.' Then departed Ithenhiela, and following the bends of the great Tes-Yukon through the high spruce forest, he came to the wigwam of Nesnabi, who stood silent beside his home.

'Whence have you come, young man,' said he, 'and where are you going?'

At this, up spoke Ithenhiela, 'Great Chief, I have come from far. I have neither father nor mother nor brother nor sister. My home was with my own people away in the South Country, and there I lived happily until the coming of Naba-Cha, who took me away with him to the cruel North Country, where the snow lasts long in winter, by the sweeping waters of the Too-Cha-Tes. Hard indeed was Naba-Cha to me and many a season passed I in misery with him; until I came away with Hottah, the two-year-old moose who brought me to your country, O Great Nesnabi, and but now has he left me.'

To this answered the kind Nesnabi, 'Ithenhiela, I have long known that you would come to me. Stay with me as long as you like, but if at the end of the week you wish to journey away, I will then prepare you for your journey farther into the West Country.'

Thus it was that Ithenhiela stayed at the wigwam of Nesnabi; but when the week was done, he came to his protector, and said to him, 'I must now leave you, and travel farther. Give me that preparation for my journey that you have promised me.'

Then took Nesnabi seven arrows from his wigwam, and said to him, 'This is enough to help you, Ithenhiela, but should you shoot at any bird or beast in a spruce tree and the arrow stick in the branches, take you care that you go not after it, for if you do, surely something will happen to you.' Hardly had Ithenhiela left the good Nesnabi, when he saw a squirrel in the branches of a red spruce tree, and, raising his bow, he shot an arrow at it. Down fell the squirrel, but the arrow lodged in the branches. At once, Ithenhiela, forgetting what Nesnabi had told him, started to climb after the arrow. As he mounted, the arrow went up, too. Up, up, they went, until at last they came to the sky, and the arrow passed through, and he after it.

Great was Ithenhiela's surprise when he entered the Sky Country. It was so different from what he had expected. He had imagined a glorious country, where the sun always shone, and where herds of musk oxen, caribou, and moose roamed at large in plenty with many of his own people camped in large wigwams here and there. But instead, the air was damp, dreary, and cold; no trees or flowers grew; no herds of animals ran on the silent plains; the smoke of no wigwam greeted his anxious eyes; the war whoop or hunting cry of no Indian of his own people was heard only, far in the distance against the sky shimmered a great white mass, like a pile of snow, a when the sun shines upon it in the early summer. Towards this great white thing ran a winding path from the very spot where Ithenhiela stood. 'I will follow it,' thought he, 'and see what I come to, and find out what lies in that blazing wigwam over there.

As he passed along, he met an old woman who said to him, 'Who are you, and where are you going?'

'I have come from far,' said Ithenhiela. 'I am the Caribou-Footed. Can you tell me who lives over there in that big white wigwam?'

'Ah,' said Capoteka, 'I know you, Ithenhiela. Long have I thought you would come here. But you have done wrong; this is no country for man. In that great wigwam over there lives Hatempka; and unhappy is he because he has lost his belt of medicine, and until he gets it again, no one will be happy in the Sky Country. The belt is at the tepee of the two blind women who live far beyond the wigwam which shines so white, and no one can get it from them. Whoever finds it, and gets it from the bad blind women, will have the daughter of Hatempka, the beautiful Etanda, for his wife.' Off then started Ithenhiela, and, travelling hard, soon came he to the home of the two old blind women. And as he entered the wigwam, he saw hanging upon the side the belt of Hatempka, and many indeed were the skulls which hung about it, for many had gone to seek the belt, but none had returned.

The blind women bade him welcome, and said to him, 'When you leave, Ithenhiela, tell us, so that we may bid you good-bye.' Now Ithenhiela had noticed that each of the two old women had behind her back a knife of copper, long and sharp.

'Ah!' thought he, 'when I leave, they mean to kill me,' for one sat on either side of the door in readiness, 'but I shall fool them.' In one part of the wigwam lay a muskamoot (or bag) of bones and feathers. To this he tied a string, which he pulled over the pole above the door. Then said he, 'I am going now, blind women. Remember I am old and fat, and when I leave, I make much noise.' At this he pulled the string, and towards the door passed the bag of bones and feathers. Immediately the two old blind women stabbed, but striking only feathers, the long knifes passed through them into each other, and both were killed. Then took Ithenhiela the belt of medicine, and went he unto the shining white home of Hatempka, and said to him, 'Great chief; be you happy now, I have brought to you your healing belt. Give me now my wife, your daughter, the beautiful Etanda, that I may leave you.'

Then said Hatempka, 'Oh! much pleased am I, Ithenhiela. You have saved my people. Now shall the sun shine again. Now shall musk oxen, caribou, moose, and bear live once more in, our country. Again shall we see the smoke of many wigwams. Once more shall we hear the voice of many hunters. Take you now my daughter, the fair Etanda, but leave me not. Stay with me, and be a great man after me.' So Ithenhiela remained at the shining white home of Hatempka.

Hence was derived the name and country of the Big Man. Still the Indians in that distant country, when the northern lights flit across the sky, see in them the fingers of Ithenhiela, beckoning them to the home he has found for them so far away.

Big Bird Story

Big Bird was a widow of a famous chief who lived with her son and beautiful daughter on the banks of a large stream. Her great ambition was to secure a rich husband for her daughter, suitable to her birth. So she told her little boy to go to the bank of the river, and to watch unceasingly to see if he could discover anybody passing suitable for a son-in-law. One day the boy ran to his mother, and with a face beaming with joy told her there was somebody passing, whom he at least would like for a brother-in-law. Big Bird was delighted and immediately took some bark, and went down to the river to meet the expected bridegroom, whom she was pleased to see was magnificently dressed in a white skin costume covered with shell-like beads. Walking before him, she put pieces of bark on the ground all the way to her camp for him to step on. There she and her daughter, having prepared a meal of unusual splendour, set it before their guest. It happened there was an old dog in the camp, and the man said he could not eat until the animal was removed. Big Bird, wishing to show her new son-in-law every hospitality, complied with his request, and, taking the dog out, killed him, and left him in the bush. The man then ate his supper, and they all went to sleep.

Next morning Big Bird got up to make a fire, but, finding no wood in the tepee went out to get some, and was surprised to see the dog lying with his eyes removed, with his flesh pecked all over, and with the footprints of a three-toed animal all around him. On going back to the camp, she told them all to take off their, shoes to see who had only three toes. They all did so, save the stranger who told her that it was a thing he never did. However, Big Bird kept begging him to remove them telling him she had a pair of new moccasins for him, which would exactly match his handsome costume. Evidently his vanity was at last touched, and he consented, and, while taking them off, said, 'kinno, kinno' (look! look!) and quickly put them on again.

The boy then called out, 'He has only three toes.'

The stranger denied this and said, 'I did it so quickly that you imagine I have only three toes, but you are mistaken.'

After breakfast he told his wife that he wanted to go for his clothes which were at his camp some distance upstream, and that he wished her to accompany him. Thinking her husband's conduct rather strange; she at first objected, but, on hearing of the numerous gewgaws at his camp, at last consented to go. So they got into their canoe and started off, the man sitting in the bow, and the woman in the stern. They had not proceeded far up stream, when rain began to fall heavily, and the girl soon noticed that the rain was washing the shining white stuff off her husband's back, and then black feathers began to appear. 'Ah,' she thought to herself; 'I have married a crow.' When he was not looking, she tied his tail, now grown to visible proportions, to the bar of the canoe, whereat he turned around, and asked her what she was doing. She replied,

'Your coat is so fine I am working with the beads.'

'Oh,' said he, 'I see I have married an industrious wife,' and resumed his paddling. She then tried to find an excuse to make her escape, and told him that the point they just passing was a famous locality for wild duck eggs, and that she would like to go ashore and hunt some for his supper. He readily consented, and as soon as she got ashore, she ran up the bank, and disappeared into the forest. The crow tried to get out to follow her; but as his tail was tied to the canoe, this was impossible, and he contented himself with calling out after her, 'Caw; caw; once more I have tricked you people.'

He then leisurely proceeded to untie his tail, and flew off for another escapade.

White Bear Story

The following story explains the reason for the ferocity of the white bear and why his habitat is different from others of his own species.

Once upon a time there was White Bear, and his nephew, Black Bear, was staying with him, with several other animals, including the fox. As the fox was always up to mischief, White Bear took away his right shoulder, and in consequence the former was very ill. White Bear took the fox's shoulder, and tied it along with a bunch of claws which he always carried. Now Fox being very sick, and not able to get along very well without his shoulder, sent for the crow, who was full of cunning, to devise some means of getting his shoulder back. After a long talk, the crow went to visit White Bear, who was very old and infirm and troubled with rheumatism. He was sitting at the fire, warming his back, when the crow came in, and the bunch of claws and the fox's shoulder were hanging from the roof above his head. The crow began to talk to him, and occasionally he would touch the bunch of claws, and White Bear would wake up with a start, at which the crow would explain that he was only touching the claws to see what they were made of. At last White Bear took no notice of the noise, and soon was half asleep, and the crow, seeing his chance, caught hold of the fox's shoulder, and pulled it off, and ran out of the camp. White Bear then woke up, and asked his nephew, Black Bear, what was the matter, and the latter, who stuttered, explained that the crow had run away with the fox's shoulder. He took so long in telling it, that White Bear got angry, and told Black Bear to get out and find a home for himself. So ever since the white and black bears have lived apart.

White Bear, to show his rage, took down the sun and put it along with the claws. Now, as everything was in darkness, the other animals could not hunt, and were starving. So they applied to the crow to get them out of their new trouble. In the meantime White Bear's daughter went for water, and as she was having a drink, something black was floating in the water, which she swallowed. Some days afterwards a child was born to her, and the infant grew so fast that soon he could walk about; and when he saw this bright thing hanging among the bunch of claws, he began to cry for it. After much persuasion White Bear gave it to him to play with in the camp. After a while he wished to play outside with it, but White Bear would not at first allow it. But as the child kept continually crying to be allowed to do so, he at last consented, but told him not to go far from the camp, and if he saw anybody coming, to run into the tepee it once. This the child promised to do, but as soon as he got out, he threw the sun up into the sky, and flew away, for he was the crow in still another disguise. When White Bear saw that he was cheated again by the crow, he was furious, and since then white bears have been always wicked.

CHAPTER 9

Comanche

Origin of Death

Coyote called all the people together to decide how many winter months and how many summer months there ought to be. They set up a large council lodge. Coyote sat down in the centre on the west side. He said, 'Well, listen to me! We are to decide how many winter and summer months there are to be.'

One man said, 'Well, let us have six cold months; let the seventh be cold in the first half, and the remain warm.'

Coyote said, 'Six cold months would be too much, we should suffer from the cold. Ten summer months would be good.'

Another man said, 'If we had ten summer months, our meat would spoil; we should suffer from heat.'

Then they debated. One little man sitting by the door, who was named Snow-Bird, said, 'Well, let us have six cold months, with one month half cold and one half cool.' Coyote was in favour of ten hot months, because he wished to play a trick on them. They were debating. The little man by the door got up, and said, 'Six cold months is plenty for us.' Saying, 'Six months,' he went out.

All the assembly rose and followed him, repeating; 'Six months.' Coyote bade them wait. 'What makes you pay any attention to that little man?' But the people did not listen to Coyote, who was thus unable to work his scheme on them. He went out last of all, saying, 'We shall have six winter months.'

All the people laughed at him. 'This is the first time you have failed to have your way.' Coyote said, 'Now we shall have six cold months. Now, then, let us have another council to name the months.' When they had gathered, he announced, 'The little man shall have just as many tongues as there are cold months.'

Then he named the months: 'October, November, December, January, February, March, April.'

All agreed. 'The little man will have seven tongues; every month one of his tongues will pass away until but one is left.'

After the council was over, Coyote said, 'Now, do all of you go over there. I shall join you, and we will decide whether our dead should return after the lapse of four days. Long ago that was our way. Today I object to our dead coming back.'

They met. He called them all to the edge of the water. He picked up a rock, held it in his hand, and spoke as follows: 'Behold, our dead people shall do as this rock!' He cast it into the water. 'This rock will not come back. Similarly, our people will not return. This earth is very large; but if the dead were to come back, it would get crowded. That is why I object to it.'

All the people agreed with him. Since then our dead have not returned.

CHAPTER 10

Coos

The Country of the Souls

An Indian who lived in a certain village suddenly became ill. He had three sons, and said to them, 'If I should die, let me lie five days before you bury me.' Soon he died, and his sons kept the body in the house overnight. On the next morning they put him outside, at a distance from the house. They laid him on a board; put a couple of boards on each side edgewise and one on top, and, although they watched him, they did not see that he had gone, because his body remained there.

His soul, however, went away. As soon as he started, he lost his way and did not know where to go. Finally he came to a wide trail. He saw fresh tracks on the trail and alongside of it. So he followed these tracks. Sticks were lying across the trail, marked with red paint by people who had touched them. Soon he came to the top of the trail; and when he began to go on a downhill grade, he heard seagulls and eagles making a noise. He wondered where those birds could be, because he could not see them. Then he came to a village. When the people from the village saw him, they began to shout from the other side, 'A man is coming down, a man is coming down!' And they all ran to their canoes and went to fetch him. But he went to the landing place and stood there smiling, because some of them had just pieces of canoes, others only half canoes, and the rest of the canoes had holes punched in one end.

When the people came nearer, he saw among them his father, his eldest brother, and many other people whom he knew. But they did not land. They only looked at him from the river, and said, 'You are a stondi [unburied].'

And his father said to him, 'Your grandmother is living down the river. Go there.' So he went to the place where his grandmother was; and when he came there, he saw his grandfather sitting by the door and whittling a small stick, while his grandmother was sitting just inside door, making a small basket. He greeted them, and they all went into the house.

The house was very clean and nice. In one corner of the room there was a small basket hanging from the wall. The old man soon built a fire, took this basket down, put his hands three times in it, and took out a small dish. Then he put back the little basket, and placed the dish in front of his grandson, who at first could not see anything in it. But when he looked again, it was full of lice. He became scared and threw the dish into the fire. The lice began to crack and snap in the fire; and the old man said to him, 'Oh, my grandson, people always eat lice when they come here first.' His grandparents knew all the time that he was a stondi, but they did not tell him. They told him however, that a woman had arrived the day before, and that they were going to dance for her, and play shinny, cards, and many other games after the dance.

After a while the man looked through the window, and saw a fish trap built clean across the river; and he thought to himself, 'I am going to cross the river on the dam this evening.' But his grandparents told him not to go down to the river, because something might get hold of him and devour him. He obeyed them and stayed in the house. But the next morning he said to himself, 'I will go down and take a swim. I wonder why they did not want me to go down to the river.'' So he left the house and began to wade out into the river. Soon eels, began to stick to his legs, and hung fast. But they did not bother him, and he kept on swimming. After he was through swimming, he took two of the largest eels into the house. His grandparents were sitting by the fire when he came in, he placed the eels near them. But the old couple became scared. The old woman crawled away on her hands and knees to the end of the house, and the old man hid himself in a corner. In the meantime the young man whittled a small stick and roasted the eels on it. When they were about to be done, they began to smell very nice, and the old people came out from their corners and partook of the meal.

In the evening, after the old people had gone to bed, the young man crossed the river on the fish weir, and came to the dance house. He looked in, and saw a woman whom he knew. She was standing in the middle of the room, and people were dancing around her in a circle. Everyone who went by touched her on the top of the head. Soon the dancers noticed him, and they began to shout, 'Do you see that stondi outdoors looking into the house?'

The young man ran away, and went back to his grandparents, who said to him, 'Whenever anybody comes here and eats lice, he becomes a resident of this village, and cannot go back any more. You are still a live person and able to go back.' But he did not want to go back yet, because he wanted to take another good look at the dance. So, when night came, he crossed the river again and went to the dance house. There the same woman was distributing presents which had been put in her grave when she was buried, saying, 'Your brother sends you this; your father sent you this; your mother sends you this.'

When the people in the house saw him, they said, 'That stondi is looking in again. Do you see him?'

So he went back to his grandparents, and said, 'My children are waiting for me, and I have to go back.' And about eight o'clock he started on his way home.

In the meantime his body, that was lying near the house covered up with boards, was getting rotten. His mouth came out of shape, and his flesh was beginning to look like a sponge. Near noontime on the fifth day, his corpse began to crack and squeak. It squeaked four times, and his sons took away the boards carefully. When it squeaked the fifth time, the body seemed to move. Then his children took off all covers from him, except a single blanket. As soon as this was done, his body stopped squeaking. Suddenly he began to move his arms and legs under the blanket, and soon he stretched his feet. His oldest son was watching him all the time. He had made a blazing fire by his side. The dead man threw off his blanket and sat up. His long hair was hanging down, in front of him, and reached way down to his waist. His son said to him, 'My father, I am watching you. I have been watching you all the time.' To this he replied something that the boy could not understand. And the boy said to him, 'My father, I do not know what you said.'

So he said to his son, 'I have some lunch here in a little basket. You may eat it. Your grandmother sends it to you.' But the boy could not see the basket at all, and shouted to his brothers, 'Come here, our father has come back!'

They all hurried up and came to see their father. They wanted to warm some water and bathe him in it; but he said, 'I am not going to take a bath, my children. I got back all right.' His eyes appeared to be swelled, as if he had been asleep for a long time. When he arose from the ground, he said to his sons, 'You need not eat the lunch I brought now. You can look for it in the water tomorrow. I have in it one cooked and one fresh flounder.' On the next morning the boys found many flounders in the river, some half cooked, and others half fresh, swimming about in the water. And this man never grew old, but always remained a young man. Only his children were getting old, very, very old.

The Underground People

In a village on Coos Bay lived a people called Baltiasa. They were big, tall Indians, and lived underground. Their food was fish, which they caught on long fish poles and then swung ashore, no matter how large the fish was. Their greatest sport was to dive in the water. They could dive and swim under water across the river and back again. They made pots of stones.

They could float large stones. Whenever they floated stones, they would talk to heaven, that the rock should not sink. They could put a rock on the water, stand on top of it, and it would never sink. They could also float on feathers. They caught oysters by putting a rock on the top of their heads and walking around under the water. Their hats were made of carbuncles, and their knives of big, hard bones. They would club each other with these knives over the head without being hurt. They were very mean, and all the other Indians were afraid of them. They abused the Indians so much that it was decided to drive them out by force. This was done, and those people made two rafts, and went down the river until they came to the ocean. But the water was very rough. So they poured seal oil on the water, and the ocean became perfectly smooth. They then sailed away, and separated later. One raft went north, and the other south. And nobody knows where they went, because they were never seen again.

The Woman Who Married The Merman

In an Indian village named Takimiya there lived five brothers and a sister. Many men from different places wished to marry the girl, but she did not want to get married. It was her custom to go swimming every day in a little creek. One day, while returning from her daily swim, she noticed that she was pregnant. Her brothers demanded to know how this had happened, but she could not give them any answer, because she did not know. After some time she gave birth to a boy, who was in the habit of crying all the time. Everything was attempted to stop the crying of the baby, but was of no avail. Her brothers therefore advised her to put it outdoors. As soon as this was done, the baby stopped crying. After a little while the mother went out to look after her boy, and noticed, to her surprise, that he was eating some seal meat, which was strung on a small stick. She looked around to see who could have given him the meat, but could not find anybody. So she took the child into the house. But the boy started crying again, and would not let anybody sleep. Her brothers told her to take the child outside, and advised her to conceal herself and watch it. A whole day she remained outside without seeing anyone. Suddenly, towards evening, a man appeared and told her to follow him, because he was her husband. At first she refused to go with him, fearing that her relatives would not know where she had gone; but after he assured her that she would be permitted to see her people, she took baby in her arms and followed him. They were going into the water. Her husband told her to hang on to his belt and to keep her eyes closed. She did so, and they arrived at a village at the bottom of the sea, which was inhabited by many Indians. Her husband was one of the five sons of the chief of this village. They lived here happy and satisfied.

The boy grew up in the meantime, and acquired the habit of playing with arrows. His mother would make them for him, and tell the child at the same time, that his five uncles, who lived above them, had lots arrows. One day the little fellow asked his mother whether she would not take him to his uncles to get some arrows. To this the father of boy objected, although he allowed his wife to go alone. She put on sea otter hides, and started on her way early in the morning. As soon her brothers saw her, they thought she was a real otter, and began shoot at her with arrows. The otter seemed to have been hit repeatedly but it would come up again, so that they did not know what became their arrows. The otter was swimming up and down the river, followed by many people in canoes, who were shooting at it, but nobody could hurt it. Seeing the fruitlessness of their efforts, everybody gave up the hunt, with the exception of the oldest brother, who followed the otter until it reached the beach. There he saw someone moving around close to the shore. Approaching nearer, he noticed that it was a woman, he recognised her at once as his lost sister. She told him that she was the sea otter, and showed him the arrows with which they had been shooting at her. She said, 'I came here to get some arrows for my boy. My husband is the son of a chief. We are living not very far from here. Whenever the tide is low, you can see our house right in the middle of the ocean. I brought you these sea otter skins that you might exchange them for some other things.' Her brother gave her as many arrows as she could carry, and she went back to her husband But before going down into the water, she said to her brother, 'You will find tomorrow morning a whale on the beach, right in front of your landing.' And so it came to pass. The whale was divided among the people.

A few months afterwards the woman visited her relatives with her husband and child, and her brothers noticed that part of her shoulders, were turning into those of a dark-coloured sea serpent. She stayed a little while, and then returned home. Long afterwards many of these sea serpents came into the harbour; but the woman never came ashore again, and was seen no more. These sea serpents had come after arrows; and people kept on shooting at them, thereby giving them what they desired. They never returned again; but every summer and winter they would put ashore two whales as a gift to their kinsmen above the sea.

The Revenge on the Sky People

There were two brothers living in Kiwe'et; the older one was a canoe builder. One day, while he was at work, a man came up to him and asked, 'What do you do with your canoe after it is finished?'

'I always sell it,' he replied, going on with his work and holding his head down.

Near the canoe that he was building lay his little dog. All at once the stranger hit the canoe builder a terrible blow, killing him instantly. He cut off his head and walked away with it.

When the younger brother and the other relatives of the murdered man saw that he was not coming home, they went to look for him. They found him dead in the canoe, with his head cut off. The little dog was barking over the dead body. Everytime he barked he would look straight up. This made them think that someone from above had committed the murder. The next day the younger brother went out to search for the murderer. He took an arrow and shot it straight into the air, and then another one, and every arrow he shot hit the neck of the preceding one and stuck in it. He kept on shooting until the arrows reached the ground.

He climbed up on this chain and got to the top, where he met some Indians dancing around a man's head that they had brought home. It was his brother's head. He asked for the man who gave them this head, but he was not among them. One of their number told him that this man's wife was digging fern roots at, a certain place, and that he could find her there every morning. He went there and found the woman digging fern roots on the banks of a river. He asked her some questions. 'Do you own your canoe?'

'No.'

'Then who ferries you across this river?'

'My husband always brings me over here.'

'And what does he do after he has taken you across?'

'He goes back, and comes after me towards evening. He stops his boat at a little distance from the shore, and I jump in with my pack.'

'What do you do with the fern roots when you get home?'

'I dry them.'

'And what do you do with them after they get dry?'

'I give them to everyone in the village, except to an old couple that live not far from us.'

'And what do you do afterwards?'

'Then I start cooking. I cook in a large pot and stir it with my hands.'

'Don't you ever burn your hands?'

'No; it never hurts me.'

'What does your husband do when you folks go to bed?'

'He goes to bed too. I always lie away from my husband, who falls asleep at once.'

After he had asked all these questions, he killed the woman, put her skin on, and made himself look just like her. He then picked up her fern roots and tied them together. Soon the husband came and stopped the canoe quite a distance away from the shore. The young man took the fern roots on his shoulders and jumped aboard. But one of his feet touched the water, and he excused himself by saying, 'I am tired and my pack is very heavy.' The husband did not say anything, and the young man did exactly what the woman had told him. He made only one mistake by offering some fern roots to the old couple. But they would not take them, and one of them exclaimed, 'This woman belongs to the earth, and not here.' Fortunately nobody from the other houses heard this remark.

When he came to the house where the murderer of his brother lived, he began to prepare supper. While stirring the pot with his hands, he burned them, and cried out, 'Ouch! I have burnt my hands.'

The husband heard this, and asked, 'What is the matter with you?'

'Oh, my finger is sore, and that is the reason why I cried out.' Suddenly, while looking up, he saw his brother's head hanging down from the roof. He could not help crying everytime he looked at it. When the husband asked for the reason of this, he answered, 'There is so much smoke in the house that it hurts my eyes.'

When night came the supposed wife went upstairs, and one of his brothers-in-law, on seeing him, said to his grandmother, 'It seems to me that my sister-in-law looks like a man.' But the old woman told the boy that the women belonging to their tribe always looked like men, and nobody spoke of it any more.

Later on, visitors from different places came and began to dance around the head, from which the blood was dripping all the time. After the dance was over, everybody went to bed. The young man took a large knife and punched a hole in every canoe in the village, except in the on that he was going to use. Then he went to bed with the husband; and soon as the latter had gone to sleep, he cut his head off, took his brother' head, and made his escape in the canoe that he had saved. In the meantime the mother of the killed man, whose place was under the bed of her son, felt the blood dropping on her face. She made a light and saw what had happened. She woke the other people, and they soon found out that the supposed woman was gone, and with her the head that was hanging from the roof. They said, 'That woman must have killed her husband,' and they went after her. But since the canoes foundered as soon as they pushed them into the sea, they had to give up the chase.

In the meantime the young man climbed down the chain of arrows and got back to his village, bringing home the head of his brother. They gathered all his friends and told them to put his brother's head on to his body again. They went to work at once. There was a small spruce tree against which they leaned the body of the dead man while they were trying to put the head back. But every time they tried, the head fell off. Finally, at the fifth trial, the head stayed on the body, which reached almost to the top of the little spruce tree. Then the boy said to his brother, 'Now you are well again.' So the man went away from the tree.

The people from above could not come down to take revenge. The people of the village then said to the revived man, 'You will be nothing but a woodpecker. The next generation will see you.' And his children were woodpeckers, and had red heads because of the blood that was dripping from their father's head.

The Man Who Married the Bird

On the river Siusean there lived a young man who was a gambler. He lost his property as fast as he could acquire it. Finally it happened that he had nothing more left. His relatives could not support him. Therefore he took his fish pole, the only thing left to him, and started up the North Fork. He came to a little waterfall, and saw in it a nice little bird that he wanted to catch with his spear. But everytime he was ready to throw, the bird would dive and thereby avoid the spear. Having made a few more unsuccessful attempts, he went down to the edge of the creek, and decided to dive in the water, to see whether he could not catch the bird with his hands. When he had dived, he saw a large house, and in it the bird he was trying to catch. The bird said to him, 'You are my husband. Come in.' He entered and heard at the other end of the house a great noise. He looked around and saw many people dancing and trying to cure a sick person. Some were gambling. He joined in the game, began to win, and continued winning right along. Then his wife asked him whether he had a sister at home, and he told her that he had a sister and a brother, and also a father who was very old and poor. He stayed in this house five days, after which the people told him that they would take him home. While they were preparing a canoe, his wife said to him, 'Here are some clothes that you may take home for your sister. Whenever she puts them on she will look just like me.' He took the clothes and went into the canoe with three companions, who gave him a piece of whale to take along.

They told him to lie down in the canoe and to keep his eyes shut. But soon he got tired of it and opened his eyes a little. Just as he did so, a breaker nearly swamped the canoe; and his companions shouted to him, 'Keep your eyes shut!' This scared him so much that he closed his eyes, and did not open them again. They were paddling under the water until they came to the beach. Here he left his companions and went afoot towards his home. While walking along he heard a noise. He approached nearer, and saw that it was his father who was wandering about the place where they had been living before, crying for his son. He approached him and asked him what he was doing. At the sight of his son, the old man uttered a cry of joy, and clasped him in his arms. Then they went towards the house, and when they came to a little creek, the old man said, 'Let me carry you across the creek.'

But the son objected, and answered, 'No, I will jump across. You can wade across. I am not going to run away; I am going home with you.' When they came to the mouth of the river, they found the cut of whale that was given to the young man by his wife's relatives. They had told him that, if he would give to each of his relatives a piece of this whale, he would find a whole whale the next day. Thus he was enabled to gain wealth from this, because he could sell it. He therefore sliced the whale, and distributed it among his relatives. The next morning he found a whale on the shore. He cut it up, and sold pieces of it to the people of the village. Thus this young Indian became a rich man. His friends, too, grew rich through him.

CHAPTER 11

Cree

The Birth of Lake Mistassini

Two brothers went out on a hunting excursion. They separated at a certain point, and each took a different route. One of them came to a small pool and saw in the water an enormous otter. He was just about to kill it when several young otters emerged from the pool. He noticed that they were of different colours, some red, some blue, and some green. Amazed at the unusual sight, he ran to inform his brother of the strange occurrence. The brother wished to go back and shoot the animals; so they started off together. As soon as the old otter made her appearance, one of the brothers fired. It dived, and immediately the water of the pool began to boil and foam and flood the surrounding land. The brothers ran in opposite directions and the water followed them At last one of them was brought to a halt at some high rocks near the post of Mistassini, and the old otter devoured him. The waters then ceased to rise; and the lake remained as it is today.

The Painted Canoe

Long ago an old man and his daughter lived by the shore of a river. They were very happy until an Indian came along and married the daughter.

The old man resolved, however, not to be so easily deprived of his only comfort, so he took his son-in-law out into the woods and left him to freeze to death.

To the dismay of the old man the daughter married again, so he at once set about treating this young man as he had done the other. In the spring at the time the sturgeon spawns he invited his son-in-law to go out with him to spear the fish. The young man happened to step on the edge of the canoe, and the old man, taking advantage of the chance thrown in his way, jerked the canoe to one side, and the young man fell into the rapid. When he came to the surface he saw the canoe in the distance, but managed by swimming hard to reach land in safety. When the old man came ashore he was questioned as to the whereabouts of the young man, and lied that he supposed his son-in-law must be drowned, as he fell out of the canoe. To his astonishment they told him that his treachery was discovered and that the young man was alive in his tent.

The old man next invited his son-in-law to go hunting with him, and again he agreed. They journeyed far from their tent and camped in the woods. At night-time it is the custom of the Indians to hang their boots before the fire to dry. The old man and his son-in-law did this, but the young man, suspecting treachery, changed the position of the boots and hung his own where his father-in-law's had been placed. The old man arose in the night, took his son-in-law's boots and put them in the fire, never dreaming that he was about to become the victim of his own treachery. He then aroused the young man and told him his boots were on fire. The young man on coming out of the tent said, 'These must be your boots. Mine are on your poles and are all right.' He then put on his boots and left his father-in-law to freeze to death. He had not gone far before he heard footsteps behind him, and upon waiting saw that the old man had tied brush (twigs of fir tree) upon his feet, and was all right.

The young man saw that there would be no peace until he could rid himself forever of his father-in-law's company. He made a canoe and painted the inside more beautifully than any canoe had before been painted. He also made handsome paddles and presented these to the old man, who was delighted and became so anxious to try the merits of his new canoe that he went out without noticing the threatening weather. He was so taken up with the beautiful way in which the canoe was decorated that he gave no heed to his course. A storm sprang up, and he was never seen nor heard from again.

The Story of Katonao

Katonao was a great warrior who was always seeking for glory. He had two sons who were very much like him in this respect. They went off to meet some other warriors, and Katonao followed to help them fight. When he had gone some distance he saw a lot of warriors on the ground dead, and he knew that his sons had passed that way. At last he came across one of his sons who was lying wounded on the ground, pierced by a number of arrows. The old man pulled the arrows from his son's body and went in search of the other son. He had not proceeded far when his wounded son overtook, him and both followed the tracks of the other son. At last they came across him fighting desperately with hostile warriors, and they ran to help him. Old Katonao tripped on his snowshoes and was captured. The two sons tried hard to save their father and endeavoured to pull him from the hostile warriors, but he asked them to let him be taken.

The hostile warriors resolved not to kill Katonao at once, but reserve him for a feast. They treated him with great cruelty on the journey, sometimes dragging him naked through the snow and tying him to the sled; exposed all night to the cold. They gave him old skins to eat. As soon as the warriors arrived home, they tied old Katonao up, and resolved to sacrifice him on the morrow. They placed him in a tent with an old man as guard. Orders were given to cook Katonao for the feast, but some of the women cried out that there were lots of partridges in the woods. The old man then asked the warriors if Katonao and the women could go hunting the partridges, and, they consented. Katonao then took up his bow and arrows and killed many partridges. In hunting these he wandered farther and farther away from his captors, and at last he made a dash for liberty. He was still naked and suffered much in making his escape. He had not gone far when he saw the warriors in full chase; so he hid in the snow and killed two of them as they ran past him. He then took off their clothes, fixed himself up, and started in search of his sons.

When the warriors came upon their dead comrades, they returned to the camp and blamed the old man for asking Katonao to go out hunting. Then they called him and killed him for the feast. When Katonao arrived at the tent of one of his sons, he found him making snowshoes. He walked on farther, and found the other son making a canoe. Katonao shot an arrow into him and chased him into the tent. The other son came up, and seeing what Katonao was doing was about to put him to death, but the wounded boy cried out for him to spare his father, so Katonao was spared and lived with his sons for a long time.

The Biter Bit

There was once an old man who had an only daughter to look after him. One day the daughter was married to a young Indian, and this so angered the old man that he put the husband to death.

The daughter married again, and again the old man made away with her husband. The manner in which he killed them was by coaxing them to the top of a hill, where he had a trap placed to break their backs.

At last the daughter married a man who happened to be a little more cunning than the rest. He ran away with the daughter and went off to hunt bear. That winter he was very successful and killed many bears. He made a large roggan or birchbark basket in which he put the bear's fat. The roggan was so heavy that it took four men to carry it.

In the spring the couple returned to the old man's wigwam, and the son-in-law made him a present of the roggan. The old man was so strong that he lifted the roggan easily. The old man then coaxed the son-in-law to go to the top of the hill, intending to serve him as he had done the others, but the young man proved too strong and cunning for the old fellow, and in wrestling he broke the old man's back. During the struggle the old man cried out to his daughter that her husband was killing him, but she had no sympathy for him, and said that it served him right.

Chichipischekwan (Rolling Head)

It happened in the darkness of the primeval world that there existed a being, it is said, who may have been a man. With him was one who was his wife. They had two sons, one being half-grown and the other a small, toddling boy.

They lived in a wigwam, not of hides, but made of many willow wands plastered over with mud to make it warm. Once in a while in later times such lodges were built for winter use; but the impossibility of their being removed from place to place brought them to such discredit among this nomadic people that they were in time entirely replaced by those of skins.

This family lived happily for a time. Every morning the father went out into the woods and seldom came home without bringing with him the choicest pieces of venison. He was happy in his work and in the companionship of his wife and children.

A time came, however, when he noticed that she had changed somehow. Instead of the happy, contented look he used to see on her face, there was now an air of restless preoccupation. A strange light was in her eyes. Every now and again she would get up and go for wood in a nearby bush. This she did repeatedly, even when it seemed altogether unnecessary. The man said nothing, but made up his mind to do some investigation in order to help her, if it were possible.

One day, some time after this, being in the bush, he saw her coming. Something in her eager gait so roused his curiosity that he hid himself behind some willows. She approached a dead tree, at the foot of which there was a large hole. She tapped! A great number of snakes came crawling out. She sat on a log that had blown down; and they crawled all around her, while she fondled them.

He was horrified! In him was born all that human abhorrence of the snake. Not stopping to make his presence known, he went back to the tent and called his two sons. 'I am going out to hunt,' said he. 'Tell your mother so when she returns.'

He walked a long time and passed many wild animals before he killed a moose. Without even stopping to take out the insides, he went home. Arriving there, he signed as if in great weariness and told his wife that he had killed moose. He explained to her where the carcass lay and asked her to go for some of the meat, as he was not feeling well. She showed marked reluctance to go; but she could not very well disobey him. 'Let me run for some wood first,' she cried.

'No,' replied the man in a firm voice. 'Go at once!'

Mumbling to herself, she started off. The man, looking at the fire saw a piece of sinew contracting with the heat. He knew that she had dropped it there while he was not looking and that it was an act of magic performed by her, in order to make shorter the distance she had to go. He scooped it out of the fire with a piece of stick and wetting it, stretched it to its utmost length thereby counteracting the effect of her act .

Having done this, he armed himself with a hunting knife and walked to where he had seen the snakes. He tapped and as before the snakes began to crawl out one after the other. As fast as they came out, he cut off their heads. He spared only one, and that a very little one. 'When the Earth is peopled by men,' said he, 'you will not have the power to interfere with those who are to be lords of it. You will be small and easily conquered.' Having made this pronouncement on the reptiles of the West, he hurried back to the tent and began to make preparations for his wife's return.

He took four things and calling his older son to him he said 'You are to take your little brother on your back and flee for your lives. Here are things which will be useful when danger approaches; this awl means a hedge of thorns; this flint gives fire; this piece of rock can form a mountain; and this beaver-tooth, a great river of water. Farewell, my own sons! Farewell! May your lot be such that good may come to the Earth through this evil that is fallen upon us. In days to come should you want to see me, look up to the Northern skies; for I shall be up there. People will call me Oochaykatak (The Great Dipper)

The boy took up his brother and fled to the West.

Some little time intervened before the mother, arrived, panting and covered with perspiration. Her path had been long and she had run most of the way. Without a word she dropped her load and hurried to the bush! A great suspicion had come over her. Sure enough, there lay her pets in a heap, dead. Only one little snake came out to tell her what had taken place. An insane fury came over her; and she ran to wreak vengeance upon her husband for the death of the reptiles.

In the meantime, the man had been making preparations; he had pulled a net over the door; and he stood, axe in hand, ready for his wife. She approached furiously; but her progress was arrested by her being caught in the net; only her head went through. The man severed it from the rest of her body, and then fled upward through the opening on the top of the wigwam. 'Chase him up to the sky,' said the head to the trunk, 'and I will go after his sons.' The body soared after the fleeing man up to the heavens; while the head sped westward after the boys.

The man may be seen up in the northern skies at night time. He is the Great Dipper; to one side is the Little Dipper, which is the body of his former wife, always chasing him but afraid to go too near the abode of the North Star, who loves her husband and therefore is ready to protect him.

The Flight of Wesakaychak

With wonderful speed the head of the mother rolled after the two boys. This was now Chichipischekwan, the Rolling Head. From afar the boys could hear her say, 'Where, where can you flee? I am going to kill you!'

Wesakachak, for that we must now call the boy, ran faster, holding his little brother. Ever nearer came the voice of his mother. Something must be done. He remembered the advice of his father; and, putting his brother down on the ground, he threw the Awl behind him, saying at the same time, 'Let it be as my father said.' Immediately, there came to be a seemingly impenetrable hedge of thorns between them and their pursuer. Once more he took up his brother and fled.

Rolling Head could not find an opening anywhere. She went up and down, but the hedge extended from sea to sea; there was no alternative but to force her way through somehow; and this she proceeded to do. Here and there she rolled, screaming with pain and fright as the thorns pricked her. How long she took to make her way through is not told; but in time she was free on the other side, bleeding all over but more furious than she had been before.

It is said that this hedge of thorns disappeared as time went on but that remains of it are still to be seen in the cactus plant in the South.

In the meantime the boy had been making his way as best he could, although he was now very tired, having had to carry his little brother on his back for so long a time and having no sleep. Once again he heard the approach of his mother as she spoke the words, 'A–a–a–ay–y! Where in the world can you flee to?'

He laid down his brother and throwing the piece of rock behind him said, 'Let there be a mountain from one end of the earth to the other.' Immediately, Rocky Mountains sprang up and once again Rolling Head found herself thwarted.

Back and forth she rolled, looking for an opening through which she could go; but she found none. Imbued with unnatural power though she was, a time came when she was exhausted. She lay down beside a wall of rock and slept. A strange sound awoke her. It seemingly came from the heart of the mountain. The sound grew louder and louder till she saw a hole forming. It was a monster worm which had gnawed its way through the rock. Today this is known as the Golden Valley trail between Banff and Mount Assiniboine.

Here was her chance! As soon as the worm was through, she followed crushing it, she then rolled into the hole, which was just large enough to let her through. Bleeding and scratched beyond recognition, she emerged the other side, her fury increased a hundredfold. Once again she gave chase to her children and was close up to them in a short time. The boy had been making slow progress, in fact he was beginning to see the futility of their flight. When he knew his mother's head to be near again, he threw down the flint behind him and said, 'Let there be a wall of fire from one end of a land to the other!' This happened. Once again Rolling Head found herself confronted by a seemingly insurmountable obstacle. She sought for a safe way through; there was none. Only one way was possible and that was to go through. Hesitating only for a short time, she rolled in to the flames and emerged on the other side, burnt and blackened. A man were dangerous in such a plight; but no creature exists that can exceed the fierceness of a woman, thwarted in her vengeance and humiliated at the same time. She gave chase once more!

After throwing the flint, the boy Wesakaychak was just able to stagger along, because, of his great fatigue. He was hardly able to keep himself from falling asleep, even as he walked along unsteadily. When he heard his mother's voice again he took this time the beaver's tooth; and, throwing it ahead of him, said; 'Let a mighty river flow here!' It was only when he found himself confronted by a great flow of water that he realised his fatal mistake. The river was in front of them and Rolling Head behind. He and his little brother were now at the mercy of their mother; he knew what that meant. His faculties cleared; and he ran along the side of the river, seeking some way of escape. The river seemed uncrossable. When about to despair, he saw two old patriarchs. They were great bitterns, old men in appearance, sitting, one on either bank of the river; exactly opposite to each other. These birds are quite large now; but in those days they were monsters in size. He ran to them and implored them to put him and his brother across the river. This they refused to do. They were not bad at heart, however; for in time they took pity on the plight of these boys. They put their necks side by side and on this hastily improvised bridge the fugitives crossed safely to the other side.

In a moment or two Rolling Head came up. 'Put me across!' she commanded. The birds refused. Now Rolling Head was a creature well versed in the wisdom of her kind. She made many flattering remarks to the bitterns. Seeing that they were pleased, she kept on till they offered to help her. Wesakaychak implored them not to do so, but to no avail. The birds once more placed their necks side by side and Rolling Head proceeded to cross.

Her naturally wicked nature was her own undoing. Recent wet weather had given rheumatism to the birds and their necks were painful. Rolling Head, when she saw Wesakaychak on the bank, began to jump up and down as she crossed. The incensed birds pulled up their necks; and she tumbled into the river. The boy, Wesakaychak, acting on the instinct which was later to bring him into such prominence in the affairs of the young world, took a stone and, throwing it into the water where his mother's head had disappeared, yelled out the word, 'Namao! Namao!' (sturgeon). The Head whisked its tail and swam away, a fish.

Thus the mother who, because of her evil ways, had lost the highest that mortal can attain, was destined forever to play the humbler role. But even against her evil will she made herself useful to man by becoming the fish now found in our rivers called by the Cree Indians.

The Younger Boy Becomes a Wolf

There was now no immediate cause for fear but still the boys' predicament was great. Fortunately it was summertime and Wesakaychak found enough berries to keep himself and his little brother alive. They were very lonely and he found it very difficult to keep the little one happy.

Be it remembered that they were the first human children. Nothing in the way of toys, with which people are wont to keep the young ones amused, were in existence as yet. Wesakaychak stripped the bark off a willow and wound it into a ball. With this he amused his little brother who cried very often.

How long these solitary children lived alone in the wilderness nobody knows. At night Wesakaychak used to look up to the skies and through his tears he would see his father, and the sense of companionship this gave him was some comfort to his lonely heart.

One day as the boys were playing with the ball on the bank of the river, they saw a canoe approaching. It was wonderful to see it come of itself against the current. There was somebody in it, but he was not paddling. The only thing he did was to hit the canoe on the side now and again, and this would serve to quicken its speed.

When he came near enough to be seen distinctly, Wesakaychak saw that the occupant was a creature similar to himself, only rougher and more hairy in appearance. The canoe stopped of itself when it came to a point opposite to where they were. The boys continued to play, and as the little boy threw the ball it took a queer curving flight, as if drawn aside from the line of its course; and it fell into the canoe.

'Oh-h! Let us have it!' cried Wesakaychak. 'It is the only thing I have to comfort my little brother with!'

The stranger placed it on the flat of his paddle and held it out. 'Come and get it!' said he in a strange, cunning voice. Wesakaychak walked into the water and was about to take the ball when, with a dexterous movement of the paddle, the stranger scooped him up and landed him prostrate in the canoe.

'Let me out!' cried Wesakaychak in anguish. 'I must go back to my little brother who needs me!' The monster struck the side of the canoe and it sped swiftly on.

'Let me go! Or else take my little brother too!' pleaded the sobbing boy; but with a self-satisfied grin, the man struck his canoe again and gradually sped on, leaving the little boy far behind do the bank.

Wesakaychak heard his brother cry, 'Brother! Brother! I will be a wolf! I will be a wolf! Oo–o–o–o–ow–w–w.' Through his tears Wesakaychak saw young gray wolf run away into the woods. He cried and cried till he fell asleep, totally exhausted.

In due time, Waymesosiw, such was the name of this being, arrived at his lodge. He place the sleeping boy on the ground, and turned his canoe over him. He seemed to be in great spirits. He spoke to his elder daughter, 'I have brought a companion for you; go and get him. He is asleep beneath the canoe.'

The girl went out, but returned in a very short time, disgust on her face. 'I do not want the swollen-faced little man,' said she.

'He is handsome,' replied Waymesosiw. 'He has been crying! You, Younger One, go and see if you like him then.'

Now, the younger of the two girls seemed to be more human than any of the family. She too went out but more quietly. Finding the boy, she took pity on him. She washed his face in the river, and, waking him up, did all she could to bring comfort into his heart. She asked about his past life, and, strange to say she seemed familiar with the main events of it. News travelled rapidly through the land in those days, for animals and birds had free intercourse with each other.

He told her what befell his little brother and she assured him that he would be able to take good care of himself; until such time as he himself would be able to look for him. A sympathy seemed to exist between them, and the boy, comforted greatly, walked with her to the lodge with every show of confidence.

In a day or two his face and eyes, which had been swollen, regained their normal state and he was seen to be a very handsome young man. The older girl was greatly chagrined at having rejected him and now did everything she could to win him over, but without any success.

Between Wesakaychak and the younger girl there was mutual attraction and sympathy. She had given him that friendship for which he had long been hungry. While courteous to the older girl, he felt nothing that had a semblance of affection for her. As time went by he grew to manhood, and he found himself in love with the younger one. Waymesosiw giving his consent, he took her to wife, thereby, incurring the deep hatred of the elder sister.

Wesakaychak Destroys the Great Moose

Waymesosiw was now desperate. He had made two great efforts to have Wesakaychak killed and both had failed. In his despair he dreamed and saw the Crimson Eagle and the Great Serpent, both of whom had not only failed to destroy Wesakaychak but had themselves been killed. Great was the joy of Waymesosiw, therefore, when he again heard his son-in-law ask his wife where he could find some sinew. Forgetting even to address him through his daughter, the old man offered to show the young man a place where he could find all the sinew he wanted.

The crafty Waymesosiw remembered that there was a Great Moose living in the Northland. He would plan to go with his son-in-law in quest of this animal. If it so happened that Wesakaychak escaped with his life in trying to kill the animal, then surely some other opportunity to destroy him would present itself.

With this design in mind Waymesosiw confided to Wesakaychak that he knew where there was a Great Moose, and would conduct the young man to its neighbourhood. Of course Wesakaychak accepted the invitation, and they made due preparation, for it was to be a long and perilous journey.

When all was ready and they were to make their start the next morning, Wesakaychak's wife had a private talk with him. She told him that she had had a dream in which she saw what was to meet them on the journey. 'A–a–ay! My husband,' said she; 'be careful when you come to the haunts of the Great Moose. My father will pretend to be lame and will be some distance behind you all the time. Watch carefully and be ready! Here is some down. As soon as the Great Moose approaches, blow on this and say the words, "Let me be like unto thee?" Immediately you will be transformed into this, the lightest of all things and you will be safe. When, in time the Great Moose is exhausted, you will know what to do. After you have killed the creature and you camp for the night, pretend to sleep but watch my father till something happens. I will be with you in spirit.'

Morning dawned and the two men were on their way to the haunts of the Great Moose. It was a very difficult trip but the old man kept easily. Many days they walked before they saw tracks which seemed to be most unnatural so great were they.

'Ough!' said Waymesosiw. 'The Great Moose!' Wesakaychak could hardly believe that any animal, however large, could have hoofs of such prodigious size. He at once secretly untied a small package from his belt and took out the piece of down his wife had given him. True to her dream he noticed that Waymesosiw dropped behind, pretending to be lame. Wesakaychak of course wisely paid no attention to this, but went on, carefully, looking for the huge animal.

Suddenly there was a mighty crash among some tall spruce trees. Wesakaychak had just enough time to blow on the down and to repeat the formula which was to bring about the change in him when the beast was upon him. With a deafening roar the Great Moose fought and bellowed, as it tried to strike and to trample on the down, which was Wesakaychak. The down, however, quietly blew around in the air, sometimes settling on his head, his nose or other parts of the great body. All day the Moose struggled but with no success. Towards evening it sank down exhausted and Wesakaychak, assuming his own shape, killed it. Standing erect on the big body of his victim; he said, 'When man inhabits this earth; such animals will not be. They are too powerful and would be a menace to life.'

It was some time before Waymesosiw came back. He had fled and left his son-in-law to his fate. Listening from the top of a high tree he had guessed from the length of the struggle that the young man was holding his own in the desperate conflict. When finally the noise ceased, he shrewdly supposed that the Moose was dead. Waymesosiw was greatly disappointed at the outcome of the fight; but he made up his mind to act as if greatly pleased, for the time being, hoping that by night he might be able to bring about something harmful to his partner.

Waymesosiw pretended great joy at the death the Great Moose and busied himself preparing the camp and cooking their evening meal. He seemed unusually jovial and told many a yarn after they had eaten, as they sat for a long time before the blazing fire. The Great Dipper had turned considerably around the North Star when they laid themselves down to sleep. Something about the actions of the old man, when they hung up their clothes on the branches, awakened Wesakaychak's suspicions. He laid down, however, and watched secretly while Waymesosiw fell asleep almost immediately. A little later he got up very quietly and, taking his clothes from where he had hung them, changed them with Waymesosiw's, which he hung where his own had been. Having done this without awakening the other, he lay down quietly and watched for developments.

Waymesosiw's snoring ended with a gasp! There was a moment's pause, and then he raised his head slowly. The big logs were still burning brightly and he had to shade his eyes to see his son-in-law across the fire. 'Are you asleep?' he asked in a subdued voice loud enough to be heard if Wesakaychak were awake but not loud enough to awaken him if he should be asleep. The latter kept on breathing regularly as if asleep but actually watching through the corner of his eye. He saw Waymesosiw get up, approach what he thought were the young man's clothes and deliberately place them on the fire before he lay down again. Then, when they were irretrievably destroyed, he yelled, 'Son-in-law, wake up! Your clothes are burning!' Wesakaychak jumped up and examined the burning clothes.

'No,' said he. 'These are yours. Mine are dry now and I will take them.'

Waymesosiw now knew that he had been outwitted, but true to his crafty nature, he made no comment. He had been worsted; but, be it said to his credit, outwardly, at least, he bore no grudge.

Morning came and Wesakaychak made preparations to go back home. Waymesosiw neither complained nor asked for help. Only when Wesakaychak was starting off did he speak of his plans. 'You have beaten me, young man,' said he. 'Go back to your wife. Your way is better than mine. I too will go home but more slowly.' For a moment Wesakaychak nearly had pity on him, but hoping to give him a lesson, he left him; he knew that the old one would not die but would eventually come through not much the worse for his experience and perhaps wiser.

Waymesosiw left alone gathered a great pile of wood; and having secured a very large round boulder, he fired it till it was red hot. Then with a green pole he began to roll it in the direction of his home. The heat from it kept him warm; and as soon as the stone would begin to cool off he would heat it up again. Thus he travelled slowly and painfully, day after day.

Wesakaychak on the other hand came easily back to his home; and the joy of his wife was great. It was summertime before Waymesosiw arrived, a wiser man and changed. His lust for killing had left him. His naturally genial temperament came to the fore and in time he was liked by Wesakaychak. Thus all was well, and the home of Waymesosiw became a place of peace and contentment.

Wisakitcax and Buzzard

Wisakitcax was travelling. He killed a buffalo, and cooked the carcass. While waiting for it to cook, he fell asleep. When he awoke, he found that Buzzard had eaten all, leaving only the bones. He lay down, concealing himself among the bones, and never moved. Buzzard, thinking Wisakitcax had left, came close up to the bones. Wisalitcax seized him by the legs and beat him. He then spat upon his head and pushed it into his anus. He walked around for about a week with Buzzard's head this way. Then he pulled it out and examined it. Buzzard was still alive, but his head and neck had become rotten, and all the feathers had come off. Wiskitcax now transformed him into the turkey buzzard saying, 'Henceforth you shall be the buzzard, and all shall know you as a carrion bird. You shall always have this mark because you stole my meat. People shall call you ugly.' Before this Buzzard was handsome like Eagle.

CHAPTER 12

Eskimo

The Woman Who Was Fond of Intestines

Once there lived an Aleut with his wife and little boy. The wife was very fond of intestines, and early each morning the husband would go out in his bidarka hunting, and return in the evening with a boat full of intestines which he gave to his wife, telling her to keep what she wanted for herself, and distribute the rest among her neighbours.

The wife was somewhat puzzled by the husband's actions; she could not understand why he went so early in the morning, where he got so many intestines, or his reasons for wishing to have them distributed among the villagers. She, of course, did not know that her husband had a mistress in the village whom he went to see while his wife was asleep, and that he desired the intestines distributed in order that his wife's rival might have a share. All of a sudden, without explanations, the man ceased going out early, and when he did go, he came back but lightly loaded. This did not in the least clear up the mystery to the wife. But one day, when he had gone somewhat later than usual, his mistress called on his wife, whom she found busy sewing a kamalayka out of the intestines her husband brought. The two got into, a conversation, and, among other questions, the mistress asked.

'Does your husband love you?'

'Yes,'

'Do you love him?'

'Do you know where he gets all the intestines?'

'No.'

'Can you guess why he has them distributed over the village?'

'I will tell you,' said the mistress, 'but you must not tell him I told you. Everyday your husband goes to the village where your parents and relatives live and where you lived before your marriage, and kills the people there and brings their intestines to you. Yesterday there were but five people remaining in the village: your mother, your two sisters, and two brothers. He killed your mother and sisters yesterday and today he went to bring the intestines of your brothers. He is in love with another woman of this village whom he visits nightly when you have fallen asleep.'

With this parting shot she left the house, leaving the poor wife weeping so bitterly that the kamalayka was hot from her tears. For the rest of the day she did not stir from the house, but sat lamenting and sewing. Towards evening her little boy rushed in announcing the approach of his father, which she generally anticipated with pleasure, and always went down to the beach to meet him; but this time she neither answered nor made the least motion. A few minutes later the little son came again saying, 'Father is here,' but all the reply he got was a new outburst of weeping.

Missing the usual meeting and greeting of his wife, the father asked the little boy where his mother was, and when told of the state, she was in, he hastened to the house, where he found her on the floor shedding bitter tears and sewing the kamalayka.

'Why do you weep? Has someone offended you?'

'No one has offended me.'

'Why then this lamentation?''

'I was thinking of my mother, sisters, and brothers and my other relatives in my native village, and I wondered how they were getting along, and this made me weep.'

He did not attempt to cheer her, but after a pause he said, 'I did not kill many animals today – two only.'

This enraged her so that she jumped up from the floor, picked up the little boy, who was near her, and threw him at him, saying, 'If my two brothers do not satisfy you, take him also.' The boy's forehead came in contact with the edge of a sharp knife on the father's breast, making quite a gash from which the blood flowed freely. This the mother noticed before escaping out of the house.

Putting aside the boy, the man made a dash for the woman, but she got out of his reach, and being the better runner of the two he did not succeed in laying hands on her. She would let him come up quite close to her, and then dash away again until he saw the hopelessness of the chase and gave it up.

In a short time the boy's wound healed, but it left a very noticeable scar. Now that his mother was gone, his father placed him in the care of his sister, with instructions that he should under no circumstances be allowed to go very far from home. In this manner he passed a few years longer, until he became the proud possessor of a bow and arrows, with which he often amused himself. One day, while indulging in his favourite sport, he began to wonder why his father and aunt forbade his going far from the house; and the more he thought about it the more anxious did he become to go, until he finally concluded 'to go just a little distance beyond that hill to see what is there'. On the way he noticed a hillock just ahead of him, at which he discharged his arrow, then ran and got it, aimed at another and another, and became so absorbed in this amusement that he did not observe how far from home it was taking him. One hillock somewhat different from the others especially attracted his attention as offering a good mark. He took aim and sent his arrow flying right into the centre of it; but what was his surprise on approaching the supposed hillock to discover that it was a barrabara, and that the arrow had gone inside through the hole in the top. When he peeped in, he was frightened at the sight of a very wild-looking woman who stared at him, and he began to cry.

'Why do you cry?' the woman asked.

'I want my arrow.'

'Come in and get it,' the woman invited. But he was too scared to do that; he however got up courage enough to stick his foot in, hoping to draw it out that way, and he had nearly succeeded when he heard the woman move. At this he ran away in tears. The woman called him back, saying, 'Do not be afraid of me. I am your mother. It is I who threw you at your father, making the scar on your forehead. Come in, I will not harm you.' When he saw that it was really his mother, he went to her and remained with her two days. During that time she told him his father's wicked deeds, how he mistreated and neglected her for another, and finally wrought on him so that he swore he would revenge her wrongs. She bade him go home, but attempt nothing for the present, and make no mention of what he had seen and heard.

During the boy's absence the father was away hunting, but the aunt was quite worked up over the long absence, and ran about the fields looking for him. When he returned she asked him all sorts of questions as to his whereabouts, but all the satisfaction she got from him was that he had lost his way and could not get back. She offered him food, which he refused to touch and he finally refused to answer her when spoken to. Toward evening of the same day his father returned, and, when told that the boy would neither eat nor drink, asked what was the matter with him; but for an answer the boy turned his back on him and went to sleep. The father then inquired of the aunt whether anything unusual had occurred and whether the boy had been far from home, and to all this she replied that all during his (father's) absence the boy's life had gone on as ordinarily, and that he was not out of sight of the house the whole time.

As the boy grew older he avoided his father more and more; and when he reached early manhood the father lost control over him and actually feared him. One day, while the older man was away hunting, the young man took his bow and arrows, some food and water, and set out to see his mother. Before going he told his aunt that he intended going quite a distance from home and not to be, therefore, uneasy over his long absence. He went to the place where he had last seen his mother, and, as she was not there, he wandered on until on the following day he came in sight of some barrabaras and two men. They answered him when he spoke to them, but when he wished to enter into one of the barrabaras they barred his way. While they were thus disputing, his mother appeared on the scene and motioned to the men to let him pass. When he came inside he was greatly surprised at the quantity of furs that was lying about in great disorder, and at the abundance of meats and other eatables that he found there. He was certain he had never seen anything like it before. After eating, his mother told him to spend the night there, and in the morning take as many of the best furs as he could carry and go back to the village of his father, in order to tempt him and his relatives to come hunting in this neighbourhood, which would offer an opportunity to repay him for what he had done. The boy did as he was told, took with him a heavy load of precious fare and started back.

In his absence, the mother and the people with whom she was living made elaborate and crafty preparations for the reception of the expected guests. In the large barrabara, where the feasts and dances were always held and where visitors were generally received, quantities of oil were sprinkled about and covered up with grass. Along the walls seal bladders full of oil were concealed, and screened with straw mats. And in this place the visitors were to be received.

The young man's father was home on his return, and received the present of furs which his son made him with much pleasure, for the boy seemed so kindly disposed that the father hoped that his natural affection for his parent had returned. He inquired the whereabouts of the hunting grounds where the son had secured these skins, and the latter told him that it was not very far, and that it was very rich, and that he planned to go back the next day to the same place, and if he and his men cared to accompany him, he would be glad to show them the way. His offer was accepted, and the following morning a large party left the village for the hunting ground.

Some of the people of the mother's village had been on the lookout, and when they saw the large party approaching, they changed themselves into wild beasts – bears, wolves, foxes, etc. The hunters marked them and shot at them, but it had no other result than to drive the beasts nearer and nearer to the village. These tactics the men beasts repeated until the hunters were decoyed into the village. Seeing so many barrabaras, the men asked the boy who the people were that lived in them. 'They are friendly people,' he replied, 'with whom I spent the night the last time I was in this neighbourhood. Tomorrow morning we will go to the other side of the village, where there is a great deal of game.' The people of the village greeted them very cordially, and assigned a place for the night to each one of them; the father and son were given the barrabara where the latter had been entertained on his previous visit. Although the mother was in the same room with them they were not aware of it, for she had concealed herself. Everywhere about them were scattered the richest furs, and the food before them was the choicest and best, and so much of it that it rather made the older man uneasy, for, though an old hunter, he had never seen anything like it before. In the evening all the people of the village, including the guests, went to the large dance hall, where the formal reception was held and the guests entertained as was customary. One by one they descended through the hole in the roof, the only entrance there was. The interior was lighted up by two rows of stone lamps filled with oil, and grass wicks. On one side of the room sat the local men, while the visitors faced them from the other; the centre was occupied by the women, and on the two sides sat seven or eight men with drums in their hands, on which they played and accompanied their singing. They would take turns; first the local men would sing their local songs, and then the visitors sang theirs. To this music the women danced with men whom they invited from either side.

Everything moved along smoothly and joyfully until the father recognised his wife among the women. She was dancing and moving towards him. At this sight he turned pale and looked for a way to get out, but the ladder had been removed. The woman moved up to him, grasped his hand, and dragged him to dance; but he resisted. The boy, who sat near, urged him and pushed him on, but all in vain. Then the woman began to sing him a song in which she went over all his misdeeds, his unfaithfulness, his cruelties, his falsehoods, as well as many of his other shortcomings, and concluded with these words, 'You and your men shall never leave this place alive.' When she had said this, all the local people, including the mother and son, were turned into birds or flying insects and flew out through the hole in the roof. The visitors, unable to follow them, remained behind. On the outside grass and wood were ignited and thrown in, which set on fire the grass and oil inside. Then the smoke hole was stopped up; and in this way all those who were inside were smothered to death. A few days later the son went to his father's village, destroying it as completely as his father had destroyed his mother's. He spared, however, his aunt, whom he brought back with him.

A Sea Otter Story

In a certain place there lived a man with his wife and nephew. One day the man went away, and on his return learned that the two had dishonoured him during his absence. When he went away a second time the woman said to the boy, 'I will die when you die.'

On his return the man noticed a number of sticks (used as tools) and asked his wife, 'Who made these for you?'

'Your nephew,' she replied, 'made them.'

Observing some wooden clamps, he inquired once more, 'Who made these for you?'

Again she answered, 'Your nephew made them.' Then the man began to prepare some roots for eating, and when he had finished he called to his wife and nephew to eat. The boy tried to eat the food, of which he was generally fond, but somehow he could not swallow it. This was so funny that it made the man and woman, laugh. The man then upbraided the boy and his wife with their criminal conduct and ended by cutting the boy's head off and giving it to the woman. She turned to it and said, 'I promised that I would die with you, and I will.' Putting on her parka, she took the head and started for the bluff close to the sea. The husband seeing the way she was going, started in pursuit, but she was already on the summit before he could come up to her. She waited until he was quite close and then turned to the head and repeated, 'I said I would die with you and I will.' This said, she threw herself off the bluff and disappeared in the water. The man stood there watching, and very soon he saw emerging two sea otters who went out to sea.

The Sad Woman

Many, many years ago the people of Atka and Attu were continually at war with each other, frequently surprising each other with fatal results. At this particular time, the Atka warriors gathered a large fleet of bidarkas, and one dark night fell on the Attu inhabitants, of whom but three escaped, two boys and a woman. The boys were soon discovered in the cave where they had hidden and killed, but the woman was not found. After the victors had departed, the woman came out; and was painfully surprised to know that she was the only human being on the island. For seven years she lived in this solitary state, and during all this time neither smiled nor laughed. She lived mostly on sea lions and sea otters, which she killed with clubs while they were on the rocks. In the eighth year her sadness came to an end in the following manner. She had as companions a young duck and seagull whom she had befriended; one day, as she was fishing along the beach, these two birds began to fight, which so amused her that she laughed out. Not long after, some suitable driftwood came ashore, and she set about building a new home. While busily engaged with her stone hatchet in trimming a log, she thought she heard a noise behind her, and on looking around saw a man. This so frightened her that she cut off one of her fingers. A little later some more Atka people came over and settled in Attu, and they are the ancestors of the present inhabitants of that island.

Another ending of this same story is that this man and woman married, and that from them all the people of Attu are descended.

The Man and Woman Who Became Sea Otters

Once upon a time there lived in a certain village a married couple, and one day the husband told the wife, 'We are going to make a feast, and we are going to invite your brother-in-law. Go and gather some herbs and roots and then go to the beach and bring some moss from the rocks.' He himself went to get some seals or ducks. On his return he busied himself preparing the dishes. This done, he sharpened his knives, and commanded his wife to call the expected guest. She knew that her husband was jealous of her brother-in-law and planned to kill him, but was forbidden by her husband to say anything to him about it. She went and called him; and as they were coming toward the house she, walking behind, thought continually of the fate that was awaiting him, yet fear of her husband prevented her from saying anything.

When they came into the house she looked at the two men and saw how much the handsomer of the two the brother-in-law was. The husband turned to the invited guest, and said: 'I prepared a feast for you; I have planned it for many years. Come and eat with me.' They sat down on the floor, having the food before them in a hollowed rock. In the meantime the woman was outside, weeping because the man she loved more than her husband was about to be killed. The meal started off pleasantly, but the husband was watching his chance, and once when the brother-in-law had an unusually full mouth and could not defend himself he jumped on him, seized him by the throat, cut his head off, and said: 'Now you have your feast.'

This done he left the house and sat down among the rocks, waiting to see what his wife would do. She went in and picked up the head, washed it, put it into an intestine bag finely trimmed with sea otter fur, and, after observing the whereabouts of her husband, started off with it towards the cliff near the house. She went quite a distance before her husband noticed her and started in pursuit, calling to her, 'Where are you going?'

She answered: 'You will see which way I am going; you killed him and you will never see me again.' As he increased his speed she began to run until she reached the top of the cliff, from which she threw herself into the water below. The husband arrived just in time to see her disappear. He stood there watching the spot, believing her drowned; but to his great surprise there emerged two sea otters, and one went west while the other went east.

He went back to the house, where he took his hunting gear and his bidarka and said, 'I will end their lives and mine too.' Saying this he launched his skin boat, got into it, and paddled away from the shore, while singing to himself:

> 'I will end their life,
> And I will end mine.
> I hear the birds singing
> That sing in the springtime,
> So I am going,'

And he upset his bidarka and drowned himself.

The Woman Who Became a Bear

On the bank of a river lived a man with his wife and several small children. One day the husband told his wife that he was ill and going to die, and requested her that when dead she should leave him on the ground uncovered, with his bidarka and bow and arrows near him. The next morning she found him dead, and she did with him as he had asked. For three days the body rested where she had left it, and around it she with her children sat weeping. But on the morning of the fourth not a sign of the body or boat was to be seen. She puzzled over the matter for a time, but the calls of her children for food kept her from brooding over it too long.

Not many days after this mysterious disappearance, a little bird settled on the barrabara and sang. Although the woman listened attentively, she could not make out what it said. About the same time on the succeeding day the little bird sang again; but this time the woman thought she heard the bird say, 'Your husband is not dead. He is living with another woman at the mouth of the river.' This same song was repeated on the third morning. Hearing this sad news, the woman felt very bitter toward her husband, and she wept a great deal. She spent the rest of the day in preparing food for her children to last them three days, and early next morning set out for the mouth of the river. From the top of every hill she searched diligently for signs of habitation. Towards noon she sighted a hut, to which she walked and went in.

There she was greeted by a very beautiful woman, whose skin was white, and who sat on the floor with her knees under the chin making mats. The newcomer inquired of the white-skinned woman whether she was married. 'Yes, my husband is hunting and will be back this evening.' As the hostess knew nothing at all of the history of her visitor, she treated her hospitably, setting food before her, and for a time they chatted very pleasantly. In the course of the conversation the white-skinned woman asked the other one what she did to make her cheeks look red.

'That's very simple,' replied the visitor, 'I boil a pot of water, and hold my face over it until it turns red.'

'I think I will do that, too; it will make my husband love me more,' said White Skin. She boiled a pot of water and held her face over it. Red Skin encouraged her in this, telling her how beautiful she was becoming, but at the same time advised her to bend over a little more. Not suspecting treachery, she leaned over; and Red Skin, who stood directly behind her, pushed the face of the woman into the boiling water and kept it there until life was gone. The dead woman was then fixed up in a sitting posture.

In the hut the deserted wife came across a piece of skin of a bear's face with the nose on it. She chewed and stretched it to make it cover her whole body, when she looked and felt like a bear. On each of her sides she put a flat rock and went outside to wait for her husband, who appeared towards evening with a load of game.

'Come out, my lovely one,' he called, 'and see how much game I brought.' No one answered; so he called again, 'Why don't you come out as you always do?' He became angry and walked into the hut, where a painful sight stared him in the face. 'I know who did it – my other wife. She shall pay for it.' He took his bow and arrows and started for his former home; but when not far from the hut a bear crossed his path. He said, 'It was not my wife after all, but this bear who tore the skin from her face.' Taking aim, he shot an arrow at the heart of the bear, but it rebounded on coming in contact with the rock. All the other arrows were wasted the same way without doing the bear any injury. The bear took off the skin, and the hunter recognised his wife.

'That's the way you treated me,' she cried. 'You made believe you were dead, and left me to provide for the children while you were living with another woman.' She abused him until he begged for pardon and mercy and promised to be faithful in the future. His pleadings were, however, to no purpose. She put on her bear skin, and thus becoming as savage as a bear, she rushed at him and tore him in pieces. With his blood on her, she ran home and destroyed her children in the same savage manner, and then ran away to the woods to live with other bears.

The Old Man of the Volcano

On the eastern side of a river was situated a populous village; on the western bank there was but one barrabara in which lived an old couple with their son. The old people were feeble, and did not think they had long to live; they therefore asked their son to go over to the village and get married. He did as he was bidden, crossed over, married, and came back with a wife. Not long after this event the father and mother died, leaving the young couple alone. At the end of the first year of the marriage a daughter was born, who, after being bathed two or three times, began to talk. Another year passed, and a little boy came to the family. As the children grew up the father became very fond of them, particularly of the boy, who very often went down to the beach to meet him as he returned from his work. For in order to provide for his little family, the father went out daily in his boat to hunt for sea animals and birds and always came back well loaded.

But one day the man came home with little game and looking very sad. His wife asked the cause of his unhappiness and he answered roughly that seals were scarce. From that day on, the poor woman could not depend with any regularity on his homecoming. Sometimes he would not put in an appearance until late in the night, and frequently he stayed away two or three days together. He brought so little game that family had barely enough to live on. When at home, he was dejected and could hardly be made to talk. His wife's questions were generally cut short by brutal answers.

Things kept going from bad to worse, and the climax was reach when the man disappeared altogether. Days and weeks passed without bringing any tidings of his whereabouts. In looking over a basket filled with various objects, the woman came across the head and claws of eagle which had been given her when she was a girl. These she shook and worked on until she made a large eagle's skin, which she put on her and flew away to find her husband, who, she feared, was starving or lying ill somewhere. She flew a long time, and came to the outskirts of a large village, alighting near a barrabara alongside of which bubbled a spring to which the women came for water. From where she was, the eagle could see a bidarka with her husband in it coming towards the shore. At the same time her attention was drawn to a young woman running to the spring to fetch some water, and, after leaving it in the hut, hurrying down to the beach to greet her faithless husband. Following her rival, the eagle swooped down on the man, and, snatching him in her claws, flew with him into the clouds; from whence she dropped him into the sea.

From this tragedy the eagle flew home to her children, whom she found safe. To the boy she gave a feather and a pebble to eat, which he did. Up to this time all those who had gone up the river failed to return, no one knowing just what had become of them. The boy, when he grew up, told his mother that he had made up his mind to go upstream. She tried in vain to dissuade him from his enterprise by pointing out the dangers and citing cases of strong and brave hunters who had lost their lives in the undertaking. Seeing that he was determined, she yielded, and gave him a needle to take with him and this advice: 'If you are in trouble, think of the feather;

should no help come from that, remember, the pebble; and if very hard pressed, make use of the needle.' The next morning he got into his boat and paddled upstream until he came to a cave into which the tide was setting with such force that he was unable to keep out of it. In the cave he felt a current of warm air and saw a smooth beach, on which he pulled up his bidarka. Pretty soon afterwards he became aware of someone approaching, and great was the boy's fright when he saw near him a large old man breathing fire.

There was, however, no harm done him, except that the old man asked him to follow. They marched into the interior, passing through dark and hot places, gradually ascending to lighter and cooler atmosphere, until they stood on the summit of a mountain whose sides sheered straight down into the sea. 'If you wish to live with me,' said the old man, 'you must jump off this bluff,' and with this he gave him a push, and the boy felt himself going down, down. He thought of his mother's advice about the feather, and by doing so became a feather and was carried by the wind back to the top of the mountain. There he resumed his human shape, and went back to his boat and proceeded in his ascent of the river, coming to a bay partly enclosed by steep black walls. In the distance, at the head of the bay, a barrabara was visible, and thither the boy pulled and landed. He went in and found a very stout old woman and a young girl, who began to weep when she saw him.

'Why do you weep?' said the old woman. 'Who is dead or drowning at sea?'

'I am not drowned. I died neither on land nor on sea,' answered the boy.

'If you are alive, come in; but if dead, stay out.'

'I am alive,' he replied, and went in.

When a few questions had been asked and answered, the old woman proposed that the young couple should marry, which was done. The young wife did not love her husband, and begged the old woman to have him killed for fresh meat, but the latter put her off by saying that he was not fat enough. At last the old woman consented to have him killed, and for this purpose told him to go to the top of the hill, to the home of her brother, and there take a bath. He suspected treachery, and was on the lookout.

At the top of the hill a stout old man waited for him to take him to the bath house; and urged him to hurry with his bathing, for he had a hot roasted codfish waiting for him. When the boy went in, the old man closed up all openings and poured hot oil on the heated rocks in order to smother him; but the boy changed himself into a pebble, and remained so until the door was opened and fresh air blew in. On seeing him come out unharmed, the old man exclaimed, 'Ah, you are different from the others!' After having eaten his roasted fish, the old man proposed to the young one to take a run along the edge of the cliffs. This proposition was accepted on condition that the old man take the lead. They started off and when they reached a steep and dangerous place, the boy shoved his companion off, and he disappeared out of sight. From here he returned home, where he found his wife sitting near the fire and the old woman soundly asleep. His wife he called outside and shot her with the needle his mother gave him, and then he shot the old woman with the same weapon.

Having had enough adventure, he started down the stream to where his mother was; and to her and others he related all that had happened to him. The chief of the village was so delighted that he gave him his daughter in marriage. After that time no harm came to those who went upstream; but they must not approach the cave at flood tide, for they will be drawn in.

Each volcano has a master. He breathes fire, and he it was who met the boy in the cave. This old man of the volcano does not like rivals, and kills all who come in his way.

An Aleut with Two Wives

An Aleut with his two wives lived in a bay far from other people. Each day the man would go out in his one-hatch bidarka to hunt, leaving the women at their work, and in the evening they would all meet again, One day he departed as usual, but did not return in the evening, and many weeks passed before anything was heard about him. Food and wood were giving out, and the poor women did not know what to do. Worry and anxiety about the fate of their husband made them old and ill; and the only thing that kept them alive was hope, for they could not believe that he was dead. From an eminence near the hut they daily took turns watching for his coming. While one of the women was thus occupied, a bird alighted on an alder bush, and said, 'Chick, chickee, chick! Your husband is not drowned. He lives. By yonder point there is a beach, near there a hillock, close to that a barrabara in which there is woman with whom your husband is at present living. Chick, chickee chick!' The frightened woman ran quickly to the hut to tell her partner in desertion the news, but the latter would not believe it. The following day the two went together, and while they sat there the little bird came and this is what it sang, 'Chick, chickee, chick! Your husband is not dead. He lives. Around the point is a beach, close to it a little hill alongside of it a barrabara in which there is a woman with whom your husband lives. Chick, chickee, chick!' Having said this, it flew away.

Both women felt that the bird had told them the truth, and they decided to find their husband. For several days they walked before they rounded the point where they saw the beach, the hillock, the barrabara and in the distance, out in the bay, a man fishing. They neared the hut very quietly, and, on peeping through a hole, were startled to see an old woman who had in the middle of her forehead one eye very much diseased, giving her a very ugly appearance. One Eye somehow became aware of the presence of people outside, and called out, 'Come in, come in!' The visitors entered and sat down near the fire, over which was boiling a pot of soup, of which they were asked to help themselves. But as no clam shells with which to dip were offered them, they could not eat. One of the visitors then asked One Eye who the person was in the bidarka fishing. She replied that it was not a bidarka at all, but a rock which at low tide seemed like a man fishing from a bidarka. She again invited her guests to eat, but they told her that they could not without spoons. The hostess tried to show her visitors how to eat without spoons by bending her head over the pot; but before she finished her illustration, the two women jumped on her and shoved her face into the soup until she was dead. Dressing her in her parka (fur cloak), and taking her to a conspicuous place on the beach, they propped her up into a natural position and left her there.

Towards evening the fisherman pulled for the shore, and, as he came close to the beach, the two women in hiding recognised their long-lost husband. He got out of the boat and went towards One Eye, and, holding before him a fish, said, 'Whenever you love me, you come to the beach to greet me.' But as he received no answer, he came to her and put his arms around her, which caused them both to fall over. While he was in this attitude, his two wives jumped out and appeared before him. On seeing them, he made a dash for his boat. They followed, and came up with him just as he was about to paddle away.

One seized the bidarka, and the other grabbed the paddle, and said to him, 'We thought that you were dead, and we mourned and suffered, while you were here all the time. Now we are going to kill you.'

'Don't kill me! I will go home with you, and we will live as formerly.'

'No, no! We will kill you.'

Saying this, they pushed the bidarka out until the water reached their necks; and there turned it over and drowned their faithless and cowardly husband.

Woman Without a Nose

At the head of a long bay lived a man and his wife apart from other human beings, of whose existence they were hardly aware. Every pleasant morning the man went hunting, returning in the evening with a bidarka full of seal meat. One day, however, he failed to come back at the usual time. This made the woman uneasy, and she kept a lookout for him, and when he finally appeared, he had only one small seal. To the numerous questions of the wife he merely replied, 'The seal are scarce, and I have to go far to get them.' She believed him. The next day he was again late, and had the same hard-luck story to tell. He looked worried, ate little and refused to talk. Occasionally he would be gone two and three days at a stretch, returning with but little game. Finally he told his wife that he was ill and about to die, and made her promise that when that sad day should come, she would dress him up as if he were going hunting, and leave him with his boat and weapons in the open air. A few days after this conversation she found him dead, and she carried out her promise. In the evening, being exhausted from much weeping and hard work, she went into the hut and fell asleep. When she woke up, neither husband, nor bidarka, nor weapons were to be seen, but on the beach she discovered tracks made by her husband in carrying the boat to the water. 'Ai, Ai, Y–a–h. This is why he died, and asked to be buried in this manner!' For a whole day and night she sat as if stupefied, trying in vain to solve the mystery. After the first shock was over, she did the best she could to adjust her life to the new conditions and accept the inevitable.

But one day while she was cutting grass, a little bird perched itself on a bush near her and repeated three times, 'Mack-la-cluili woani.' The woman listened attentively, and concluded that the bird meant for her to go in search of her husband. She hurried home to put on her torbasas (soft skin shoes) and belt, and set out.

Over hills and valleys she walked before she came in sight of a bay, where she noticed a man in a bidarka fishing, and she suspected him of being her husband. Not far from her was a hut, to which she directed her footsteps; and on going in, she saw a woman around the fire cooking seal meat. A better look at the woman disclosed the fact that her face was quite flat; there was not even a sign of a nose. Yet she sniffed the air and said, 'Fati. I smell a human being. Where did it die, on sea or on land?'

'I died neither on sea nor on land,' said the newcomer, 'but came to find my husband.' On the floor was a large knife, which the visitor picked up unperceived, and, watching her chance; attacked the noseless woman and cut her head off. Her body was carried outside, the head replaced; and she was made to look as natural as possible. This done, the deserted wife hid near by to await the coming of her faithless husband.

As he approached, he called, 'I am coming!' but receiving no reply, he shouted again, 'I am coming!' Still no reply. A third time, 'I am coming! Are you angry again today? I did not go anywhere.' When he pulled up his bidarka, he spoke again, 'Why are you angry? Here I am.' He went up to his mistress, and, on touching her, the head fell off.

Just then his wife appeared, and said, 'This is how you died.' He looked at her and then at the mistress, and began to weep. Turning his back on both of them, he got into his bidarka, pulled away a short distance from the shore, turned it over, and drowned himself.

The Woman with One Eye

Once upon a time there was a man and he was married to two women. He was a fisherman. He was fishing for a long time and he saw a sand-spit and there was fire burning there and he saw smoke. Then he went ashore. Soon as he came to the house he saw an old woman with one eye. That old woman asked him if he was married, and he said, 'Yes.' Then he gave the old woman some of his fish and went back to his place. He came to his home and told his women if he dies to put him in a barrabara and his bidarka and bow and arrows, spears and knives.

His wives said, 'Yes, we will do what you say.' Then he died after that; then the two ladies put him inside the bidarka and put his things inside the bidarka and some other things into the barrabara. Those two ladies were crying like anything. That other lady, the one carrying the stern of the bidarka, dropped her end of the bidarka, being too heavy for her. That man he laughed a little, he smiled a little. That head-lady said, 'This dead fellow laughed a little.'

And that lady who dropped her end she was growling, 'You think dead people will laugh.'

'I saw him laughing myself,' that lady said. Then they walked on again to the barrabara. It was a long ways to that barrabara. That lady, she was tired all the time and she dropped her end again. When she dropped her end the man laughed again, and he did not want the ladies to know that he was not dead, he was making out that he was dead all the time. They brought him to the barrabara. Then these two ladies were crying all the time. They went home to go to sleep. Then at night that man he woke up, he took his bidarka, to the beach and he loaded his bidarka with his things that he had in the barrabara, then he started off for that woman with the one eye.

When those two ladies woke up in the morning they went to the barrabara to see if that man is there. When they came to that barrabara, they did not find that fellow in there. Then they were crying more again.

The Boy with Seal Flippers

Kawhachnanign, chief of a village, had a wife and two sons. The older was the darling of the mother, while the father preferred the younger. This boy had one marked peculiarity – his hands and feet were like those of a fur seal. When he was walking, his flippers would interfere with each other, causing the child to fall. The villagers were greatly amused, but fear of the father kept them from manifesting their fun publicly.

One time when the chief and his men were out hunting, a party of warriors from another village came to attack Kawhachnanign and his people. Learning that the men were all gone, the visitors decided to have a grand feast that night, and in the morning to kill all the old people and ugly women and children, and take with them the younger women and some of the children. They pulled up their bidarahs (large open skin boats) on the beach without fear or hindrance. All the small boys, who were just then playing near the water, ran away out of danger except the boy with the seal flippers, who could not keep up. He was captured, gazed at, and made much fun of by the visitors. The mother, when she learned of the whereabouts of the child, advanced towards the warriors, weeping and singing, 'I do not love him, but his father loves him. Send him to me.' They let him go; and as he walked towards his mother, he fell every few steps. This scene the warriors enjoyed hugely. When he fell, someone picked him up and sat him on his feet again, and this would be succeeded by another fall and more laughter. The mother suffered a great deal, but could not interfere; and when the boy at last reached her, she took him in her arms and ran home weeping.

While the warriors were feasting and making merry, Kawhachnanign and his men were on their way to the village; and when they noticed the campfire and the bidarahs on the beach, they knew that the enemy had but recently arrived. They therefore landed in a small cove on another part of the island, and under cover of darkness, got into the village unperceived. The chief found his wife in tears, and asked her the cause of her grief, and whether anyone had been injured. In reply she took the crippled child and gave him to the father, saying, 'Take your child, I do not love him,' and related all that had taken place. He did not say much, but lay down to think. Early in the morning, when it was light enough for one 'to see the lines in the palm of the hand', Kawhachnanign with his men fell on the sleeping and unsuspecting warriors and cut their heads off. Not feeling himself sufficiently revenged, he went to the village of the enemy, killed the old and ugly, and brought the others back as captives.

Ughek

In a very large and populous village lived a half-witted man named Ughek. On account of his meanness he was much disliked by all the people. To the evening parties where the men gathered in the large hall to play, sing, and dance in a circle, he was never invited. The women were not permitted to take part in these joyous festivities; but when bringing in the cooked seal meat, ducks, and berries and oil, for the men, they were allowed to dance in and, after depositing the food, to dance out again. Ughek, who resented the treatment he was receiving, got even with his neighbours by hiding near the dance hall; and as the women passed, he plucked the dress of one, pinched a second, and tripped a third, and in this way made himself thoroughly disagreeable to the community.

The chief determined to put up with him no longer. He therefore called a meeting, which decided to leave the village for a time; but Ughek should not be taken. The next day the village, except for Ughek, was deserted. For two days he did not mind his new situation; but at the end of that time he began to fear lest the schwichileghk (sea monster, half human and half beast, which is covered on the body with seashells and on the head with kelp) would come out at low tide and eat him, as he had done to others.

On the evening of the third day he gathered all the oil lamps from the other barrabaras into his own, filled them with oil, and lighted them. This done, he played on the drum, sang, and danced. Every now and then he turned his head toward the beach, and once his attention was drawn to a stone. He went out to it, and said, 'You are here alone, as I am. It is lonely for you. Come with me. In the barrabara where I am it is pleasant, many people are dancing. Come with me.' Since the stone made no answer, he attempted to force it to come with him by carrying it, but he could not lift it. He went once more into his hut, continuing his singing. Again he approached the stone, asking it to share his joys, and again the stone refused. The attempt to move it was a little more successful, for he advanced it two steps at least. He went back to his music, and from there to the stone. The third time he transported it as far as the doorstep. He danced and sang a little more, and finally got the stone inside and said, 'I am all alone. The people have gone and left me to starve. I am afraid of the schwichileghk. I will put you over the door, and, if he comes, you fall on him and kill him.'

Having placed the stone over the door; Ughek was free to go on with his entertainment. About midnight his joy was cut short by the odour of kelp, which became stronger with each minute. Ughek had his eyes on the skin door, which fluttered, and through which a moment later a head of kelp was seen, and from it these words came in a roaring voice; 'It has been a long time since I have eaten anything, but now I shall have a good feast.' The schwichileghk, for it was he, advanced slowly, but when about halfway in, the stone fell down and killed him.

Ughek raised the stone, cut the monster into small pieces, which he cooked, and filled all the dishes he could find in the village. Not many days later the villagers returned, and Ughek, on hearing them, ran off and hid. Not seeing any trace of Ughek, the chief and his people concluded that he was dead, and celebrated the event with a dance. As the women were advancing with their cooked meats; Ughek sneaked in and played his old tricks on them. One of them ran into the dance hall, shouting excitedly, 'You thought Ughek dead; but he is not. He just now tripped me.' It was decided to call him in, and invite him to tell all that happened to him during their absence. Ughek came in, and began playing on the drum, singing and dancing. That done, he asked permission of the chief to set refreshments before the people. When this was granted; he went out and brought in the cooked schwichileghk. Each person took a piece of meat, chewed and swallowed it, and dropped dead. Ughek himself returned to his hut to live with his stone, and there he is now.

The Brother and Sister Who Became Hair Seals

In a certain family there were twelve brothers and one sister. She lived in a hut away from the rest of the family. There were no other men living in the neighbourhood, and, so she was somewhat surprised when some man came to see her at night. She did not know who it was, but suspected that it was one of her brothers, and in order to find out which one of them it was, she prepared some red paint, and when the man was about to leave she dipped her hands into the paint and put them on his shoulders. The next day, as all her brothers were outside playing, she went among them and detected marks of paint on the shoulders of the oldest. Going back to her barrabara, she sharpened her knife and placed it alongside of her. That night, as usual, the man came and slept with her, but as he started to leave she threw her knife at him and cut the sinews of one of his legs. The following morning she went about her work as customary, when someone came to announce that her oldest brother was sick, the sinews of one of his legs being cut.

She went to him, got him out of bed, and set off with him. Their mother, learning the state of affairs, said, 'We reared them that they might be a help to us and work for us; but now they have gone and ruined themselves.' The two went a long distance until they arrived at the bluff, over which they threw themselves, and a short time after they appeared as hair seals.

The Loon and the Blind Man

There was once a woman who lived alone with her two grandchildren. Her husband had died. In the village where they lived there had been some kind of sickness. The woman's son and her daughter-in-law had died and she was left alone with her two grandchildren. They lived there alone, all three of them. Now the boy became a man and started hunting. He took his sister and his grandmother to another place where he liked to hunt. He made a house there. He made it strong, so strong that the bears wouldn't tear it up. On the top of it he put a skylight. He was a good hunter and could catch all kinds of animals.

Now this grandmother was old; she wasn't strong. When she worked hard, she got very tired. After a while, she started thinking that her grandson made too much work for her. She started thinking wrong about her grandson. The boy had sun goggles made out of wood and his grandmother took them and hung them over the fire of the lamp. Next morning, he started out hunting. He hunted all day and in the evening he started off home wearing his goggles. When he was walking home, he noticed he couldn't see far; he was beginning to lose his sight. At home, he was given food by his grandmother. He said to her: 'I can't see far; I can't even see the meat you have given me.'

She said: 'I am sorry that you are going blind; you are our only hunter; now who will get meat for us?' When he awoke in the morning, after sleeping, he was blind. He could only see the dim light of the skylight, nothing else. He went out, but he couldn't see anything around the house.

And by summer, time, he still couldn't see. All summer long he went out from the house and sat by the door. Soon he couldn't even see the dim light shining through the skylight of the house. And in the fall, he still couldn't see. He sat by himself, thinking: 'We are so lonesome; why don't some people come here to see us?' When he wanted to walk, his sister led him around. When he was in the house, he just lay on the bunk, not doing anything. He thought once, while he was trying to go to sleep, that maybe, his grandmother could make his eyes better. He remembered that the old women are often like medicine men and have power. He said: 'Grandmother, can't you use your strength and give me something to cure me?' But she didn't say anything.

It was winter now and the grandmother said that the meat they had was getting less and less and that there wouldn't be enough when summer came. Then they started to eat the old meat they still had stored. The grandmother and the little girl kept busy all day; they got wood and water. Every day they went out and were gone all day. They were beginning to starve and the last of the old, rotten meat was being used up.

Then Tiptan, that was the boy's name, heard his grandmother say: 'The sun is shining; the sun is coming up now.'

He said: 'Oh, there will be lots of animals coming around now when the sun is getting warm.' And just before the two women left to go out gathering; he let his sister take him outside. He felt the snow; it was soft. 'Is it summertime?' he asked.

She said: 'The snow is almost gone now.' And when it came to evening, and the two women came back, his grandmother gave him food. He didn't eat much of it; it tasted bad and it smelled bad. When they were going to sleep, he heard something outside. He called his grandmother and she went out to see. There was the bear right close to their house.

And he asked his grandmother, saying. 'Give me my bow and two arrows and take me out to let me shoot the bear.' She got him ready to shoot the bear, facing him toward it and directing his aim. He shot an arrow and he heard the bear coming rolling down off the roof.

While he thought of how he had got the bear, his grandmother said: 'You missed the bear; you hit the itkax' (the wooden frame of the skylight of the house). Then they went back and went to sleep.

The next morning, while his grandmother and his sister were getting ready to go out, he said to his grandmother, 'Leave me water to drink.' She gave him some and he drank but there was caribou hair in it. He blew this out of his mouth and started drinking again. It wasn't clean. Then they left him alone and went away. When it came toward evening, and the grandmother and sister came home, he smelled some good, tender meat. He said: 'That smell is good; they must have cooked some meat, real tender.' But when they gave it to him to eat, it was rotten again. Next day, he smelled good meat again but was given only rotten meat to eat and his water was dirty again. He thought that he would get up first in the morning but his grandmother was up before him and gave him bad meat again. Again, he asked for water. He said: 'Give me clean water.'

But his grandmother said: 'It gets dirty from the dirt falling down the top of the house.' She blew on it and it was cleaner.

He said: 'Let me stay out all day.' They led him out and he sat in the warm, summer sun and listened to birds. He sat there a long time.

Now while he was sitting, he listened and he heard a loon making a noise over his head close by. And he called to the loon, 'You can fly around and see; you must be happy.'

And the loon said: 'Xya–Xya.' This is the noise that the loon makes. And after he made that noise, he said: 'Tiptan, xayn' (Tiptan, come!). So he went toward the sound of the loon. And when he came to the edge of the lagoon nearby, the loon came to his side.

The loon said, 'Let me put you on my back and let us go down to the bottom of the water in the lagoon. Hold your breath and don't try to breathe.' And the loon put him on his back and told him to hold on under his wings. 'When you can't breathe, hold on hard to my sides,' the loon told him. When they went down under the water, the boy couldn't hold his breath any more and he pressed the loon's sides. Then they came up the first time. And the loon said, when they came up, pointing toward the shore, 'Can you see yet?'

'Yes, I can see the edge of the lagoon,' said the man.

The second time they went down, he held on as long as he could. When they came up, the loon asked him, 'Can't you see yet?'

He answered, 'I can see the willow branches along the water.'

The third time he held on again. Then, when he pressed the loon, they came up again. 'Can you see the stones on the mountain?' asked the loon. He said he could see that a little bit now. Then they went down for a fourth time. When they came up, the loon asked again and the young man said he could see the small single stones on the mountain.

And the loon took him down again. When he was almost drowned, they came up. The loon asked him again and the young man said, 'It's about the same; I can see only the small stones on the mountain.'

The loon answered, 'We will go down again to the bottom, and when you get off, go up on the bank and open your eyes.' This is what they did. He went up the bank and opened his eyes and he could see as far as he could see.

After that, he looked at the loon and saw that the bill of the loon wasn't quite right. He said 'I will sharpen it for you.' He did so and then he said, 'Now you can catch any kind of food you want.' And so the loon has a sharp bill. And after that, the loon told the man to go home. On his way he saw all kinds of animals.

Soon he reached home. He saw the bones of the bear and the skin lying nearby. He went into the house and looked at the water and he saw all kinds of worms in it. He drank some and lay down. After a while, his grandmother and sister came in. They said they had walked far and they hadn't done anything. He asked for water. When his grandmother brought him some, he opened his eyes and said: 'Maybe you like these worms, you better drink it yourself.' She was frightened and they went to bed without saying anything.

In the morning, he thought to himself, 'How shall I punish my grandmother?' He didn't want to kill her. He went out and began to fix his kayak to get ready for hunting. At the edge of the sea he saw some belugas (Delphinus albicans, the small white Arctic whale) swimming and heard their noise. He didn't try to catch any of them. He went out in his kayak and caught a little seal and then went home. Then he told his grandmother and sister, 'There are belugas out there; another man was out there and he caught one. You must help me while I go to hunt them. When we go out, I will spear one and you two will hold the rope for me.'

The next day they went out. He tied the rope to his grandmother's wrists and then speared a beluga. But he didn't spear it in the usual way; he speared it over the flippers. It started to swim away and it dragged the old lady with it. She cried, 'My knife; my knife!' but the beluga dived and didn't come up again and the old lady was pulled under. When the beluga didn't sound again, he knew that he had done right.

Then he took his sister home and he said to her: 'Now I'll get married and since you are growing up, you must marry, too. Then we will all live together and I'll never be blind again.' He married a woman from another place and his sister also married into that same village. He became very rich and caught foxes and other animals, but he didn't shoot birds.

CHAPTER 13

Flathead

Coyote Makes Spokane Falls

Coyote and Fox were travelling together and they were coming up from below. When they got to where Spokane Falls now is, Coyote said to Fox, 'I believe I'll get married. I'll take one of the Pend d'Oreille women for my wife.'

So he went to see the chief of the Pend d'Oreilles about getting one of the women for a wife. The chief was not willing to let his women intermarry with other tribes, so he told Coyote he could not have any of the Pend d'Oreille women for a wife.

Coyote said, 'Now I'll put falls right here in the river, so the salmon cannot get past them.' That is how Spokane Falls were made.

Coyote and the Woman

Coyote went on across the river. As he was going up the mountain side he heard the dogs barking furiously. He looked to see what they were barking at, and he saw a mountain sheep running ahead as fast as it could.

On the top of a high steep cliff stood a woman who kept hallooing to Coyote to come on and kill the mountain sheep, to shoot him quick before he got away.

Coyote went around the mountain side, and came up where the woman was. The mountain sheep was right in among a pile of rocks. The woman kept showing Coyote where to stand when he shot the mountain sheep, but she kept behind him all the time.

When they got very close to the edge of the cliff, she was showing him how to aim, and then all at once she pushed him over the edge. Coyote fell down, down into the middle of the river, and lay there dead.

About a month after that, his partner Fox was fishing in the river, and he saw something white at the bottom. He looked again and saw that it was the bones of his partner. He fished him out of the river, jumped over him, and Coyote came to life again.

Fox said, 'What have you been doing again?' Coyote told him about the mountain sheep and the woman that had pushed him over the cliff.

Fox said, 'Go back on the same trail and play blind. Get the woman to go in front of you to show you the way, and when you are at the edge of the cliff, push her over and kill her.'

Coyote went back over the same trail, and he played blind for the woman to lead him and show him how to shoot straight. He kept her in front of him, and every once in a while he would open one eye just a little bit to see if they were near the edge of the cliff. When they were close to the edge, Coyote pushed her over and she got killed.

This happened between Grandstell and Darvy.

Coyote and the Medicine Trees

Coyote took to the trail again, and went up to Medicine Trees between Ross's Hole and Darvy. Coyote was going down the mountain side, and a big mountain sheep ran after him. There were big trees standing at the bottom of the mountain.

Coyote ran and the mountain sheep ran after him. Then all at once Coyote ran out to one side. The mountain sheep ran on down the mountain and right into the big trees at the bottom. One of his horns stuck in the side of the big tree. It is away up high now and can be seen quite plainly.

Every time the Indians go by there, they give earrings or beaded moccasins or anything they happen to have to that horn, because it is big medicine. That is why the trees are called Medicine Trees.

Coyote and the Crying Baby

From there Coyote went on to a place called Sleeping Child. As he was going through the woods, he saw a child in its cradle-board leaned up against a pine tree. The baby was crying and crying just as hard as it could cry. Coyote called for the baby's mother, but he could get no answer. He called again and again for the mother to come and take her baby. But the mother didn't come.

Then he took the baby to quiet it, and he said, 'I know how I'll stop your crying.' He put his finger in the baby's mouth for it to suck. The baby sucked a while, and when Coyote took his finger out of the baby's mouth there was nothing left but the bones.

He put in another finger and another, until there was nothing left of all his fingers but the bones. Then his hand, then the arm, the other hand, the other arm, his feet, his legs, all of him, and then there was nothing of Coyote but the bones.

In a few weeks Fox came along that way, and he saw the bones of Coyote lying on the ground. He jumped over them, and Coyote came to life again.

Coyote said, 'I have slept a long time.'

Fox said, 'You were not asleep. You were dead. What for did you go near that baby? It is one of the Killing People. That is the way it kills every one that goes through these woods.'

Coyote said, 'It kept on crying so hard that I put my finger in its mouth. It felt pretty good, so I put in another and another until it was all of me. Give me a knife and I will go back and kill that baby.' So Coyote went back and killed the baby.

Coyote and Rock

Coyote and Fox went on from there to a place called Ross's Hole. Coyote had a very fine new blanket. As they went along they saw a very nice big smooth round rock. Coyote thought it was a very nice rock.

He said, 'I think you are a very nice rock. You're the nicest rock I have ever seen. I guess I'll give you my blanket to keep you warm.' So Coyote gave the blanket to Rock.

Then Coyote and Fox went on their way. Pretty soon it began to thunder and lightning. Coyote and Fox went under a tree for shelter. Now Coyote had no blanket to keep the rain off his nice beaded clothing, and he was afraid his clothes would get spoiled.

He told Fox to go back and get the blanket from Rock. Fox went and asked Rock for the blanket, but Rock said, 'No.' Then Fox came back, and told Coyote.

Coyote said, 'Go back and ask Rock if I can't please have the blanket for a little while. I'll give it back to him again after the rain is over.'

Fox went back and asked Rock again, but Rock said, 'No, he can't have it. I want it myself.' Then Fox went back and told Coyote what Rock had said.

'Well,' said Coyote, 'he is awful mean. I think he might let me have the blanket for just a little while. He never had a blanket before. What for should I work hard and get a blanket just to let him keep it? I'll not do it. I'll take my own blanket.' So Coyote went back and jerked the blanket away from Rock.

Then all at once it cleared up. Coyote and Fox sat down to smoke. While they were smoking, they heard a crushing, crashing noise. They looked up and saw Rock come rolling toward them as hard as he could. They jumped, and ran down the hill as fast as they could run. Rock was going awful fast, and going down the hill he got pretty close to them. Fox jumped into a hole in the side of the Hill, and Rock just touched the tip of his tail as he went by. That is what made the tip of a Fox's tail white.

Coyote went on down the hill, jumped into the river, and swam through and came up on the other side. He saw Rock go into the river and thought he would sink to the bottom, but Rock swam through all right, came up on the other side, and went after Coyote. Then Coyote ran for the thick timber. When he got to the middle of the thick woods, he lay down and went to sleep. Pretty soon he woke up, and heard the trees crashing and crackling, then he knew Rock was after him yet.

Coyote jumped up, and ran for the prairie. Rock came on after him on the prairie. Coyote saw a big bear, and Bear said to Coyote, 'I'll save you.' Pretty soon Bear and Rock came together and Bear lay dead.

Then Coyote saw a big buffalo, and Buffalo said to Coyote, 'I'll save you.' Rock passed on, he struck the big buffalo, and Buffalo lay dead.

Coyote ran on till he came to where two old women were standing, who had stone hatchets in their hands. They said to Coyote, 'We'll save you.' Coyote ran in between them, and Rock came right after him. Coyote heard the old women strike Rock with their hatchets. He turned and saw Rock lying on the ground, all broken to pieces.

Then Coyote noticed that he was in a big camp. Pretty soon he heard the old women say, 'He looks nice and fat. We'll have something good for our supper now. Let us eat him right away.' Coyote sat and studied. When Coyote wished for anything it always came to pass. So he wished that all the water would dry up.

After he had made the wish, he said, 'I am very thirsty. I wish you would let me get a good drink of water.'

The old women said, 'There is plenty of water here. You may have a drink.' But when they looked in the pails they found that every one was empty, and all the little streams close by were dry.

Coyote said, 'I know where there is a creek that has water in it. I will go and get some water for you.' He took the pails and started off. When he got out of sight, he ran away. The old women waited for him a long time. Then they began to blame each other for letting him go. At last they quarrelled and killed each other.

Coyote in the Buffalo Country

Coyote travelled on from there. After a while he had nothing to eat. He was pretty nearly starved. He went into a tepee about noon and lay down to rest. He was very weak because he had had nothing to eat for a long time.

He heard some one halloo, but he couldn't see anyone. Then some one called again, and after he had looked carefully for some time he saw Eagle a long ways off.

Eagle told him that far away from there was a very rich country where there were plenty of buffalo all the time. 'I am going there,' said Eagle, 'but you can't go, you're too poor.'

Then Coyote got mad. He said, 'I can go any place I want to. I am going to go there.' Coyote started out; and in fifteen days he got there. The place is on the Missouri River, not far from Great Falls. There was a big camp of people at this place. Bear was their chief. The people did not like Bear at all. When they killed lots of buffalo, Chief Bear would always take the best pieces for himself, all the good meat, and the nice chunks of fat.

Coyote wanted to be chief himself, so he went out and killed a big buffalo and stripped off all the fat. Then he cut the meat in strips and hung it up to dry. After that he built a big fire and heated some stones red hot.

Chief Bear found out that Coyote had killed a buffalo, and he came to look at the meat. 'This is nice meat,' said Bear, 'I'll take this.'

Coyote said, 'I saved some fat for you.' Then Coyote took one of the red hot stones, and put plenty of fat around it. Then he shoved it into Bear's mouth. This killed Bear, and then they made Coyote chief.

Bear had been a great Medicine Man, and whenever he wished for anything it always came to pass. It was Bear who had caused the buffalo to stay around in that country all the time, so when Coyote became chief all the buffalo went away. In ten days the people were starving. Every one said, 'Coyote is no good of a chief.'

Coyote went out to hunt for buffalo. He was all alone, and he hunted for five days, but he couldn't find any buffalo at all. He was ashamed to go back to the people without anything, and so he kept right on.

In a little while Coyote met Wolf.

'Where are you going?' said Wolf.

'I am going to travel all over the world,' answered Coyote.

Wolf went on ahead, and pretty soon Coyote heard a wagon coming after him. He looked around and saw that the wagon was full of meat. Coyote lay down by the side of the road, and pretended he was dead The driver stopped his horses. 'This is pretty good fur,' said he. So he threw Coyote into the wagon and went on.

Coyote ate and ate all the meat he could hold. Then he jumped off the wagon, and ran away. Pretty soon he met Wolf again.

'Well,' said Wolf, 'you look fat. Where did you get the meat?'

Coyote told him that he had played dead and lay on the roadside. The driver picked him up, threw him into the wagon, and drove on 'Now,' said Coyote, 'he picked me up for my fur, and your fur is much finer than mine; he'll take you quicker than he did me.'

Wolf lay down on the road, and pretended he was dead. Pretty soon the wagon came along. The driver stopped his horses and jumped out. 'Ha, ha,' he said, 'Wolf looks as if he were dead, but I'll see this time.' So he took a big club and hit Wolf on the head, and then right away he hit him another lick.

Wolf was pretty nearly killed. He jumped and ran away as fast as he could. He was awfully mad at Coyote. He said, 'I know Coyote did this on purpose. I'll kill Coyote, that's what I'll do.'

Wolf ran, and Coyote ran. After a while, Wolf overtook Coyote. 'I'm going to kill you,' said Wolf, 'that's what I'm going to do to you. What for did you play that trick on me? I am going to kill you right now.'

Coyote said, 'Wait, I have something to say to you. Wait till I have said it. Then you can kill me after that.'

'All right,' said Wolf, 'what is it?'

'Well,' said Coyote, 'there are only two of us. It isn't fair for us to fight alone. Let us get others to fight with us. Then it will be like one tribe fighting another. Let us get some other fellows to fight with us, and let us fight fair.'

'All right,' said Wolf.

Wolf went in one direction, and Coyote in another. Wolf saw a bear, and he said to Bear, 'Come with me and fight against Coyote.'

'I will,' said Bear. So Wolf and Bear went on together. In a little while they met Bore. Wolf said to Bore, 'Come with us and fight against Coyote.'

'All right,' said Bore. So they took Bore along. Then there were three in this party, Wolf, Bear, and Bore.

Coyote had gone the other way, and he had Cat and Dog in his party. Coyote and Wolf had agreed to meet at Butte. Coyote had said, 'If you get there first, wait for me, and if I get there first I'll wait for you.'

Wolf and his party got there first, and they waited for Coyote and his party to come up. Pretty soon Bear looked out and said, 'I see Coyote and his party coming. He has Cat and Dog.'

'Yes,' said Bore, 'and Coyote is a brave man, but we'll do the best we can.'

Coyote was all dressed up – nice beaded moccasins and everything very fine. Coyote was a great chief. Then Coyote and his party came up, and the two crowds fought. Coyote killed all of his enemies. Then he went on alone.

Coyote and the Two Shells

From there Coyote went on down to where Missoula now is. Coyote was walking along between Lolo and Fort Missoula when he heard some one call his name. He stopped and looked around, but he couldn't see anyone. Then he started on a little trot, and he heard his name called again. He stopped and looked right through the trees, and there, by the side of the river, he saw two women sitting down.

He went across the river and up the hillside to where the women were sitting. When he got close to them he thought he would marry them, because they were good looking women. So he went and sat down between them.

When he got between them they stood up and went dancing down the hill to the river. When they got close to the river, Coyote said, 'Wait, I want to take off my clothes.' Coyote had nice clothes on, all beaded and trimmed in shells. He was a great chief.

The women said, 'No, we don't want to wait; we will have a nice time dancing.' They danced right on into the river, and they pushed Coyote down and drowned him.

Some time after that, his partner, Fox, was around the river looking for something to eat. He looked down in the river and saw something lying at the bottom. 'Why,' said he, 'that is my partner, Coyote,' and he pulled him out, and jumped over him, and Coyote came to life again.

'Oh, my,' said Coyote, 'I have slept too long.'

Fox told him, 'You were not asleep; you were dead. What for did you go near those women? You had no business near them anyhow.'

Coyote said, 'Now, I'll go back there and I'll kill them both.'

Coyote went back and climbed half way up the hill. Then he set fire to the grass. The women started to run, but they couldn't get away. Both of them were burned to death.

They were Shells, and the reason the side of a shell is black is because they were burned that time.

Coyote Kills the Giant

From Spokane Falls Coyote came on up to Ravalli. There he met an old woman, who was camped close to where Ravalli Station is now. The old woman said to Coyote, 'Where are you going?'

'Oh' said Coyote, 'I am going to travel all over the world.'

'Well,' said the old woman, 'you had better go back from here.'

'Why should I go back from here?' asked Coyote.

'Because there is a giant in this valley who kills every one that goes through,' replied the old woman.

'Well,' said Coyote, 'I will fight with him and kill him.'

Then Coyote started on the trail again. He saw a great big tamarack tree growing on the hillside, and he pulled it up and threw it over his shoulder and went on his way. He said to himself, 'I'll choke that giant with this tamarack tree. That's what I'll do.'

Pretty soon he saw a woman that was nearly dead. 'What is the matter with you?' asked Coyote. 'Are you sick?'

The woman said, 'No, I am not sick.'

Coyote said, 'I am going to choke the giant with this tamarack tree.'

The woman said, 'You might as well throw that stick away. Don't you know that you are already in the giant's belly?'

Then Coyote threw the tamarack against the hillside, and it can be seen close to Arlee, a little station on the Northern Pacific Railroad. It stuck against the hillside and grew. All of what is now Jacko Valley was filled by the giant's belly.

Coyote went on from there and he saw lots of people lying around. Some of them were dead, and some were pretty nearly dead. 'What is the matter with you people?' asked Coyote.

They all said, 'We are starving to death.'

Coyote said, 'What makes you starve? There is plenty to eat in here, lots of meat and fat.'

Then Coyote cut chunks of grease from the sides of the giant and fed them to the people, who got better. And then Coyote said, 'Now, all of you people get ready to run out. I am going to cut the giant's heart. When I start to cut you must all run out at O'Keef's Canyon or over at Ravalli.'

The giant's heart was the rounded cluster of mountains north of Flathead Agency, and there are marks on the side which show the place that Coyote cut with his stone knife.

Coyote began to cut the giant's heart with his stone knife. Pretty soon the giant said, 'Please, Coyote, let me alone. You go out. I don't want you to stay in here. You can go out.'

Coyote said, 'No, I won't go out. I am going to stay right here. I'm going to kill you.'

Then he started to cut the giant's heart. He cut the giant's heart off and then ran out. The giant was dying, and his jaws began to close. Wood Tick was the last to come out. The giant's jaws were just closing down on him when Coyote caught him and pulled him out.

'Well,' said Coyote, 'you will always be flat. I can't help it now. You must be flat.' That is the reason Wood Tick is so flat.

Coyote and Fox Separate

Coyote kept on alone until he met Fox, his partner. They went on together until they came to the white man's camp. They had had nothing to eat for along time, and they were both very hungry.

Fox said to Coyote, 'You play dead and I will take you to the white man and sell you for a sack of sugar. Then, when the white man cuts the string that tie your feet, you must jump up and run away.'

Coyote agreed to this plan. Fox took him and sold him to the white man for a sack of sugar. He took the sugar and went away. The white man took his knife and began to skin Coyote's legs. Coyote yelled and tore, and finally he broke the strings that held his feet, and ran away. He was awfully mad at Fox, and he said, 'If I find my partner I will kill him sure.'

After a while he met Fox and he said, 'Where is the sugar? I want my share of the sugar.'

Fox said, 'Why didn't you come right back? I was so hungry I ate it all up.'

Fox said, 'I'm going back now. I am not going any farther.'

Coyote says, 'I am going to keep right on.'

So they parted there. Fox went back and Coyote went on alone.

Coyote and the Little Pig

Coyote kept on alone for a while. When he was tired of travelling, he built himself a little house and stayed in it for a while. Then he started out again. When he had been travelling for some time, he came to a place where the road divides.

The three pigs had come there before Coyote, and each had taken a different road. They went out to find homes for themselves. When they parted, they said they would come back every month and see each other.

They found nice homes, but Coyote came after them. He killed the oldest brother, then the next oldest, and then he was looking for the youngest brother, Little Pig. Little Pig was the smartest of them all.

After a while, Coyote came to where Little Pig lived, and he said, 'Hello! Little Pig.'

Little Pig said, 'Hello!' But he kept the door of his house closed tight. He had a very nice place.

'Let me in,' said Coyote.

'Who is it?' said Little Pig.

'It's me,' said Coyote.

'Well, who is me?' said Little Pig.

'It's Coyote, and I want to come in.'

'You go away, Coyote,' said Little Pig. 'I don't want you here.'

Little Pig was pretty smart. Coyote thought, 'He's pretty smart, but I'll fool him, I'll kill him yet.'

Then he said, 'Little Pig, don't you know there is a nice garden about half a mile from here – cabbage and potatoes and everything in it?'

Coyote wished for the garden, and it was there. The next morning Little Pig got up early and went to the garden and helped himself to everything.

The next morning when Coyote got to the garden, he looked at all the things. He saw that Little Pig had been there and helped himself to everything and then gone away. He looked around and saw Little Pig down the road about half a mile. He ran and Little Pig ran. Little Pig got into the house first and locked the door and wouldn't let Coyote in.

Coyote knocked at the door, and said, 'Little Pig, let me in. I have tobacco and kinnikinnick. We will smoke together.'

'No,' said Little Pig, 'I don't smoke. I don't want your tobacco and kinnikinnick. I won't let you in. You want to kill me.'

Then Coyote went away. That night he came back and knocked at the door. 'Let me in,' said Coyote.

'Who's there?' said Little Pig.

'It's me,' said Coyote, 'I don't want to hurt you. I want to help you. Let me in.'

'Who are you?' asked Little Pig.

'I am Coyote.'

'Go away, Coyote. I don't want you here.'

'I want to tell you something,' said Coyote.

'Well, what is it?' said Little Pig.

'About half a mile from here is a nice big orchard, and all kinds of fruit in it.'

'All right,' said Little Pig. 'Tomorrow morning I will go there and get me what I want.'

Coyote wished for an orchard to be there, and it was there. Early the next morning he got up and went to the orchard. When Coyote got there, Little Pig was up in a tree gathering apples. He was pretty badly scared when he saw Coyote.

Coyote said, 'What have you got there? Some nice big apples?'

'Yes,' said Little Pig. 'I have some nice big apples. Don't you want me to throw you one?'

'Yes,' said Coyote. 'Throw me a nice big apple.'

Little Pig took a big apple and threw it just as hard as he could. Coyote tried to catch it, but he couldn't. It hit him in the eye and knocked him down. Little Pig jumped down from the apple tree and ran as fast as he could. Coyote jumped up and ran after him, but Little Pig got in the house first, and he locked the door on Coyote.

Coyote knocked and knocked, but Little Pig wouldn't let him in. Coyote said, 'I'll come down the chimney.'

'All right, come down the chimney, if you think you can,' said Little Pig.

Little Pig began to build a fire. Coyote came down the chimney, and fell into the fire, and was burned to death. Fox was not there to step over him, and so he never came to life again, and that was the end of Coyote.

CHAPTER 14

Fox

Dispersion

The Foxes used to dwell at the North, by the shore of the sea. There they lived until many nations came together and fought against them. Of all the nations, only two there were that did not war against them; they were the Ioways and Otoes.

There was a certain young man in the camp of the Foxes, and he had the knowledge and use of mysterious power. He beheld how sore the Foxes were pressed. And when the nations came and camped round about the Foxes, hemming them in from all sides, he blackened his face and fasted.

All this took place in the summer, at the season of ripening corn. By and by the young man came out of the fast. Speedily he sat down by a drum and began to beat upon it. At the same instant he sang a song; it was a song of prayer calling for deliverance. The song contained power; for, lo, it began to snow!

All night long it snowed soft, silent, and deep.

The fighting men of the enemy had withdrawn to their lodges, and there great sleep fell over them all. In the morning the snow lay deep everywhere. When the sun hanged high, it began to be noised about in the camp that the Foxes had escaped; and then a great cry went up, 'They have gone! They have gone!'

Thereupon the camp was moved with a great stir; bodies of men ran to and fro, seeking whither the Foxes had fled.

In the days when the Foxes were hemmed about and surrounded by the nations, a thousand men came together. They were the oldest in the nation. They called the young men together and spoke to them in this wise:

'The end of our days is nigh at hand, and we have but a short while yet to live. We feel it best to free you of the burden of caring for us. We are now going forth to meet the enemy; and we will fight as long as life and strength in us, will permit. We shall never return; and when we die, it will be at the hands of the enemy, and, we hope, after we have caused them sacrifice. We leave a parting wish with you, young men: Protect the women and children. Treasure the mystery-bundles, and take care that you never lose possession of them.'

And the old men went forth to battle, and never a one came back.

Of those that went into the northwest, four hundred women and a man were made captive. The name of the man was Takamisaw. They were led away with hands bound behind their backs.

One night the women began to wail for their people, and they cried to the manitou for deliverance. Lo, and their prayer was not in vain! Deep sleep fell over their captors, and that same night they made their escape. By day they lay in the reeds of the hollows, and by night they journeyed over the plains. They were seen by the enemy on the fourth day of their flight, but they were able to make their escape.

At last they overtook their people.

At the time, Wabasaiy was chief of the Foxes. He let the foe take him captive. He was led away to a place where a great throng gathered to behold him. There he was bound fast to a tree; his back was against it, and he stood straight. The warriors sat on the ground in front, and watched him in the face. The people drew nigh, and began to mock and reproach him. Stiff and rigid he stood for a long while, and without a word he took his abuse.

Then all of a sudden out came one of his arms, and he pointed his forefinger at them who mocked. Speedily a deep breath he took, and snapped the cords over his chest. The cords fell to the ground, and he walked forth from the tree. The people opened apart, and gazed upon him with wonder as he passed out of their midst.

Verily, he was a manitou, and not an ordinary mortal.

The Foxes journeyed northward until they came to a place where they parted in three directions. Some went past the head waters of the Mississippi, and fought their way through the land of the Sioux; then they turned southward, and journeyed over the great plain country; again they changed their course, and went eastward until they came to the broad Mississippi; they crossed the water and came to Rock River; they saw the land was good; they seized and held it, and there they dwelt.

Others went away into the northwest. It is said that they journeyed across the plains, and arrived at the source of the Missouri.

Here they stopped to live, and joined themselves with other nations. The rest continued northward, and there they scattered again. They stopped among the lakes, and there they dwelt.

There they can be found even to this day.

The Blackhawk War

The Sauks and Foxes were living together at the time in the Rock River country. White people had been coming in for some time and helping themselves to the land. Wherever they selected places to live, there they settled down and began to make homes for themselves. The people beheld these doings, and were not at all pleased. When they made protests, the reply they got was that the land was no longer theirs, that it was now the white man's.

About this time came officers of the government, and the chiefs and head men met them in council. The white men presented a paper. It said that an agreement had been made between officers of the government and head men of the Sauks and Foxes; that according to the agreement, the people had given up the possession of all the Rock River country in return for which the government had paid money, sugar, coffee, pork, tobacco, salt, and whiskey; and at the bottom of the paper was signed the names of the men of both sides who made the agreement. The principle man on the side of the government was the head official at Shallow Water (St Louis); and the principle man on the side of the Sauks and Foxes was Kwaskwami. The agreement had been made in the wintertime.

The whole business came with great surprise upon the chiefs and councillors. The paper made clear one thing: it verified the ugly rumours that had gone from mouth to mouth about Kwaskwami. It was known to all that he had gone to spend the winter near Shallow Water. His object was to be near a trading post where he could dispose of his pelts as fast as he got them. But it was rumoured that he spent much time at the post, and that he hunted little; that he hobnobbed with the big official there, and that he had much money to spend; that he drank a great deal, and was often so drunk that he was absent from his camp for a long period at a time; and that all the while, even up to the time of his departure, he had plenty of food to eat. Now, all this was very strange, and the people wondered how it had come to pass. Then, as now, they knew and they kept tab on the wealth of one another, and it was easy to guess the limit of one's possessions. Moreover, it was particularly easy to guess how much a man like Kwaskwami had. He was just a prominent man of a small group of people who happened to have their camps near by one another. This small band made up the party that went to camp near Shallow Water. It was men in this party who signed the paper with Kwaskwami; and it was the people of this party who spread the gossip about Kwaskwami and his doings at Shallow Water post. Kwaskwami and the men whose names were on the paper denied ever having touched the pen. They must have lied, or else they were drunk at the time and did not know they had touched the pen.

The chiefs and councillors tried to explain to the officers the position of Kwaskwami, that the man was not a chief; that he had no power to make a treaty with another nation, that his act was not known before or at the time he did it; that he was not made a delegate to make a treaty on behalf of his people; and that what he did, he did as an individual. They tried to explain to the officers that it was necessary, when a question came up about the cession of land, to let the whole nation know about it; and that when a cession was made, it was necessary first to get the consent of every chief and councillor:

It was of no use to talk about these things. The officers said that the agreement had been made, and that both parties would have to stand by it; that they had come; not to talk about the treaty, but to tell the people to move as soon as possible across to the west bank of the Mississippi river.

Naturally the people were loath to leave their old homes; but some had made up their minds to make the best of a bad bargain, and go to the new country. Those most of this mind were the Foxes. Plwicig was chief of the Foxes then, and he led his people over across the river. With the Foxes went a band of Sauks.

Among the Sauks was a man who had been prominent in council; his name was Keokuk. Most of the Sauks were not for going, especially men of the younger class. There was at this time among the Sauks a great warrior; he was of the Thunder Clan, and his name Big-Black-Bird-Hawk. The young men rallied about him; and talked to him about holding the old home, even if it meant war with the white man. He was not willing at first, because the number of his Sauk warriors was not big enough for a long, hard fight; and they had few guns and little ammunition, though they all had bows and arrows. He had fought with the English and with the Shawnee Tecumseh; and knew what it was to fight against the government.

In the midst of these events, he was visited by emissaries from other nations, from the Potawatomies, Kickapoos, Winnebagoes, Omahas, and the Sioux – all of them offering help to drive back the white man. A prophet among the Potawatomies told of a vision he had of the manitou, by which power came to him to foretell events. He said that the Big-Black-Bird-Hawk was the man to lead the nations and win back the old homes of the people; that when the fight began, speedily would rise the dead to life again, and the warriors would be without number; that back would come the buffalo and the game folk that had disappeared; and that in a little while the white man would be driven to the eastern ocean and across to the farther shore from whence he came.

In the end the Big-Black-Bird-Hawk was prevailed upon to go to war. No sooner had he begun, when he discovered that he would have to do the fighting with only the warriors of his own nation and a few others that came from the Kickapoos and Foxes. The chief of the Potawatomies who had urged him so strongly to fight gave the alarm to the white people, and took sides with them as soon as the fighting began. Instead of the Sioux and Omahas coming to his help, they fought against him, and when the Winnebagoes saw how things were going, they joined also with the whites. Indeed, there was little fighting between the Sauks and the white men; most of the fighting was between the Sauks and the other nations. It was the Winnebagoes who made the Big-Black-Bird-Hawk captive. They turned him over to the white men, who carried him away to the east and kept him there a prisoner. After a time he was permitted to return to his people, whom he found living on the west bank of the Mississippi. A short while after he died some white men stole his skeleton and placed it in a great building, where it was on view. The great building caught fire, and it was burned up with the bones of the warrior of the Thunder Clan.

The reason why these other nations took sides with the white man was partly because they were urged to do it, but the main reason was that they now saw a chance for them to get back at the Sauks, but they had occasion to regret what they did. When the war was over, and when the white man knew nothing about it, the Sauks, with the help of the Foxes, went at the various nations; they went at them one at a time. And of them all, the Sioux were the only ones who came back to fight. This war was the last of the wars with the Sioux. They were driven out of the country which the white men call Iowa. Such was how the Sauks and Foxes came into possession of Iowa. It was a right which the government acknowledged when it came to the purchase of the country from the Sauks and Foxes.

The Origin of the Sauks and Foxes

The Foxes are an ancient people, more ancient than all others; and every nation that ever came for a visit bore testimony to the fact. They are even so ancient that none among them ever knew when first the Foxes came upon earth. It must have been a great while ago when the great manitou placed the first of our people here on earth.

They dwelt a long time by the sea. Old men used to congregate at the shore, where they could sit and look out over the sea. On one these occasions they beheld an object coming from afar, and making straight for the shore where they were. They watched, and saw that it was a huge fish. For a while its head reared above water; and then it ducked beneath; up came the tail a-switching. Thus it was first the head out of the water, and then the tail.

When the fish drew nigh, the people saw that its head was like the head of a man, and they were astonished. They watched it come to the shore, and when it arrived in water too shallow for swimming, it rose, and every part that was lifted out of water became the same as a man. The tail was the last to change; it became legs and feet after leaving the water behind.

Behind the strange being came a great school of other fishes, and the same thing happened to them. They changed from fishes into people. They went up from the water and followed their leader. He was bigger and taller than all the rest. He was their chief. He led them off to a place close by the town, and there they made themselves the same kind of a town. Everything they saw they copied. Everything they saw the Foxes do, they went and did the same.

The Foxes asked them who they were, why they left the sea, what manner of life they had while there. But the new folk were unable to tell. All they knew was that they had lived in the sea, that one day they followed their chief into shore and became transformed into people when they quit the water. Nothing more could they tell.

Thereupon, because they knew nought of themselves while in the sea, the Foxes named them Osagiwag, which is 'people who come out into the open'. They gave the name as a symbol to show that they came from under the water, that they came out from one kind of creatures and entered the form of another; and that they came out one manner of life and entered into another which they knew nothing of before. It was a sign that they came out to become a race of people

The Fox was the first of men on earth. He came before all others. He was red at the face, at the hands, at the legs, all over his body everywhere. He was red, like the colour of true blood within him. Such was the way he was made by Wisaka, and such was the way he looked when his maker let him step forth on earth among the manitous.

Among the manitous he mingled. He was present at their councils and had the right of speech. The manitous looked upon him with wonder; and made comment when he passed in and out among them. He was very much of a manitou.

Afterwards came other Foxes; manitous like the first. By and by they grew great in number. As time went on, they took on the food, the looks, and the nature of the people that they now are.

Things have changed since those times. The people are now in distress. They no longer reap the good of the land which is theirs; little by little it is slipping from their hands. Bird and animal kind is vanishing, and the world is not as it was in the beginning. With this the manitou is displeased. On some day in the future he will take it upon himself to destroy this earth. He will then create it anew and place his chosen to dwell there once more. In that day, the Fox will look as he did in the beginning; they will be red all over the body, red as the blood within him.

Witchcraft

There are some persons among us who are witches. It is not safe to anger such people, because of the risk of having to suffer. A witch works evil in various ways. All that a witch needs to do is to touch a man on the shoulder, and it will not be long before the man will feel pain there. A witch may brush against a man on the hip, and the place will soon be big with swelling.

Witches have great power, and they can work evil at a distance. I once knew of a witch that had something in a knot as big as my thumb. There was magic power in the knot, and the power was of long range. The witch would speak to the power in the knot, and tell whom and where to hit. If the witch said to hit so and so on the thumb; so and so would be struck on the thumb and suffer swelling there. It never failed to do execution. Magic power, the same as a witch, enters a lodge by way of the door.

Witches like to travel by night. They often spit fire as they pass; the flash is frequently so big as to light up the whole landscape. Very often they seem in great hurry, passing by with a whir and a hiss in their wake. A witch frequently goes forth in the form of a bear. The swing of its walk is slow, and a grunt comes with every step of the foot, and at every grunt is a flash which lights up the path in front.

It is possible to kill a witch, but not always on the spot. A witch is said to live four days after a fatal wound. One who dies without any sign of previous illness or as soon as one has been taken with sickness is usually looked upon as one who has been a witch.

It seems that the manitous do not like witches to visit the graves the dead. Hence every grave is guarded by four manitous. They station themselves about ten paces northwest from the grave. They keep watch by turns; one stands guard while the other three sleep.

Witches are accustomed to visit a grave at night. A witch approaches with a whir, and lands at the grave with a thud. It stamps on the ground, and immediately up from the grave rises a ghost. The object of the witch's coming is to take the ghost on a wandering journey in the night.

As soon as a witch arrives, the manitou on guard moves up and lays hold of the witch before it can get away. If the witch makes a promise not to visit the grave again, the manitou is likely to let it depart. But usually the guard wakens the other manitous, and they cut the witch up into pieces, which they scatter over the grave as a warning to other witches. The manitous depart at the coming of dawn, and return again at dusk.

CHAPTER 15

Hopi

The Emergence

In the Underworld all the people were fools. Youths copulated with the wives of the elder men, and the elder men deflowered virgins. All was confusion, and the chief was unhappy. He thought, and at sunset proclaimed that on the morrow all the people should assemble around him. On the following morning all came into the court. They said, 'We heard you announce, you have sent for us. What is it you wish, perhaps you wish to tell us something.'

'Yes,' said the chief, 'I want to tell you that I have been thinking much and I am saddened by your evil actions. Now, I announce that tomorrow morning early, all the women, maids and female children and infants, all females, shall remain here in the village and all the men, youths and male infants, all males, shall cross the broad river and remain there on the other side.'

Neither the men nor the women were much displeased at this proposal, and discussed it overnight. 'Now it will be determined who the lazy ones are, perhaps the women, perhaps the men, we shall see.'

On the following morning the males all swam the river, carrying the infants on their back, and leaving the women in the houses, which belonged to them. Before swimming the river, the men and women divided all kinds of seeds between them, all the store of seeds was divided.

The men carried their hunting weapons with them and caught deer and antelope. They nursed the infants by cutting up small bits of venison which they gave to the infants to suck, and it was as good as mother's milk to them, they grew fat and strong. The women planted, so did the men, both were alike industrious, neither were lazy, and there were abundant harvests on both sides of the river. The women regretted the lack of flesh food, and longed for copulation and child bearing, but the men had plenty of flesh food and were indifferent. This continued for three years, then the women's gowns had grown ragged and their fields were poorly cultivated. On the fourth year the men had again abundant harvests, but the women obtained little or nothing from their fields, and they were hungry and unhappy. 'Okiwa sikwi nawakina,' was their constant cry.

On the morning of the fifth Shoyaluna (Winter solstice ceremony) after separation, the woman chief came to the river brink and called across to the men, 'I want to tell you something,' and a youth heard her and told the elder men and one of them went to the river bank and called,

'What is it you want to say?'

The woman chief was all in rags and looked miserable. She said, 'I have been thinking, let all the men and youths assemble on your side and all the women and maids on this side and let us discuss,' and this was agreed to, and they thus assembled. The woman chief spoke first: 'We are all in rags, and we have only a few ears of corn left to eat. We have no flesh food, no copulation, no child bearing. We are sad.'

'Anchaai, (true),' said the chief.

The woman chief said, 'Let some men come over here.'

'Sooni,' said the chief, 'let the women come over here.' The women were all glad of this permission and ran into the river and swam across, and the men received them gladly. The men had built fine houses and these they gave to the women. They had also woven many fine gowns and girdles and these they also gave to the women, and there was abundance of corn, and plenty of the flesh of elk, deer, bear, and antelope.

At that time, at sunrise the sky was wide, the horizon was far around, but at noon the sky vibrated, it alternately compressed and distended. The horizon was not so far around as it is in this world. In the daytime, in the Underworld, it was beautiful, there was bubbling water in commotion, all around the landscape; but at night the sky contracted and it was disagreeable. There were both sun and moon at that time. Then the bubbling waters increased and encroached upon the dry land and pressed close up towards the people. They became sad. The chief thought and said, 'Perhaps there is a huchi (hole doorway) in this tokpela (sky).'

There were four mountains, at the cardinal points, and at the mountain at the Northeast lived Spider woman and Pyuukanhoya and Palunahoya (the Twins). The Hopi War chief (Kaletakmonwi) made a war prayer stick for Spider woman and a tachi or puvwubshunni (nodule club) for the Twins, and prayer feathers, and sent a youth with these to the mountain. Spider woman thanked the youth for the prayer stick and prayer feathers and asked what he wanted. The Twins danced with glee on receiving their presents. 'What do you wish for these things?' asked Spider woman.

The youth said, 'We are surrounded with bubbling water and it is covering all our land. Where is the good place to go to, the good houses, perhaps you know.'

'Yes,' she said, 'I know. In the above is a good place, tell all your people to hasten and come here.' The youth returned and after the elders assembled and smoked, he told all that had occurred. Women prepared food for the journey, and then all the people started, carrying the altar slabs on their backs and went to the mountain, the house of Pyuukanhoya. They all went up the mountain to its summit, and the water flowed close behind, covering everything, but the mountain grew a little faster than the rise of the water and after a time the mountain summit was almost touching the sky. Spider woman planted salabuyi (spruce plant) and it grew up against the sky, but the sky was hard and the spruce could not penetrate. Again Spider woman thought, perhaps reed will pierce through. So she planted a reed, and it grew four days and reached the sky and found a small crevice which it penetrated.

Badger climbed the stalk and reached its tip, but he could not get through to see anything, so he returned, saying, 'I am very tired, I could see nothing but earth.'

The elders thought. 'What man knows? Perhaps Locust?' So they asked him and he said yes, he knew. Locust is very brave, he never winks his eyes. (They are like the eye glasses of the American.) So he climbed the stalk and went through and reached the tasselled tip of the reed, and looked around, and there was water everywhere. Locust carried a flute, slung on his back; he drew it out and began to play upon it, and at the Northwest the Yellow Cloud chief appeared. He was very wroth and darted yellow lightning at Locust which went close past the eyes of Locust, but he never winked, and went on with his flute playing.

Yellow Cloud said, 'What kind of man have we here? For sure he is brave, for sure he is a man!'

Next to the Southwest Blue Cloud appeared and he too was wroth and flung his blue lightning at Locust and it passed through him from side to side, and he only continued to play as before, and Blue Cloud said the same as had Yellow Cloud.

Then at the Southeast, Red Cloud came up very wroth and darted the red lightning which passed through Locust from belly to back, and he continued playing as if nothing had occurred. Red Cloud expressed his wonder and admiration as the preceding Clouds had done.

At the Northeast White Cloud arises and casts white lightning which passes through Locust from head to tail, and he continued playing as if nothing had happened to him. The four Cloud chiefs drew together and came close to Locust and talked with him, demanding to know from whence he came. They said, 'This is Cloud land; what do you here? You are a good man and brave, perhaps you are an orphan?'

'No,' said Locust, 'I have many people behind me in the Below.'

'It is well,' said the Cloud chief, 'You are brave and deathless; your heart and those of your people must be good; go tell them to come and all this land shall be theirs.'

'Kwakwai (thanks),' said Locust, who then returned and told his people. Then Badger went up and widened the crevice so that people could pass through, and while he was doing this, Locust told his adventures to the people, and said the place above was just like the place they were then at, all water.

The people again were saddened at this, but the chiefs thought, and said, 'Well, it is no worse than here, and may be better, let us go up and see.' The people climbed up the reed for eight days, stopped each night at a joint from which a great leaf grew out and the people slept on it. That is why these leaves are called totokya, sleeps.

When all had emerged, the Twins who each had the resilient lightning, shot it in every direction and made canyons and through these the water flowed away. The Twins then made all the rocks of mud, and made all the mountains, made everything that is of stone. Pasha (finished).

After the Emergence

In bygone time all people lived in the Below, in the lower house; after a time they passed up to another house; after another lapse of time they passed up to a third house, and after more time had elapsed they again passed upward, by means of the reed, and emerged from the sipapu upon this fourth or upper house, this is tuwa kachi, land (earth) surface, upon which they now live. The four houses rest above each other, as you may see illustrated upon the rattle of the Flute society, the four gourd discs of the Flute moisture rattle, these discs being called the naliyum kihu naachvee, the four houses situated above each other.

In the Below, people were numerous, men, women, and children. The women became angry with the men and were constantly reviling them for their laziness, declaring that the women had to do the greater part of the work, both in the fields as well as in the houses, and that the men neglected to weave gowns and girdles and other wearing apparel for them. The men retorted that the women were the lazy ones, that they did not stay at home and attend to their domestic duties, but idled in each others houses gossiping; and each accused the other of marital infidelity. After this evil state of quarrel had long continued, the men said it will be better for us to separate, let the sexes live apart, then it will be seen which of them has been at fault. The women readily agreed to this, and so the people separated, the men going away and leaving the women in possession of the land and houses. The village was near a river which was very wide and deep and swift flowing, and the men made a wun a shibvu (slender-pole receptacle, wood vessel, box) in which they crossed the river. All the males went across, men, youths, children and infants. The men nursed the male infants by giving them little bits of fresh venison to suck. The men built houses and planted, and at the end of one year gathered large harvests; the women had but little skill in fieldwork and only obtained a scant harvest, and the men came down to the river bank and displayed their abundant field fruits and taunted the women. It was an evil time and both men and women were foolish, when they became amorous they resorted to artificial means to gratify their desires. The women used stick covered with buckskin, and also the peeled stem of the conical cactus called oko, and with these imitated copulation. The men used the liver of the deer and antelope, and also the squash and gourd. For this purpose the men plucked a gourd, cut a round hole in its side, and filled it with the blood of the hare (sowi), warmed it before the fire, and imitated copulation. In six moons, one of these gourds gave birth to Tawiya mana, Gourd girl, a very beautiful maid. During this separation of the sexes, a young man, not a maid, imitated copulation by using the primary wing feather of the eagle; she conceived and was carried to San Francisco Mountains, where she gave birth to Kwatoko.

Also during this evil time, a young woman, not a maid, was sitting in her house in great misery; her body was hardly covered, for her gown only hung over her in ragged shreds; she was very lousy and was picking the vermin off and scratching herself. While thus engaged her person was almost wholly exposed, and the sun rays coming through a crevice in the wall, fell upon her vulva, and she moved with pleasure and then fell asleep. She told of this occurrence to some elder women, and it came on to rain, and the water began to drip through the roof, and the elder women said to her, 'Lie over yonder and let the rain drops fall upon you,' and she went over and lay down, spreading her legs apart, and the rain drops fell upon her vulva, and again she moved with pleasure and fell asleep. She conceived and gave birth to twins, the first born was Pyuukanhoya and the other Palunahoya. In four days there were able to walk and run around, and they were foolish and full of mischief, breaking and destroying food vessels and cooking utensils; they were very dirty and their noses always snotty.

When the Twins had grown to be of the size of a boy about twelve years old, they frequently asked their grandmother, the Spider woman, who was their father, and where did he live. But Spider woman evaded direct answer, saying 'How should I know?' At last she told them that Sun was their father, that he lived at the place of Sunrise, and she would go with them and they should see him. She perched upon the helix of the ear of Pyuukan. She spurted some medicine and filamentous substance spread before them, making a smooth path to the doorway of the house of Sun. There sat Tohoo (Lion), Honauwu (Bear), Chua (?Rattlesnake); and Katoya (the mythic serpent) sat on the hatchway.

The Twins successfully spurted medicine upon these watchers as they came to them, saying as they did so, 'Itakwa kaichivuyuta (our friend, do not be angry),' and each watcher at this in turn lay down quietly, and they passed on and stood looking down the hatchway.

There were many beautiful young women and maids down there. They were the daughters of Sun. Some of them looked up and said, 'Who are these dirty, snotty-nosed young ones, I wonder?'

The wife of Sun said, 'Pakivitai (Come in, you two),' and they went down the ladder. In the middle of the floor was a mound of turquoise and on its top was a large abalone and this was the seat of Sun. Around the floor were many other smaller chosbushi tutukwi (turquoise mountains, mounds) on which were seated the wife of Sun and his daughters. The wife of Sun grows angry at the Twins. The daughters ask them who they are, and where they come from; but the Twins sit silent.

Then the daughters say, 'You may sit there, on these two mounds, and be brothers until our father comes home, then we shall know.' Sun came home, from the below, coming up a ladder leading through a hatchway in the floor. He always comes with a great noise.

As he emerged, he said, 'What do I smell? There are strange ones here.' The daughters had put the Twins away in the omauvonya (cloud altar) before Sun came home, and when he demanded that the strange ones should be produced, the daughters brought the Twins from the beautiful omauvonya, in which they had been covered with beautiful clouds of all colours. The Twins run to Sun, claiming him as their father, but he says 'Haki, haki (wait a while).' Sun brought out his great pipe of turquoise, on the sides of which clouds are painted, and filled it with tobacco and, ramming it with a stick, he lit the pipe and gave it to Pyuukan, and the Twins smoked it, passing it from one to the other. They swallow the smoke and by virtue of Spider woman's medicine the smoke appears in the sky as clouds.

After the Twins had smoked the pipe out they again claim Sun as their father, but again he says, 'Haki, haki!' There was a high mountain, its top almost touching the sky; Sun showed this to the Twins and told them to go up to its top and sleep there. Spider woman tied a turkey feather to the right side of Pyuukan and another turkey feather to the left side of Palunhoya. They went up to the mountain top and the wind blew cold from the North. The wind brought ice around them, and but for the feather wrappers they would have perished. As it was, they were almost frozen, and sat there through the night with chattering teeth. In the morning Sun called up to them, 'Are you dead yet?' and they came running down, and at the prompting of Spider woman said, 'Oh, no, we had a fine sleeping place, only it was too hot, it made us sweat,' at the same time they pretended to be wiping the sweat from their brows.

'Now surely you know we are your sons,' they said, but again Sun said, 'Ha'ki!'

He led them to a place where there was a smooth path, and there were four large hollow spheres of metal. In each of these spheres was a hot fire, and Sun bowled one along the trail and told Pyuukan to run after it and catch it; he then bowled the other and told Palun to run and catch it; and then he bowled the other two at them, calling to them to be sure and stop, them, which they did. He next called to them to pick them up and bring them to him. They were very heavy, but the Twins spurted medicine on them and they became very light, and they took them up in their hands and brought them to Sun.

Then Sun recognised them as his sons. He cleansed and decorated them, and his wife was no longer angry, and he sat each of them on a turquoise mound. He showed them beautiful clouds in one room, asking them if they wished to take some of these, but the Twins said no; he showed them beautiful shells, ornaments of all kinds and beautiful garments, and all manner of animals, these he proffered as gifts to them, but the Twins did not want them. 'Well,' he said, 'you must desire something, tell me what it is.' So they said they wanted weapons to destroy the monsters that ravaged their mother's land. Then Sun gave them bow and arrow, and resilient lightning.

Witch and Coyote Establish Death

At the sipapu came up Pahano (White people), Hopi, Yota, Yochemu, Tashabu, (Navajo, their old name, Yotahuni) and Payutsi. Atkyuka, the west, direction of the below, was where people first came up, far in the west. There are four great waters separated by sand, and on the land, on this side of the fourth great water, and close beside it, is the place of the sipapu; there the water is always in commotion.

Mahuil (locust) has unwinking eyes, is brave. Reed locust sat on the tip of the reed planted in the underworld; his eyes never close, hence he never sleeps. He sat on the tip of the plant and sang, and the reed grew up through the sipapu in one day. He looked around and there was water everywhere. The Clouds were angry because of this intrusion, and Yellow, Blue, Red, White, Black and All-colours successively launched their lightning (the lightning of each cloud of its own colour) at Locust, but he never winked an eye; the lightnings passed through him and harmed him not. And the Clouds said, 'Surely you are brave, you have won; tell your fathers and mothers, your children, all your people to come up.' Then Yaupa (Mocking bird) climbed the reed and the people followed him, but they could not come up swift like Mocking bird; they were four days climbing and wherever they slept at night, long leaves grew from the stem and on these leaves the people slept, and when people reached the surface, Mocking bird was there to meet them. (Wikyatiwa knows the story of Masauwu (Skeleton) at the sipapu, I do not. Masauwu linked his left arm under the right arm of each person as he emerged and thanked him for coming.) Mocking bird knows all tongues and as the people emerged from the sipapu he taught them Hopi talk. After a while he ceased to speak Hopi and began teaching the emerging people American talk, then he ceased speaking that, and in turn taught other emerging peoples the speech they now use, Yota, Payutsi, Yochemu, Navajo. This is why peoples speak with different tongues, Mocking bird thus taught them. Mocking bird taught the different societies their songs in the Below.

After all had reached this earth surface who were permitted, the Americans built beautiful stone houses, large, rectangular and many storeyed and the Hopi imitated them but the Hopi houses were smaller and ruder. The Yota made shade houses of willow; the Payutsi, wind breaks of sage and greasewood ; the Navajo made the hogan; and the Yoche sought shelter among the rocks.

People brought no corn up the sipapu; there was no corn. People were constantly thinking and saying, 'What shall we eat?' Muiyinwu had six kinds of corn that he brought from the Below, and he laid the six ears in order, and these were yellow, blue, red, white, black and spotted. He laid these ears besides each other and all the people were gathered around them.

The American was beside the largest ear, and he took it, and Muiyinwu thanked him for doing so and said, 'You shall have all knowledge.' The Hopi was standing on the opposite side next the smallest ear, and, as the American had done, so did the Hopi, he took the smallest ear because it was next him. And Muiyinwu thanked him also and said, 'You shall have the kachina and their knowledge,' and in token of that he gave the Hopi an ear of sweet corn, as that is the kachina corn.

This left three ears for the four remaining people, and Payutsi was constantly saying, 'What kind am I to get? When am I to get an ear of corn?' but no one gave any heed to him.

The Navajo took the largest ear of the four, saying, 'I have many wives and I need much food. I am roaming constantly; tonight I sleep here, where shall I sleep tomorrow? I encounter many and I am a fighter, and after the arrow pierces me to kill, when I fall on my back I will die kicking.'

'Alas,' said Payutsi, 'which ear am I to get?'

Then Yota said, 'I am constantly climbing the mountains in search of game and am always hungry and I need strong food,' so he took the next largest one, and the Yochi took the one that was left.

Then Payutsi said, 'I don't want any corn, I can live very well on grass seeds and cactus fruit.'

Four days after people came up, Powako (Witch), who had followed the Hopi closely up the reed, killed the Hopi chief's daughter, perhaps with an arrow, I know not, he killed her with his wizardry. The people said, 'Why did this bad fool come here, let us slay him,' and the chief grasped him by the throat, but Witch besought the chief to refrain from killing until after he looked down the sipapu. And the chief and Witch went back and looked down the sipapu, and there they saw the maid seated and leaning her back against the door of a house close by the base of the reed. She was brushing her hair with a broom brush and she looked up and smiled at her father.

Coyote is one of the pets of Witch, he followed him as a dog does a man. He was standing also at the sipapu and looking down, and he said, 'Every one will die and go down to the Underworld again,' and he threw down a large flat stone.

Before this Witch had said that in four days the maid would return to this upper world, but when Coyote threw down the stone, Witch was vexed and said, 'Now she can never come back.' All the people were angry at Coyote for this and drove him away, because only for his foolish action people who died would have been able to revive and walk around on this world four days after death.

Muiyinwu gave the Hopi and the Americans all vegetation now cultivated, but he told the Hopi he could not accompany them, that the Americans had all knowledge and strength, and that the Hopi should follow their trail and would find good places to live in, for the Americans know how to choose. 'It is easy to follow their trail,' he said, 'for the Americans have heels upon their shoes.' So Muiyinwu went to the Underworld again and resumed his seat upon the flowery mound.

The Americans, strong and wise, travelled straight and far to the eastward, and the Hopi elders said, 'Let us look for the American trail,' and the Hopi divided into different groups and spread out in diverging directions, south, east, north. They found traces of fire and dwellings where the Americans had stayed, and the Hopi followed them far, but were never able to overtake them, so the Hopi turned again toward the west.

In the return journey the Bear clan were the first to reach Tusayan and they came up on this mesa at the steep sand drifts near the 'Cape of the Lost Children', and from there travelled southwest and halted for a time at Tukl'novi where was the house of Spider woman. Afterwards they came down to this point of the mesa and built this house, this very house you (Alexander M. Stephen, field collector) live in.

When people diverged from the sipapu, my people, the Snake clan, travelled far and for a long time and halted at Tokonabi and built many houses there. After the youth brought the Snake woman who gave birth to all kinds of snakes and these snakes had bitten many children and killed them, the Snake clan migrated and travelled southward till they came to (?), and there they stayed and built the big house. They lived there a long while and then they travelled eastward and came to this region, and when they came to Mushoninovi they were halted by Masauwu who barred the trail. He made four lines of meal across it. He said, 'There are people up yonder on the mesa point, they are the Bear clan. I know them, but who are you? All this region is mine and I do not like to see strangers entering here.' The Snake clan built houses there, and one day they beheld something stalking toward them and what was it? It was large and terrible; there was no skin nor hair on its head, only a bloody skull sat on its shoulders. The chief of the Snake clan was sitting crouched on his heels, looking steadfastly at the approaching object, and when it drew near he saw that it was Masauwu, but he never moved, for our chief had no fear. Then Masauwu embraced him and said, 'You are the brave man, your eyes show no fear, you have won.'

The Hopi obtained from Muiyinwu all their typical plants except the squash and kokomkau (black corn) and these Masauwu gave them. Masauwu pashaadta (his field), in which he cultivated these plants, is in the valley southeast from Walpi and not very far across the main drainage arroyo. It is now held and cultivated by me. I inherited it from my mother's ancestors of the Squash clan who won the field from Masauwu. All the Masauwuki (shrines) also belong to me as I inherited them also.

The Reed clan joined the Snake clan while yet at the valley house. The Reed Clan came from Lemeba, the knoll on the east side of Mushoninovi where the traces of their houses are still to be seen.

Birth of the Twins

A Hopi maid longed for copulation, because she had heard it was sweet, but she knew nothing of it, for sure she was a virgin. She was constantly longing, and one day while she was seated in her house she spread wide her legs, and drew up her dress, uncovering her person. She cried, 'Tawa! inaa! pash anchai uhnumi kanakwa, Sun! my father! for sure you do not (love) care for me.' There was a crevice in the house roof, and through it the sun rays penetrated and fell upon her exposed vulva, and the sensation was pleasant and she moved with delight. This was in the early summer when the corn was knee high. Clouds came up and the rain fell and the maid went under a projecting cliff for shelter, and again she longed, and she drew back her dress, exposing her person, and spread her legs and the falling water collected in a pool on the edge of the cliff and flowed over in drops, and again it fell upon her vulva, and again the sensation was pleasant, and she moved with delight. Like the antelope, she gave birth to two upon the same day; the first born was the child of the sun, Pyuukanhoya, the other twin was also the child of the Sun but is also called the child of the Water, Palunahoya, Echo.

The Twins Slay Kwatoko

A long while ago we had neither bow nor arrow, nor any flesh of deer for food. Pyuukanhoya had a tacki (a nodule of iron ore, covered with deer skin and fastened with a pliant flap to a stiff short handle). Kwatoko was a great eagle, as high as a man and the spread of his wings as wide as a large house. He swooped down and carried off men, women and children. He ate the maids, saying their flesh was sweet, and he also ate men and women. Pyuukanhoya and his brother Palunahoya are always together and Spider woman is their grandmother. (Sun is their father, but who is the mother?) Huzruin wuqti (Woman of Hard Substances), seni, but I don't know. The Twins went to Tawa kiku, Sun house (in the East), and said, 'Alas! my father, Kwatoko is daily devouring Hopi, Acoma, Zuni, Tinneh folks, and we have no weapon but this tacki.' In Sun's house was an iron fireplace. It was like that American cooking stove, only much larger. There was a great fire in it, and Sun opened its door and thrust in both the Twins, and then through a hole in its top he poured a lot of water, and the steam hissed and bubbled, and he closed the door and there the Twins remained some time.

Then he opened the door and out the Twins came bounding and dancing and, just as children do, they hugged Sun round the knees and Sun hugged them close to his bosom, saying, 'For a truth you are my sons. I did this to try you. Now I know. Now glad am I to fondle my children!' Then he washed them with hot water in a large earthen vessel and made them beautiful, and then he asked them what they desired. It was then they told him of Kwatoko and of his evil deeds and they begged Sun to give them weapons that they might slay him. In Sun's house at the northwest corner is the kwiniwi yumo kobi. This is Cloud house. In it are all the different kinds of clouds and in this chamber were two beautiful jars, and Sun, Pyuukanhoya, and Palunahoya, in this order, entered the chamber and sat down before these jars. From the jar in front of which Pyuukanhoya sat, Sun took out beautiful yellow lightning and gave to him; and from the other jar where Echo sat, Sun took out beautiful blue lightning and gave to Eco. These Twins are mere children, little chubby boys, and they hugged the lightning in their arms and danced around Sun crying kwakwai! kwakwai! thanks, thanks, just as any children do when they receive a gift that pleases them.

They slept in Sun house four nights and on the fifth morning Sun said, 'My boys, come with me.' He placed his shield, the sun disc we see, on his right arm and sat crouching. Pyuukanhoya on his right thigh, Echo on his left thigh, and he embraced them with his left arm and maintained them in this position, pressing them close to his bosom. Sun ascended with a rushing noise, as he always does, and at noon he arrived over this region, about halfway between Mt Taylor and San Francisco Mountains, which are both called Nuvatikyauoi. And he asked the boys to look down and see if they knew where they were, where their home was.

The Twins recognised the mountains and said one to the other, 'Yonder is our house.'

And Sun said, 'I am glad my sons are knowing ones (intelligent). Surely that is your home.' Sun is father of the hawks, and he called one and said, 'Here are your two brothers, take them on your back down to their home,' and they both got on hawk's back and descended. As they touched ground, Hawk took off his feather shirt and wiped the sweat from his brow, saying, 'Whew! How hot it is!' (Hawk marks his cheeks, diagonally, with his two finger tips dipped in black. Pyuukanhoya marks his cheeks vertically with his two fingers dipped in white.) Before calling Hawk at noon, Sun and his Twins ate food. Sun did not carry food with him, he finds it at houses on his road across the sky, which is like the travelled roads of the American. People live there in houses. This is why people now always eat at noon. After eating he called Hawk and the Twins got on his back, Pyuukanhoya on his right shoulder, Echo on his left, and Hawk descended in circles and when halfway down he called to Eagle to come to his help, as he was very tired, and Eagle came rapidly and circling under Hawk received the Twins on his back where they occupied the same positions as on Hawk's back. Hawk turned half over as he transferred the Twins. Eagle descended in spiral flight and deposited the Twins at the house of their grandmother, Spider woman, about halfway between Mt Taylor and San Francisco Mountains.

And the Twins ran in crying, 'Oh my! Granny!'

She was crouching at her fireplace on her knees and elbows, her face almost in the ashes, and without turning her head, she said, 'Sho! I have no grandchildren. Kwatoko ate them some time ago.' (This is repeated four times.) Then she looked up and recognised them and dried her eyes, for she had been crying, and hobbled toward them and hugged them. She asked where they had been and they told her, and she said, 'Surely the Sun is your father. But, now, my children, do not wander far from the door, lest Kwatoko seize you.' Spider woman had not seen the lightning, for the youths carried it wrapped in a mantle slung across the shoulder just as Sand chief carries the prayer sticks for offerings at the directions. They stayed four days in their granny's house.

At this time rabbits were hunted only with the muzriko, the straight throwing club. On the fifth day (the tenth of the whole adventure) the Twins went on a rabbit hunt, and Kwatoko sat on the peak of a high conical mountain watching them. He swooped down upon them, calling to them, 'Get on my back and I will carry you.' They got on his back and he soared high in air with them and when at a very great height above the peak, he turned over and let them fall to earth. There were five mountain peaks, or five conical, peaked mountains. They fell on the central peak and rolled to the bottom where they lay as if dead. Kwatoko alighted on one of the peaks and called to his children who were in a cave house in the central mount, to come out and eat the Twins, 'For,' said Kwatoko, 'I know you must be hungry.' But the Twins were not dead, only shamming and two young Kwatoko went up close to Pyuukanhoya and two others to Echo, and just as their mouths opened to bite, Pyuukanhoya turned his head and called ish ish! and the young monsters drew back afraid. (The same incidents occur to each of the Twins.) Kwatoko called to his children, 'Why don't you eat?'

The young ones said, 'We are afraid of them, they make a noise.'

'You are foolish', says Kwatoko 'that is only a noise from their entrails. They are dead, go and eat them.'

Again the young ones tried. The Twins this time turn their heads and say kaimu, no, and the young Kwatoko called to their father. 'For sure they are alive, for they speak.' Then Kwatoko turned his head toward the Twins and called to his young to try again to eat them, but the Twins then turned over and, rising, opened out their mantles, and Kwatoko was looking squarely at them. The Twins bestrode their mantles and gathered up their lightning and threw it at Kwatoko and killed him, and the lightning darted from their hands to the object aimed at and returned again to their hands.

The Twins then said to the young ones, 'Your father is killed. What will you do now, how will you live, where is your mother?'

And the young ones said, 'She will return when suv wuyoki comes,' small drop rain, the soft gentle rains, the female. (Wu wukava yoki, great drop rain, the male.)

The Twins then said, 'Go you to your house, we will remain here.' The young ones went to the central peak and the Twins lay down and waited. After a time, clouds arose and the gentle rain fell, in spots first, and then it fell everywhere and Kwatokwuqti came hovering over the conical peak. At each peak was a Kwatoko, two male, two female, and at the central peak the four young, two male, two female.

Kwatok woman hovered over the central peak and her heart was broken. She called to her young when she alighted, 'I know you are hungry, here is something sweet to eat.' And what was it? Two young villagers, a youth and a maid. They were beautifully arrayed with necklaces, eardrops, fine white mantles, etc. and they were instantly devoured by the Kwatokhoyamu. In the Kwatok house the door was of wood, bones and skulls were lying around the mountain and all kinds of beads that had been worn by the victims, but there were no bones or other debris near the door. Then the anger of the Twins was aroused and Pyuukanhoya rose up and cried Wu! And Echo repeated it, and Kwatok woman turned around and looked at them, and they launched their lightning and killed her.

Pyuukanhoya took hold of a young male and female, and they began to cry. 'Hush!' said Pyuukanhoya, 'I will not harm you. You have no people now, Your father and mother both are dead. This will no longer be your home, but yonder, on the rock cliffs, owa tuyuka (rock cape), you shall live, and your name shall be monwu (owl).' So these two winged their heavy flight. When they reached the cliff, the owls called back huhu! huhu! And the female's cry was the same, but shriller. Then Pyuukanhoya sent the other two to a similar cliff, but in opposite direction and when they reached it they called back kaka! And these were the first crows.

After this Sun, who was the first maker of bow and arrow, gave them to Pyuukanhoya so that he might hunt antelope and deer.

Early Monsters

The early monsters are reckoned as consisting of four, Kwatoko, Chaveyo, Wuko Chaizrisa (Big Elk), Wuko Cchubiyo (Big Antelope). The giant elk was of form like the modern elk, but of stupendous size, and exceedingly fierce; he slew many people with his horns. The Natashka are of infrequent mention because they were the young of Chaveyo and seem to have remained at their home in the mountains, depending upon Chaveyho to feed them; and his ravages, like those of Kwatoko are always spoken of as having been for the purpose of procuring human bodies for food, especially bodies of children. The giant elk also devoured the bodies of the people he killed, and goring and thrusting with the horns seems to have always been his method of dispatching his victims. The giant antelope also destroyed people and devoured them. Chaveyo wore a skin mask. Bits of cedar wood strung together were laid over the top of the mask. He had large stone arrowheads strung together in horizontal rows across his breast as a sort of mail or armour. His heart, as also was that of Kwatoko, was of stone, just like the stone war axe. Kwatoko had no weapons other than beak and claws. Chaveyo received from Sun a sivvwuvwapi, metal whip, sabre, which he carried in his right hand, like a staff, as he trotted along, listening for the footsteps of a possible victim. He was constantly looking for victims, men, women and children. He carried a deep burden basket on his back in which he placed the bodies of his slain. The edges of the basket were fringed with jingling olivella shells, and these also fringed the outside of his legs, so that he made a jangling sound as he trotted along. He had breeches of buckskin. He also had a bow and arrow, and the resilient lightning, but this he does not seem to have used in slaying, only the metal pliable weapon. Children wept when they heard him trot by.

All the monsters were killed by the Twins with their resilient lightning.

The Twins Slay Chaveyo and Giant Elk

Pyuukanhoya and Palunahoya lived with their grandmother on the west side of Nuvatikyaobi (Mount Taylor, which has the same name as San Francisco Mountains). The Twins desired to go to the house of Sun, their father, and Spider woman, the grandmother of the Twins, gave them medicine, which was some kind of meal, and of this they were to chew a little and spurt upon the guards at the door of Sun house. The Twins went far to the place of Sunrise, where Sun house is entered through a canyon in the sky. The guards are upon this side of the entrance of the house of Sun. He keeps them near his doorway, just as the Pahano (Americans) keep dogs fastened near the doorway of their dwellings. They are Bear, Mountain Lion, Rattlesnake, and tubka nami piyukta, canyon together closing and opening (rapid motions). The Twins were nukushhoya (dirty young ones), but Sun washed them with yucca and combed their hair with tumo ala and they became bright skinned and handsome. This washing also gave them great strength and activity.

Tokpela pash ani huzru, the sky is very hard, and the sides of this canyon are vertical (reaching to the Above infinitely) and they are constantly opening and closing, and would crush anyone (unauthorised) who attempted to pass through into the house of the Sun, and the other guards are always angry. This charm which Spider woman gave the Twins, they spurted upon these guards and quieted them, and they spurted upon the sides of the canyon, and it remained open long enough for them to pass safely through the sky into the house of the Sun.

When the Twins reached close to the sky, the path lay along a narrow tawi (terrace or ledge) on one side of which was a tuhpela (face of a vertical cliff, a wall) and on the other a precipice, which goes sheer to the Below, the Underworld. An old man sat there with his back against the wall and his knees drawn up close to his chin, and when Pyuukan was passing, the old man suddenly thrust his legs out, trying to knock him over the cliff.

Pyuukan leaped backward and saved himself, and in reply to the protest of the Twins, Old Man said his legs were tired and he had thrust them out for relief. Then Pyuukan remembered the Spider woman's charm, and he spurted a little of it upon the old man, who then sat quite still with legs drawn up, and the Twins passed on toward the canyon, at the entrance of which were the other guards.

Entering the Sun house, the Twins were greeted by Tawa numaiadta (Sun, his wife) who placed them, laid them down, in the omauponya, cloud altar (which is described like a bed of mats in a recessed nook of the house), Sun after descending (going in through the sky), at the west, passed through the Below to his house in the east, and entered there, wiping the sweat from his brow, saying, pashutu huu, pash ani nu manwi, how hot it is, and how tired I am. He sniffed around and said, 'I smell strange children here. When men go away from their homes their wives receive the embraces of strangers. I believe you have children by some stranger. Where are they? Bring them to me.' So she brought the Twins to him and he put them in a flint oven and made a hot fire. After a time he opened the oven and the Twins came laughing and dancing around his knees, and he acknowledged them to be his sons.

One day the Twins went to the pool near Mount Taylor and soon also came Chaveyo. He stooped over on hands and knees and drank four times, emptying the pool at each draught. He then arose and smelt the Twins and approached them, and he flung his shivvwuvwapi at them, but Pyuukan sprang in the air and as the weapon passed under him, he caught it in his hand. Chaveyo then flung his lightning at them, and Pyuukan caught this as he had done the weapon. Pyuukan flung the weapon at Chaveyo, but although it stunned him, it glanced off his flint shirt without piercing. Then Pyuukan flung the lightning which struck Chaveyo and staggered him. Then Pyuukan flung his own lightning, knocking him down, and Palunahoya flung his lightning and killed Chaveyo outright.

Big Elk was one day lying down in a valley near Mount Taylor and the Twins went out against him. Muyi (mole) met them and said, 'Do not go alone against him; he is very fierce and strong and may kill you; wait here and I will help you.' Mole then dug four ki yukuli, one under the other, and made the Twins remain in the upper one. Mole then dug a long tunnel, and, coming up under Elk, plucked a little of the soft hair from over his heart region, and Elk turned his head and looked down. Mole said, 'Oh, do not be angry at me, I want just a little of your soft hair to make a bed for my children,' so Elk allowed him to continue the plucking. But Mole took away enough to leave the skin quite bare over the entire heart region. Returning to the Twins, he told them what he had done, and each twin threw his lightning wounded Elk, who then sprang to his feet and charged upon them. The Twins concealed themselves in the upper kiyukuli and Elk gored at them, but could not harm them. Again he charges upon them and thrusts down at them with his horns, but they retreat to the second chamber; again he comes at them as before, and they retreat to the third chamber. They then retreat to the fourth chamber, and when Elk makes his fourth attempt to reach them he falls dead. Kona (chipmunk) then comes scurrying up and, after thanking the Twins, he tells them that he has come to show them how to cut up the monster's body, and with his sharp teeth he proceeds to do this. Pyuukan thanked Chipmunk, and stooping down he wetted the tips of the two fore fingers of his right hand in the blood that issued from Elk, and, drawing his finger tips along the body of Chipmunk, he made the marks which it still carries.

After all the monsters were slain, the village people became numerous.

Pyuukanhoya Slays Chaveyo and the Nataska

Sun is father of Kwatoko and Chaveyo. Kwatoko had a wife with wings and feathers like himself. Hahaiyiwuhti was the wife of Chaveyo, and the children she bore him were the Natashka, of whom there were four. Long ago, Chaveyo and his four sons, the Natashka, lived in a house at Nuvatikyaobi (San Francisco Mountains). They were constantly roaming and slaying any people they came upon, especially children.

At Palavaiyu (Red River, Little Colorado), Spider woman had a house, and Pyuukanhoya dwelt there with her, for she was his grandmother, and she knows everything. Pyuukanhoya desired to go to the house of Chaveyo, and Spider woman told him how to proceed. She made him a pinon gum garment resembling the flint shirt of Chaveyo. Pyuukan put on this garment and crossed the river, and soon Chaveyo and the Natashka met him and inquired where he was going. He said to see them; they expressed their gladness at this and invited him to come straight to their house, which he did. Spider woman perched on his ear, invisible, and directed him. Reaching their house, Chaveyo dug a shallow pit and caused Pyuukan to sit in it, and then piled a great quantity of wood over the pit and set it afire and went to his house. Mole dug under to the pit and brought Pyuukan into the tunnel where he sat in comfort. After the fire had quite burned down, Chaveyo and his sons went out and looked into the pit, and there sat Pyuukan quite unharmed. 'For sure this is the strong youth, the good youth,' Chaveyo said, and he brought him into his house. Chaveyo and Pyuukan then took off their garments, hanging them on the same peg projecting from the wall, and sat down and had food. Spider woman then stole the flint garment of Chaveyo and made Pyuukan put it on, and Chaveyo went to the peg and took down the delusive gum garment of Pyuukna and put it on, for it so closely resembled his own he did not perceive the deception. Chaveyo then invited Pyuukan to sit down beside him on a large pile of wood near the door and, when they were seated, Chaveyo poked some embers under the wood pile and it was soon ablaze. When the flames got high enough the gum garment took fire and Chaveyo burned with it, but Pyuukan sat unharmed in the blaze, protected by the flint garment, and sat watching until Chaveyo was quite consumed. Then Pyuukan slew the four Natashka and with the flint (metal) whip (sabre) of Chaveyo cut off their heads and brought them back to the Hopi at Red River. The Hopi saw the heads and made imitations of them, and those imitations were just the same as those which you still see worn by the Natashka kachina. The early Natashka looked exactly like that.

Salyko

A great whirlwind once devastated the surface of the earth, this was in early days and people got water by pulling up a bunch of grass and the cavity filled with water. The tuft of grass was always replaced after drinking.

There came a little old man, a dwarf, who said that when Shotukinunwa instructed the boy, Waiakniwa, concerning planting, the boy forgot the proper method. Dwarf said he would instruct them when the planting time came. But the people were now perishing of hunger. They prayed to Masau, but he said he could not help them. He said, 'Dwarf has two sisters married to Salyko. They perhaps may help you.' They prepared an altar, each member of the tribe preparing a prayer stick instead of the sticks being prepared as usual by the chiefs only. The altar was made on a sand dune as this was prior to houses. Masau's younger brother came to them and asked what they were to pray for. They said rain, but he laughed at them and said rain would do them no good if it came. The ground being bare, it would form a deluge and drown them all. They must pray to Dwarf's sisters for food, corn. Salyko could not come to them for when he came to earth wherever his foot touched a chasm was formed.

Nashungewe, the oldest of the Hopitu, told them when he heard what Masau's brother said, 'If the coming of Salyko will open the earth, let us prepare a rock for him to rest upon.' A rock was then rolled in to the altar in the space left between the prayer sticks they had set out for the sisters. Then Nashungewe said, 'We know not what to sing, so let us get our rattles and stand in silence.' All the men, women and children stood thus around the altar, but no one dared to start any ceremony till a boy ten years old went up and selected the largest rattle and sang a song which was strange to everyone. Suddenly a sound like rushing water was heard, but no water was seen, a sound also like great winds, but the air was still. The sisters' prayer sticks had disappeared and a great hole had been made in the rock. The people were frightened and ran off, but the boy kept on singing. In a little while the boy shrieked and some of the old men went back and tried to bring him away, but he was fastened, so the old men again withdrew. The boy soon afterwards came to them and they saw that his back and legs were cut and bleeding and in the wounds were splinters of yucca and willow. The boy said he had seen the Salyko, but could not tell how Salyko looked, his wives were very beautiful and elegantly painted. They wore great headdresses displaying all the kinds of corn they were to give to the Hopitu – white, yellow, red, black, blue, blue and white speckled, red and yellow speckled, sweet corn, chico (a small sweet corn), kwapi (a seeded grass), and all these bunches of corn were wreathed around with clouds. The wives also were decked with beads around their necks and in their ears. They wore moccasins and wrapped leggings, fine white blankets and a bunch of turkey feathers on their foreheads, signifying good will and abundance. The boy went back to the altar and shook his rattle over the chasm from which there came a deep sound in token of assent to the requests the boy made for his people. The women then gave him baskets to set before the rock. The chief of the Hopitu then told the boy that he (the boy) should be chief of Salyko's altar and the boy said he knew that already because none but those who had been scarified as he had been could look upon Salyko. The boy told all the men to prepare each a bundle of eagle feathers. In a few days he told them to come with him to Salyko's house (the rock). The boy put his hand in the mud and impressed his hand mark upon the rock and it dried instantly, four others tried, but the impressions remained wet. The fifth dried, and so the test continued until others were chosen. So they were whipped by Salyko with yucca and willow but they made no outcry. This pleased Salyko and he told them to go to the altar and abstain from salt and meat for ten days and at the end of that time he would appear to them with his two wives and instruct them in the rites they must perform when they sought his aid. At the appointed time they appeared and Salyko distributed five grains of each of the different kinds of corn to each of the initiated. The two wives distributed in the baskets of the women all kinds of garden vegetables. Then Salyko took off his mask and clothes and laid them on the rock, saying he would return soon, and so disappeared down the chasm. Baholikongya then appeared and told the initiated youths that Salyko had lied, that he could not return unless some one of the youths was brave enough to take his mask and clothes to the bottom of the chasm and give them to Salyko. Then the wives said if Salyko could not return they would stay with the Hopitu, but Baholikongya said that would be very wrong as soon they would be unfaithful to Salyko. So they also slipped off their clothes and left them on the rock and disappeared. When the time came for Salyko to return, none of the youth was brave enough to carry him his mask, so Nashungewe took it and as he stood over the chasm became transformed into Salyko, but all the youths were afraid to be initiated. Salyko was then offended and prompted Masau to steal the paraphernalia. This Masau did and disguised himself as Salyko and danced in mimicry over the mesas. Salyko was angry at this and pursued him, but could not catch him. Another time Masau and his two bothers came disguised as Salyko and his wives and led the people to perform many impious acts. This continued for a long while until it happened that Masau while masquerading as Salyko came bearing a branch of cedar in his hand instead of willow. Then the people saw they had been cheated and unmasked Masau but he got off with the mask. This enraged Baholikongya and he punished the people for not regaining the mask. And Muingwa withered the grass and corn and great distresses ensued. Finally the boy chief one day caught Masau asleep and so regained the mask. The Baholikongya withdrew the punishments, but said that henceforth Salyko would never more return, but that the boy chief should wear the mask and represent Salyko and his festival should only be celebrated when a proper number of novices were willing to be initiated.

The festival is still celebrated and the novices duly flagellated, the ceremonies occurring about once a year. The moral is that men should be proven ready to suffer pain and hardship with fortitude in providing food for the family and that the woman's province is to prepare the food and preserve a store of seed for future plantings.

The Jamestown Weed Maids (Toothed Vagina)

The Chimona mamantu (Jamestown weed maids) were white skinned like the Pahano Americans, they were large and plump and beautiful. They had the fashion of the Tewa women of clipping the front hair even with the tip of the nose. The Chimona grew in front of their house; they passed through the plant to enter or leave their house. The site of this chimonki (Jamestown weed house) is a short distance south from the south end of Tewa, on a ledge or terrace, on the east face of the cliff, and about fifty feet below the summit.

A Hopi youth's heart throbbed tumultuously, he grew amorous and went to the house of the Jamestown weed maids; one of them peered through the plant and invited him to enter, which he did. He saw many beautiful women and maids. They were all naked except for a big belt which each wore round the loins, the ends of the girdle fastened at the back, its fringe hanging behind the legs. They welcomed him and set before him wafer bread and other meal foods, for they had great abundance of corn. After he had eaten, the mama monwi (girl chief) directed the others to sweep the floor and spread a dressed buffalo skin upon it. They made the youth lie down upon this skin and then all the women in succession copulated with him, the women lay atop of the youth, not in the usual manner. The vulva of these women was very large and had teeth. The last one to copulate was a maid and as she finished the act, with her vulva, she bit off, and ate with her vulva, the penis of the youth. He did not die from his injury, but when he came home to Walpi and told of the disaster, the people pitied him, the women lamenting the ill that had befallen so handsome a youth. The Hopi chief was unhappy and thought long, then he made a prayer stick and prayer feather and went to the house of Pachibkwasha, near the little ooze springs on the cliff trail leading to the Gap, north from Tewa, the oozes called Kukuchva (lizard spring). He was welcomed and on entering saw many men and youths. There were two chiefs there, one sitting on each side of the fireplace in the corner, and on the wall near each were hanging from pegs, pipes and tobacco. There were no women. These Lizard men gave the chief buffalo meat and fat, and after he had eaten, the two Lizard chiefs filled each a pipe with tobacco. The Hopi chief brought out his pipe and tobacco, and each smoked his own pipe. After they had smoked and knocked out the ashes, Lizard chief asked the Hopi chief what he had come for. The Hopi said, 'I came to bring you this prayer stick and prayer feather.'

Lizard chief thanked him and passed them to the other chief who also gave thanks. 'What do you wish in return for these?' asked Lizard chief.

Said the Hopi chief, 'The women who are Chimona women are evil, with their vulva they have eaten the penis of one of our handsome youths.'

'Anehai,' said Lizard, 'in four nights we will send one of our young men to the Chimonki.' So the Hopi chief thanked the Lizard and returned home. On the fourth evening, following the Hopi chief's visit, a Lizard youth went to Chimonki and, being invited, entered and they set food before him, wafer bread and corn food. The Chimon wuhta wonwi (woman chief) asked what he had come for, and he told them that in four nights there would be assemblage at the Lizard house and it would be well for the Chimona to have assemblage also at their house, and exchange visits.

'Eskwaili,' said the Chimona chief, and this was agreed to. On the fourth day the Chimona washed themselves at Sun spring and trimmed their hair anew, flush with the tip of the nose. This they did with a single pair of metal shears, which was the only pair they possessed. This part of the hair that hangs over the face was then rolled tightly up on a twig, which upon being afterward unrolled hung over the face in beautiful wavy locks. The Lizards washed themselves at Yunyaiva and then the chief sent some of the youths to gather several pouches full of sumac berries. Others made kwashi of buckskin, and the sumac berries having been crushed on a mealing stone, the kwashi were filled with this berry pulp, making them red and these kwashi were hung around on pegs in the walls to dry, inside the Lizard house.

This work being finished, all ate food in the afternoon, and the younger men admired the kwashi and said to each other, 'I would like this one, or that one.' The Lizards whitened the front of their bodies with clay, and with malachite made a blue stripe down each side of the belly. They made leggings of buffalo skin and wore them, like the Komanchi. Then with buckskin strings they fastened on the kwashi, and all sat down inside along the base of the wall on each side of the house. They sat chukukiyuta, squatted, listening for the approach of the Chimona. They also spread buffalo skins upon the floor.

The Lizards squatted and listening heard cries of 'tu vai yuh yuhyu!' which the approaching Chimona made, and when they reached the entrance of Lizard house, the Lizard chief urged them to enter speedily, which they did. There were a great many; among them being wuhti, boli, and mana. They were all naked excepting for the big belt around the loins and fastened behind; and they danced before the Lizards. The young men nudged each other and whispered their amorous desires to one another; these women were very large, white and beautiful, and their vulva were very large. The women at the close of each measure sang 'ewe yuliwa eeee' and then disposing themselves so as to form four sides of a square, faced toward the men, and stretched out their arms, with outspread palms, straight before them. After dancing for a while, the Chimona chief invited the Lizards to go to the Chimona house, and about half of the Lizards went there, the remainder staying in their own house to entertain the Chimona. Those of the Lizards who went in procession made a cry as they went p-p-p-yuh-yuj! and reaching the Chimona house were invited to entered and thanked for coming. The Lizards then went capering into the chimonki in an irregular group and danced and sang as Chukuwimkya; the women, naked but girt with the big belt, were sitting around against the walls looking on. The Lizards sang the Chukuwimkya song ahe ahe, keeping time to this strain by drawing the prepuce, with both hands, back and forth, and the women looked on eagerly and fidgeted amorously. At the close of the dance one of the maids ran to the fireplace, and taking up a gourd of water dashed it upon the fire, extinguishing it and leaving the house in total darkness. Then all copulated promiscuously. This first copulation was with the artificial kwashi and the sour seeds with which they were filled took off the edge of the vulva teeth. The Lizards then slipped the strings with which these were fastened and cast them away, and copulated naturally, and assuredly it was sweet. This promiscuous copulation was maintained at both houses until all the women were completely exhausted.

Kwatoko, the Woman Stealer

The ravages of Kwatoko extended over all the earth. He preyed upon the Hopi, Tewa, Zuni, Navajo, Yoche, Yuta, Payutse, Kohonina, all peoples. He carried off women and maids and took them to his house, in the Above. He slept with one four nights, then killed and ate her. This was his custom.

A Hopi youth went toward the San Francisco Mountains; on the pinon tablelands near the base he came upon the Pinon maidens. Their mantles are of pinon bark, their skirts of grass. At that place were also Spider woman and Mole. After the ordinary salutations had passed, they asked where he was going and he told them that Kwatoko had carried off his young wife and he was going to try to bring her back 'That is well,' said Spider woman, 'we will help you.'

At her prompting the Pinon maids washed themselves and gathered a lot of gum and washed it, and they made a garment in exact imitation of the flint shirt worn by Kwatoko. They washed themselves and the gum so that Kwatoko might not detect the imitation by its smell. When the garment was finished, Spider woman gave the youth a little of her medicine (which as usual was in the form of fine meal) and perched upon the helix of his right ear, invisible, and said that she would whisper him guidance in what was to come. Mole led the way to the mountain top, the youth following him, but the Pinon maids remained in the pinon tree dwelling place.

When they reached the topmost peak, Eagle swooped down and they got upon his back and he soared aloft with them. When he had carried them to a great height and began to tire, Kihsa (Cooper's hawk) swooped close and they were transferred to his back, and he carried them upward. When he tired, Masikwayo (Gray hawk) took them on his back and mounted till he tired, and then Palakwayo (Red hawk) received them, and thus for an immense distance upward, these birds continued their flight, relieving each other of the adventurers upon tiring. They thus soared to the very far above till the huchi (doorway) was reached that led to the house of Kwatoko, and there the youth and his two companions entered and went to a white house which was that of Kwatoko. Before coming to the ladder leading up to its terraces, Spider woman prompted the youth and he gathered a handful of sumac berries and gave them to Lizard, who thanked the youth and after chewing the berries gave them back to him. The youth (in all his action he is prompted by Spider woman) then went to the house ladder, each rung of which was a sharp knife, which would cut in two the hands and feet of any who attempted to climb it. The youth rubbed the edges of these knives with the chewed berries and instantly their edges became dull, and he was able to climb the ladder without cutting himself.

Entering the house, the youth saw the flint shirt hanging on a peg in a recess, and he at once exchanged garments, putting on that of Kwatoko and hanging up the gum imitation in its place. He looked in another recess and saw Kwatoko sleeping in the arms of his (the youth's) wife. He called to her, and said that he had come to rescue her. She said she was glad he had come, but feared he could not accomplish this, because no one ever left the house of Kwatoko alive. He said, 'Have no fear, I will soon have you again.' The medicine of Spider woman prevented Kwatoko from hearing this conversation, but he soon awoke and put on the gum imitation shirt without perceiving that his own had been stolen, and, seeing the youth in his house, asked what he wanted there.

The youth said he had come to take his wife home. Kwatoko said, 'Let us gamble to decide that, and you must abide the consequences; if you lose, I shall slay you.' To this the youth agreed.

Kwatoko brought out a great pipe, larger than a person's head, and filled it with tobacco and gave it to the youth, saying, 'You must smoke this entirely out, and if you become giddy or nauseated, you will lose.' So the youth lit the pipe and sucked it, but he did not exhale any smoke, he kept the pipe full aglow, and swallowed all the smoke, and felt no ill effects, because where he sat the reed had grown, and Mole dug long tunnels to its roots, and bored them, and placed the hollow stump of the reed in the anus of the youth and as he swallowed the smoke it passed down through his anus and out through the bored roots, into the tunnels that Mole and dug.

Kwatoko sat in wonder and as the youth finished the pipe, Kwatoko said, 'Surely you are a wonderful man; tell me, what has become of the smoke?' Going to the door the youth showed him the smoke issuing as dense clouds at the four cardinal points. Then Kwatoko was unhappy, for the youth had won.

Kwatoko thought he could cheat the youth with a trick, so he brought out two deer antlers, saying, 'We will each choose one and he loses who fails to rend the antler prongs apart,' but the one on the northwest side was a real deer antler, while the one on the southeast side was an imitation antler made of the brittle stems of chimona (datura meteloides). The youth, hastily prompted by Spider woman, was quick to propose that he should choose first, and Kwatoko opposing, said, 'Sooni (I must chose first),' but the youth four times insisted on having first choice and finally Kwatoko consented, so the youth chose the imitation antler and easily rent the prongs apart. Kwatoko tried hard to rend the prongs of the real antler, but he knew it was hopeless, he could not break them, and he said, 'Assuredly, you are a knowing man,' and he was unhappy, for the youth had won a second time.

Kwatoko had two fine large pine trees growing near his house, and they were his pets, so he said to the youth, 'You may chose one of these trees, and I will take the other and whoever plucks one up by the roots shall win.' Now Mole had burrowed under one of them and had gnawed through all its roots, quite cutting them off, and had run back through his tunnel, and was sitting at its mouth, peering through the grass anxious to see the youth win, and Mole was glad to think that he had again outwitted Kwatoko. The youth chose the tree that Mole had prepared and, helped by Spider woman, plucked it up and threw it over the cliff, and although Kwatoko struggled with the other tree he could not move it. So he said, 'For sure, you are the strong man,' and he was unhappy at his third defeat.

Then Kwatoko spread a great tunushvonya (meal ready to eat) and said to the youth, 'You must eat all of this food at one sitting, or else you lose.' So the youth sat down and ate of meats, stews and porridge, emptying one food basin after another, and trays and baskets full of all kinds of wafer bread, etc., and still his belly showed no signs of swelling, and Kwatoko sat looking at him in astonishment. But Mole had burrowed under the youth, and all the food he ate passed through his anus, and Mole carried it all away into the large hole he had dug to receive it. And then for the fourth time the youth was the winner.

Kwatoko then made a great wood pile and said to the youth, 'You must get up and stand on the top of this, and I will set it on fire, and if you are unharmed, then you may try me in the same way,' and the youth climbed up the pile and stood erect on its summit. Kwatoko then fired the pile at the northwest, southwest, southeast and northeast and it was soon all ablaze, but the flint arrowheads of which the garment of Kwatoko was made, were also coated over with ice and the heat of the fire melted it, so that water trickled down and prevented the flames from touching the youth, and all the wood burned down and left him unharmed. Kwatoko was filled with wonder and said, 'What a man you are!' and assuredly Kwatoko was unhappy while he observed the youth making another great wood pile. Still Kwatoko felt secure, thinking that he wore his own fireproof garment, and mounted the pile, and the youth fired it at the northwest, southwest, southeast and northeast, and the pile was soon ablaze, but as soon as the first flame touched the gum imitation garment, it burned it with a flash and Kwatoko was consumed.

Spider woman again prompted the youth and he went over to the ashes of Kwatoko and, putting some of her medicine in his mouth, he spurted upon them, and pashiichi loma taka , instantly a handsome man became visible. Then Spider woman said to him, 'Will you for sure refrain from killing people and forsake all your evil habits; will you henceforth be a good man?' Kwatoko assented with many fervent anchai, assuredly. Then Spider woman told him that hereafter the Hopi would pluck a feather from his arm, from his shoulder, from his thigh, and would make with them their prayer feather when they prayed for rain. Then the youth ran to the house and hugged his wife, rejoicing, and opened all the recesses in the house and freed all the captive women of the Hopi and of the stranger peoples, and there were a great number. And the eagles and the hawks conveyed all these people down to San Francisco Mountains and they returned to their homes.

The Sipapu Is Sought by the Birds

Before reaching this present world, people sat upon the leaves of the reed which grew in the daytime only. It remained stationary at night, and where the joint is, and there is where the leaves grew, and people slept on them, hence that joint is called totkya (sleeps). It is uncertain how many days the reed grew until it reached the sky. Its point was sharp and it penetrated a crevice and grew through the sky one day. People slept on it another night and next morning just as the sun rose the reed reached through the sipapu and people emerged.

Before people got on the reed the Lalakontu sent out the dove, and it flew around the sky seeking for the sipapu. It flew all around the horizon, but could find no opening and came back tired. The people reviled it and called it a fool. The mochini, which pertains to the Agave society, then flew around, but it already knew where to look for the opening and flew directly over head and found it. It came back and told of its discovery.

There was only a grey, dim light when people came out from the sipapu because there was no sun there.

The Migrations of the Eagle Clan

After the segregation of our people and the wandering which succeeded, my family followed the running water, suffering many hardships on our way to the north. We reached a point of high rocks from which could be seen a beautiful valley spreading out and reaching away up to the mountains. The walls of this valley were of red and yellow rock like that at our old home in the south. So we said we would stop here, and then houses were built. We had lived here many days when one of our hunters returned bringing with him the skin of a bison which he said had been given him by a man who, though a stranger, talked in our hunter's tongue, telling him that he lived at the Red rock and had been living there for three plantings, that before he came, others of his family had been living there and had built houses high up in the side of the rock. Also he said that his family had the horns and hoofs of the deer and that they had come from the land of beautiful water. When he had told us of these things our chief sent a large party of men to see who these people were and what they were doing in the land of the Eagle. After an absence of one moon they returned to us filled with wonderful stories about these strangers; that they made coverings for the feet and back from the leaves of the yucca; vessels of many kinds from the grasses that were growing around their houses. In methods similar to those we now practice they confined the running water in ponds for domestic use and for irrigating the gardens. They also had the kiva and the kachin kihu (house, shrine) where the things pertaining to the kachina were kept. They also observed the Feast of the Fire, the Coming (arrival) and Going (departure) of the Kachina, and the Feast of Masau. They also had the sipapu and before it stood the tiponi.

All of these things having been told to our chiefs and old men, it was decided that our chief, and his assistants, taking the tiponi with them, should go to these people, and if they found them willing, should set it up with theirs and join together in songs. Then our chief said if it was well for people to join songs with these others for a season, an eagle and a deer would come and drink together from the spring that furnished water to the chief kiva of the strangers. And it must be engraved upon the rock for it would prove that these strangers were our brothers.

After our chiefs and those who went with them arrived at the Red rock house they found that the story which had been told was true and they saw many other things. The house in the canyon was high up in its walls and was larger than had been represented, many of its rooms held but one family while others held five families, some of them more. After they had seen everything, they stated the object of their visit and these strange people complied, and on the next day our tiponi was placed beside theirs and their chiefs and ours and all the people began to sing together. They sang for two days, but there came no sign of the eagle or deer and so they continued singing for six days. On the morning of the seventh day an eagle and a deer were seen at the spring nearest chief kiva, the eagle perched upon the rock on which the deer was standing and drinking from the spring. Then all the people shouted with gladness for they now knew that what the old man had told them was true, and after this a general feast was proclaimed to last for seven days. At the time, all the garden products were ripe and the corn was ready to be eaten on the ear. So all the people went down from their houses and for six days they stayed out in the corn fields, visiting from one field to another, and each night the men gathered together preparing themselves for the dance which was to be celebrated on the seventh day. On the day after the dance my people got ready to go home and the strangers loaded them with all manner of presents and were very sad at parting.

When our chief returned and told all that had happened, my people were very happy. It was not long after this that intermarriage began, and in a few years we were closely mingled together. We had always called ourselves the Hopituh and we found that these people of the Red rock house called themselves by the same name, hence we were convinced that at one time we had been the same people, but how long ago we knew not.

For a long while we visited each other until a very wild and numerous people to the east of us called the Komanchi, came amongst us, stealing what they could, killing many, and ravishing our women, and doing great harm to us who had always given them food. This condition lasted a long while till finally the chiefs said we must leave, and go to a country where these bad men could not find us. So we left that land and travelled south for days and then followed a running stream toward the west to where another stream coming from the north joined it (junction of San Juan and Colorado). At this place we stopped and built some houses because our women and children were tired.

After many days we were led by the Spider woman upon the big mesa and she pointed out to us a great shining white rock, on the east of which lay the country of Masau. Masau was the chief to whom we were looking for the fulfilment of the promise of land where we were to build and plant until the coming of the white chief who was to protect us from all our enemies and give us many things, implements to dig and to break wood and stones. So we sent some of our warriors to look for a place for us. They went beyond this great white mesa and were gone many days, so long were they on the journey that of all those who went out but seven returned. They told us of a mesa upon which an eagle had built its nest, where grass and wood were abundant, but no water. 'While yet on our way we saw a beautiful valley in which antelope and deer were playing. Here although the herbage was not so abundant as at other places we had seen, yet there was water, and a peculiar kind of tree which bore wool.' They talked about what they had seen for many days, and at last my people started on their way to this valley. Two days brought them there and they saw what had been told them by the others. Great herds of antelope and deer were playing along the edges of the mesas and up the canyons. These animals were not at all startled by our coming, they would come up quite close to us and our children would run among them before they would turn and trot off. All this occurred after twenty moon years (twenty four and one half years) of travel, when our people had become greatly dissatisfied with constant change. So it was determined to go one day's march further, when if the grass and water should grow scarcer, we should return to the place were the deer were seen. So we started on our way and came to a place occupied by those now of Oraibi. For fifty moon years (sixty-one years) peace was perfect, then the Snake people began to come among us explaining the methods of battle. Then began a period of trouble.

The Migrations of the Horn Clan

Among the mountains whose peaks were always snow covered and where the trees were always green, where from the hillside the plains were seen over which roamed the deer, the antelope and the bison feeding on never failing grasses, twining through these plains, now on this side, now on that, were streams of bright water beautiful to look upon, a place where none but those who were of our people ever gained access. Here we lived happily for many years, free from quarrels, and corn and game were plentiful. Our gardens were large and heavy rains made the corn grow high. Our chief was then a very old man, his hair was white, his body was bent with age, and he walked with a stick. He could not hunt as the others did, but we gave him portions of all things, corn and meat. After many years he died, a wizard blew in his ear, and his head swelled so that it burst; then the people were very sad. When the time came to select a new chief, dissensions arose and the people fell to fighting, killing and driving each other from one place to another. Then the chief of the Horn people said, 'My people, we must leave, for nothing good will ever grow again where so many bad people live.' Our people then left, going to the west for five days when the footprints of Masan were found describing ten concentric circles which our chief said meant that we should stay there for a certain number of plantings and should build a house, not on a mesa or mountain top as formerly, but in the valley where water would be plenty and where we could protect our sheep and growing crops from wolves or any other enemy that might wish to destroy our property.

We stayed there a long time, planting and storing our grain, we had great quantities of everything. Finally a change came, our chief died and left us without anyone who could lead us. Again we could not agree and we had many quarrels, but no fighting. Destroying each other's crops and stealing each other's planting grounds was common, just as the White man does with us today, telling us that he will give something, but never does unless it be a lie.

One day with the rising sun there came to us an old man, one whom the old people recognised as he who many years before had been the chief of our whole people. Seeing that we could not govern ourselves in peace, he had returned to take care of us for a while or until we found a new chief in whom we could have confidence. He first reproved our chiefs, then he talked to the men about the bad way they were behaving and said he wanted them to go back to where they had left off and renew their dances. This they promised to do and finally did, but not until they had been very greatly shamed by many of the scoffers, those who did not plant, but ate at all times. After the dances had been once more reinstituted and all were doing their work without quarrelling, the old man called all the people together. He told them his time was come, but he who should first find the footsteps of Masau should be their chief, that when they had gathered their crops then growing they must leave that place and go to the north. After all the crops had been taken care of, the people left, travelling up a canyon until they came to a running stream. It chanced that one of the men while hunting found the footprints of a strange being. They were in the form of a spiral, or were they concentric, made in decreasing circuits while the being searched for something of value. When the hunter returned home he told his people who then became excited over the event and demanded of him to show them where this strange place was. On the morrow he led them to the place, and they saw the foot marks leading up the steep side of the canyon. On the rocky canyon wall were the marks of both hands and feet showing that this person had climbed up to a cavern which was nearly at the summit. After many efforts to ascend all failed until one bold fellow found a way to the summit of the mesa. He soon came to the place over the cavern, which he entered by lowering himself by means of a rope made of yucca fibre. After a careful search he again found the footprints. He now felt sure that this strange being, could be no other than Masau and so called to his friends in the valley. They at once took up the cry and some hurried to the mesa summit to join the adventurer while others went to planting as to have food when the stores on hand were exhausted. While the men planted, the women gathered stones to build houses. Another party of men made ladders and pecked and cut steps into the canyon wall by which to climb to the cavern, as it was intend to make storing place for grain and other products. It was two plantings before the steps and ladders were finished. During all this time no chief had been appointed and the people became excited over this matter as the person who had discovered the footprints of Masau refused to accept the office. He said he feared the people would soon tire of him, and then trouble would begin again, but he suggested that a youth be appointed who should be taught all the customs of the people – all that people know – so that when he should become a man he would be able to talk to the people and teach them how to do. A youth was accordingly selected, but as he was too young to undertake the conduct of affairs, his grandmother acted with him until he had grown old enough to look after the welfare of the people. This youth belonged to the Mountain sheep clan. After the steps and ladders were finished the chief priest went up to the cave to consecrate it for the reception of the crops, and when they reached the rocky platform, they were surprised at the size of the cavern. They measured it by paces and found it three hundred nineteen paces deep by eight hundred fifty paces long. They determined to have the house built in this cavern and on descending found the people willing to do so. In one season they conveyed all the rock and mud up to the ledge and excavated two reservoirs for water. During the second season they erected the outer walls of the great house; on the third, they roofed and finished the entire building. When the crops had all been harvested and stored in this new house a grand festival was proclaimed and joined in by all the men. Immediately following was a feast in which the women alone participated.

At this time the people had covering for the feet made from rabbit or fox skin. Sometimes the wolf skin was used, but very rarely. Sandals were made of yucca leaves. Yucca was plaited also into coverings for the head and back. The women had robes made from the skins of sheep and antelope, fastened at the waist with a yucca girdle. The chiefs wore blankets during the feasts, made of some white substance, not wool, for it was very fine and a strong thread could be made from it (probably cotton, more likely yucca). The women made robes from rabbit skins which were used as they are today to sleep under.

After we had been at this place a long time there came to us from the south a Wolf man (Wolf clan) who said he was tired and hungry and needed rest, but the chiefs were a little afraid to let this stranger come up to the house until they knew more about him. So the first night was passed in talking to him and inquiring how he chanced to stray upon our house as he was the first person who had arrived since we were at that place. He talked in the same tongue as my people which led some to think him another chief who had come back. They talked all night at the foot of the steps and when morning came it was seen that he was a brother, he belonged to one of those families who through much dissension had left our pleasant home of the east. Now the former fear changed into gladness and he was taken up to the house where he was compelled to relate all that had taken place since his people left ours. For ten days he was busy telling all that he knew or had heard. After he had stayed with us for some time he was allowed to depart for his home in the south, but there were also sent with him seven men who were to see the country and buy anything they could from our brothers as tokens from which we might learn something concerning their daily vocation and what other people (if any) came among them. When these man started on their long journey to the south, one of the chiefs put on the rock a picture of the wolf fastening his tail to the straight path leading to the south, showing that the Wolf clan belonged to us but had gone off, but his clan was still preserved amongst us.

As time passed and the messengers who were sent to the south did not return; another party went in search of the missing men. Those who went on this second expedition were selected with great care from the Eagle clan because those men were swift, not blind, and never tired. When this party departed, men with eagle wings instead of hands and feet were pictured on the wall of rock. These men were absent three moons and when they returned they did not bring the men for whom they went to search. They said that the seven had married and were living in a beautiful canyon a short distance to the east from where our brothers were living. From this day on dissatisfaction took the place of contentment and, after struggling for many years to keep the people together, our chief followed to this beautiful canyon, Antelope spring canyon about three miles south from Keam's canyon. It took many days to get all my people down to the new home because we would get lost among the many little canyons and the trail was very crooked. But we got to our friends at last and soon had houses, using the cavernous recesses in the canyon sides and putting up a wall in front, these answered very well until we found the time to build good houses. But the other Hopituah, our brothers, after a time prevailed on us to go to their houses not far distant, where we built houses beside them. And we have been living here to this day.

CHAPTER 16

Huron

The Making of the World

In the beginning there was nothing but water, a wide sea, which was peopled by various animals of the kind that live in and upon the water. It happened then that a woman fell down from the upper world. It is supposed that she was, by some mischance, pushed down by her husband through a rift in the sky. Though styled a woman, she was a divine personage. Two loons, which were flying over the water, happened to look up and see her falling. To save her from drowning they hastened to place themselves beneath her, joining their bodies together so as to form a cushion for her to rest on. In this way they held her up, while they cried with a loud voice to summon the other animals to their aid. The cry of the loon can be heard to a great distance, and the other creatures of the sea heard it, and assembled to learn the cause of the summons. Then came the tortoise (or 'snapping turtle'), a mighty animal, which consented to relieve the loons of their burden. They placed the woman on the back of the tortoise, charging him to take care of her. The tortoise then called the other animals to a grand council to determine what should be done to preserve the life of the woman. They decided that she must have earth to live on. The tortoise directed them all to dive to the bottom of the sea and endeavour to bring up some earth. Many attempted it – the beaver, the muskrat, the diver, and others – but without success. Some remained so long below that when they rose they were dead. The tortoise searched their mouths, but could find no trace of earth. At last the toad went down, and after remaining a long time rose, exhausted and nearly dead. On searching his mouth the tortoise found in it some earth, which he gave to the woman. She took it and placed it carefully around the edge of the tortoise's shell. When thus placed; it became the beginning of dry land. The land grew and extended on every side, forming at last a great country, fit for vegetation. All was sustained by the tortoise, which still supports the earth.

When the woman fell she was pregnant with twins. When these came forth they evinced opposite dispositions, the one good, the other evil. Even before they were born the same characters were manifested. They struggled together, and their mother heard them disputing. The one declared his willingness to be born in the usual manner, while the other malignantly refused, and, breaking through his mother's side, killed her. She was buried, and from her body sprang the various vegetable productions which the new earth required to fit it for the habitation of man. From her head grew the pumpkin vine; from her breasts the maize; from her limbs the bean and the other useful esculents. Meanwhile the twins grew up, showing in all they did their opposing inclinations. The name of the good one was Tijuskeha, which means, something like saviour, or good man. The evil brother was named Tawiskarong, meaning flinty, or flint like, in allusion probably to his hard and cruel nature. They were not men, but supernatural beings, who were to prepare the world to be the abode of men. Finding that they could not live together, they separated, each taking his own portion of the earth. Their first act was to create animals of various kinds. The bad brother made fierce and monstrous creatures, proper to terrify and destroy mankind – serpents, panthers, wolves, bears, all of enormous size, and huge mosquitoes, 'as large as turkeys'. Among other things he made an immense toad, which drank up all the fresh water that was on the earth. In the meantime, the good brother, in his province, was creating the innocent and useful animals. Among the rest he made the partridge. To his surprise, the bird rose in the air and flew toward the territory of Tawiskarong. Tijuskeha asked him whither he was going. The bird replied that he was going to look for water, as there was none left in that land, and he heard there was some in the dominion of Tawiskarong. Tijuskeha then began to suspect mischief. He followed the course which the partridge had taken, and presently reached the land of his evil brother. Here he encountered the snakes, ferocious brutes, and enormous insects which his brother had made, and overcame them. Finally he came to the monstrous toad, which he cut open, letting the water flow forth.

The spirit of his mother warned him in a dream to beware of his evil brother, who would endeavour to destroy him by treachery. Finally they encountered; and as it was evident that they could not live together on the earth, they determined to decide by a formal combat which of them should remain master of the world. It was further agreed that each should make known to the other the only weapon by which he could be overcome. This extraordinary article of their agreement was probably made necessary by the fact that without such a disclosure the contest would have lasted forever. The good brother declared that he could be destroyed only by being beaten to death with a bag full of corn, beans, or some other product of the bread kind; the evil brother rejoined that he could be killed only by the horn of a deer of or some other wild animal. They set off a fighting ground, or 'list', within which the combat was to take place. Tawiskarong had the first turn, or, as duellists would say, the first fire. He set upon his brother with a bag of corn or beans; chased him about the ground, and pounded him until he was nearly lifeless and lay as if dead. He revived, however (perhaps through the aid of his mother's spirit), and, recovering his strength, pursued in turn his evil brother, beating him with a deer's horn until he killed him. But the slain combatant was not utterly destroyed. He reappeared after death to his brother, and told him that he had gone to the far west, and that thenceforth all the races of men after death would go to the west, like him. And it is the belief of, all the pagan Indians that after death, their spirits will go to the far west, and dwell there.

CHAPTER 17

Iroquois

Three Brothers Who Followed the Sun under the Sky's Rim

This happened in old times, when there were not many people. There were three brothers, and they were not married. They were hunters, and had spent their lives hunting. When the brothers were young, they enjoyed the excitement of hunting; but as they grew older, it did not give them so much pleasure. The youngest brother suggested that for new experiences they walk to the edge of the earth where the sky comes down and touches the big sea of salt water.

There is salt water west, and this world is an island. The other brothers thought the plan a good one; and when they had prepared everything, they started on the journey. They travelled a good many years, and a good many things happened to them. They always went straight westward..

At last the brothers came to a place where the sun goes under the sky's edge. The sky bends down there, and sinks into the water. They camped there for a month, and watched the things that happened there. They noticed how the sun got under the rim of the sky and went away quickly. Some men came there and tried to get under the edge of the sky, but it descended quickly and crushed them. There is a road there. Now they noticed that when the sky came up, the water sank lower; and that when the sky went in the waters the water rose higher.

The younger brothers desired to pass under the rim of the sky when the sun slipped under on his road; but the elder brother said that the happenings were too evilly mysterious, and that he was afraid. The younger brothers ran under the rim of the sky quickly, and the rim was very thick. They kept on the road, and water was on each side.

They were afraid that the sky would come down and crush them. Now, the oldest brother, it is said, watched them; and when he saw that nothing happened to injure his brothers, he began to run after them. The younger brothers turned from their safe place to encourage him; but the sky came down on the sun's road and crushed him, but they saw his spirit shoot by quickly. The brothers felt sad.

On the other side of the sky everything is different, so it is said. Before the brothers was a large hill; and when they had ascended it, they saw a very large village in the distance. A man came running toward them. He was in the distance; but he came nearer, and he called out, 'Come!' It was their elder brother.

'How did you come so quickly, brother?' they asked. 'We did not see you come.'

The brother answered only, 'I was late.' He passed by on a road.

An old man came walking toward them. He was youthful and his body was strong, but his hair was long and white. He was an old man. His face was wise looking, and he seemed a chief.

'I am the father of the people in the Above-the-Sky-Place,' he said. 'Hawtnu is my son. I wish to advise you, because I have lived here a long time. I have always lived here; but Hawtnu was born of the woman on the island. When you see Hawtnu, call quickly, "Niawe skano." If you fail to speak first, he will say, "You are mine," and you will be spirits, as your brother is.'

The brothers proceeded and saw a high house made of white bark. They walked up the path to the doors. A tall man stepped out quickly, and the brothers said, 'Niawe skano!'

And the great man said, 'Doges, I have been watching you for a long time.' The brothers entered the house. Now, when they were in the house, the man said, 'In what condition are your bodies?'

The brothers answered, 'They are fine bodies.'

The great man, answered, 'You do not speak the truth. I am Hawtnu, and I know all about your bodies. One of you must lie down, and I will purify him, and then the other.'

One brother lay down, and Hawtnu placed a small shell to his lips, and put it on the brother's mouth. He also tapped him on the a neck, and sealed the shell with clay. He began to skin the brother. He took apart the muscles, and then scraped the bones. He took out the organs and washed them. Then Hawtnu built the man again. He loosened the clay and rubbed his neck. He did this with both brothers; and they sat up, and said, 'It seems as if we had slept.' Hawtnu said, 'Every power of your bodies is renewed. I will test you.'

The brothers followed Hawtnu to a fine grove of trees surrounded by a thick hedge. All kinds of flowers were blooming outside. 'My deer are here,' said Hawtnu.

A large buck with wide antlers ran toward them. 'He is the swiftest of my runners. Try and catch him,' said Hawtnu.

The men ran after the deer, and rapidly overtook him. 'He has given us good speed,' the brothers said. They soon discovered that they had many surpassing abilities, and the great man tested them all on that day.

They returned to the white lodge, and the brothers saw a messenger running toward them. Upon his wide chest was a bright ball of light. It was very brilliant. In some unknown language he shouted to Hawtnu and dashed on.

'Do you understand his words, or do you know that man?' asked Hawtnu. 'He is the sun, my messenger. Each day he brings me news. Nothing from east to west escapes his eye. He has just told me of a great war raging between your people and another nation. Let us look down on the earth and see what is happening.'

They all went to a high hill in the middle of the country and looked down through a hole where a tree had been uprooted. They saw two struggling bands of people and all the houses burning. They could hear people crying and yelling their war cries.

'Men will always do this,' said Hawtnu, and then they went down the hill.

The brothers stayed a long time in the upper world and learned so much that they never could tell it all. Sometimes they looked down the earth and saw villages in which no one lived. They knew that they were waiting for people to be born and live there. In the upper world they saw villages, likewise, awaiting the coming of people. Hawtnu told them a good many things and after a time told a messenger to lead them to the path that the sun took when he came out on the earth in the morning. They followed the messenger and came out on the earth. They waited until the sun went over the earth and had gone to the west. Again then they went under the edge of the sky in the east, and came out in their country again. It was night, and they slept on the ground. In the morning they saw their own village, and it was overgrown with trees. They followed a path through the woods, and came upon another village. Their own people were there, and they went into a council house and talked. They told their story; and no one knew them except their own sister, who was an aged woman.

'The war of which you speak took place fifty years ago,' the sister said.

The brothers did not care for the earth now, but wished themselves back in the upper world. They were not like other men, for they never grew tired. They were very strong and could chase animals and kill them with their hands. Nothing could kill them, neither arrows nor disease. After a while, both were stuck by lightning and were killed.

CHAPTER 18

Mandan

No Tongue

At a certain village headed by a certain chief there once lived a man and his wife and their two children, the elder a girl; the other one (some two years younger), about seven or eight years old, a boy. The woman used to leave the village and go into the woods to do her work of preparing and dressing hides. One day the man followed her to a lonely spot in the woods, and killed her. He cut off one leg, and hid the rest of the body. The leg he smeared with the hair and blood a of a deer, then he built a fire and cooked it.

After a while, the two children came that way, and their father gave them their mother's flesh to eat. Then he left them and went back to the village. After a while, the children also returned to the village. There they found themselves avoided by all. Their father had given out the report that they had killed their mother and eaten her flesh.

The chief soon called a council to decide what should be done with the children. After some debate, it was determined that they should be taken by the police out into the woods and lost. So the next day the police took the two children a long ways into the woods, and left them there without food. The children wandered around for several days, living on berries and such roots as they could find. Then, finally, they made their way back to the village again. Once more the children were taken far into the woods and abandoned by the police; but after much suffering, they returned once again to the village.

Then a council was again called; and it was decided, at their father's urgent plea to lose the children once more, and then to leave the village, and move inland for a long stay. So once more the children were taken far into the woods and left; and that night all the inhabitants of the village packed up their belongings and went away.

The boy and girl wandered around for many days, barely subsisting on berries and roots. Then, at last, hungry and tired, they got back the village, only to find it deserted with no food to be found. They cried about the village for some time, and at last found the trail which their people had left.

This trail they followed for several days and finally; exhausted and almost dead with hunger came to the tepees of their people. It was evening, and they ventured to enter the camp. Within was a poor old woman. When she saw them, though she recognised who they were, she felt sorry, and asked them in and gave them food.

Then she told them that she would hide them for a day or two, but that all the people were against them; and they must go away. She told them to go back to the village on the river bank, and told them how to find her house. In the house, she said, was a cache; and she gave them directions for finding it. In the cache were corn, beans, squash, and fat, with such dishes, robes, and such utensils as were needed for sewing and cooking. In some way, however, the presence of the children in the camp was suspected; and the police were sent around to search every tepee. When they came to the old woman's house, she sat by the door. They asked if the children were inside; and she did not answer. Then they entered, and found them.

The chief and the headmen debated for a long time as to what should be done with the boy and girl this time; and finally it was decided to send them back to the old village with the police, and give orders to have them killed there. So, on the following day, the police took the two and went back. But when they came to the village, they felt sorry for them and did want to kill them. So they rolled the two children tightly in a large heavy hide and bound it firmly round the middle with a thong. The bundle thus made they placed on the very edge of a high, steep bank, at the base of which were many stones. To the bundle they fastened another cord, which they tied to a stake, so that, if the bundle rolled off, it would hang suspended over the edge of the bank.

Thus they left the children, who could do nothing to help themselves, and who were so placed that the slightest stirring might cause them to go over the edge. The boy and girl cried almost continuously, stopping on now and then to caution each other against struggling or moving. A long time they lay thus, weeping, and wondering what they had done deserve such a fate. Then by and by they heard a crying from the direction of the village. At first they thought that it was people; but as it came nearer; they recognised it as the howling of a dog.

It was a very old dog, whose teeth were nearly worn out; and she was very weak. The dog came up, and began to chew on the thong which fastened the children to the stake. She chewed for a long time, crying, and resting occasionally; and all the time the children were fearful, lest they be pushed over the edge. Finally the dog began to chew on the thong which bound the hide, and the children were still more fearful. But, as the dog chewed, she pulled on the bundle, and gradually drew it back from the edge of the bluff. At last she broke the thong, and the hide loosened. The little girl was able to get out and help the little boy out.

Then they started back to the village to look for the old woman's house; and as they went along, the old dog (which they had thankfully petted and caressed) followed them. They had no trouble in finding the old woman's house, and they found the cache just as she had described it. From it they got robes, utensils, and food enough to last them for some time; and the old dog was not forgotten.

For a long time they lived thus in the old woman's house, going out the daytime to gather roots and berries, and returning at night. After a time; however; the weather began to grow colder; and the girl suggested that they go down into the bottom land and build themselves a winter house in the woods. So they went down, and built a very little house, just big enough for themselves and the dog. They built it just like the earth lodges, with a frame of poles covered with grass and then with earth; and in it they were snug and warm.

By this time, however, their food taken from the cache was gone, and they began to be very hungry. All the berries were dried up; and they could not dig roots, because the ground was frozen and the snow was coming. So they had to live entirely on the berries from the wild roses. They lived thus for some time. Every day, as they went out to gather rose berries, they noticed how thick the rabbits were so one day the little boy told his sister to make him a bow. The next day the sister worked at the bow, and finally succeeded in making a small one which he could handle. Then the little boy went out with his bow, and practised a great deal. Finally, on the first day, he managed to kill one rabbit, which he took home to his sister. She dressed the rabbit; and saved the skin. After this, the boy kept on hunting with his bow, and soon became a good hunter, and would bring in a number of rabbits every day.

Thus they lived along comfortably for some time, together with the old dog. One day the boy got close to a wolf on the edge of the bank, and managed to kill it. He dragged it home, and they made a robe from its hide.

One day, after thinking for a long time, the girl told her brother that she thought he ought to go up on the hill and fast and pray, as the warriors do. In that way, they might get many good things, and good spirits would come to him. The boy did not understand what she meant at first; but she explained it to him and he agreed to go. They had plenty of rabbits on hand, so that he did not need to hunt.

So the sister took the rabbit skins and made him warm mittens and other warm things to wear, for it was very cold. Then she told him to remember whatever appeared to him, and if he was asked for anything, he must at once give it. So, after dressing warm, he went up on a high hill before sunrise, and stood there all day, fasting and praying. Meanwhile the sister sat at home in the house. She was sorry for her brother, all alone and cold on the hill, and he was so little. And she cried all day.

When he came back at night, she asked him if he had seen anything; but he said that he had not. The next day he went again, very early, as before and stood on the hill all day; and his sister stayed at home and cried. That night, when his sister asked him if he had seen anything, he said that he had. He said that two men came to him out of the air, just as the sun was coming up. One of them asked him for something; but he did not just understand him, and, before he could answer, the man said to his companion, 'He not want to give it.' And they disappeared before he could answer. As they went away, they sang a song.

The next morning the little boy prepared to go up on the hill again His sister told him, if the men came again, to quickly give them what they asked for. So he went up on the hill, and again the men came just as the sun was rising. One man asked him for his tongue. The little boy took his knife with one hand, and tried to pull out his tongue with the other. But it always slipped from his fingers, and he could not hold it. And again the men disappeared. As they went, they sang the same song.

When the boy told his sisters what had happened, she got a little stick and made it very sharp. In the morning, when the little boy was ready, to go up on the hill, she gave him the stick, and told him to stick it through his tongue when the men came, and then he could pull it out and cut it off easy. So the little boy went up on the hill; and his sister cried and cried at the thought of her poor little brother having to cut off his tongue. The men came once more, just at sunrise and one of them again asked the little boy for his tongue. He pierced his tongue with the sharp stick and thus was able to pull it out. He cut it off and handed it to the man. Then the man said, 'That is a brave man! No one can get the best of him.' And he said to the boy, 'I will make you a great hunter and warrior; and you will be very powerful.' Then the two men went away as before, singing the same song.

The little boy went back to his sister, crying, and with the blood running out of his mouth and over his clothes. His sister cried more then ever when she saw him. But she washed him up, and made him as comfortable as she could. He felt very bad for several days, but after that he was all right again.

One night there came two strange persons to their lodge, and the boy asked his sister to wait on them. After eating, these men went out without saying a word to them. Then the boy began to hunt again, and one day, on the edge of a high bluff, he met two men. They spoke to him, and said that they were the two men who came his lodge one night, and they said they had a nice meal. They told him that they had been killed under that bluff, and that they made their home there now; that they knew all the hardships which he and his sister had endured; and that they were the ones who helped them get through all this hardship. They continued to talk to the boy, saying they knew that two persons had come to him when he was on the hill. The one that had promised to make him powerful was the Sun; they said, the other one was the Moon. The Sun would do all that he had promised; but No-Tongue must be very careful, for the Sun wanted him to die young. The Moon, they said, would help him, and keep him from being killed.

Then the two men said they would continue to help No-Tongue (for such he was henceforth called) and his sister. They told him that they would get all the spirits together, and make a big buffalo corral. They said he must go out and pick out a place for the corral on the next day, and then come and show them where it was. After this, the two men went away.

On the following day, No-Tongue went out and picked a place for a corral in a deep coulee, ending in a sort of pocket. Then he took the men to see the place. They told him that he and his sister must stay in the house the next day while the spirits built the corral. So the next day .the boy and the girl stayed in the house. Toward evening, the two men came to them, and told them that the corral was done. But they said that the scaffolds for the meat were to be built the next day, in the woods around the house, and that they must neither go out nor look out.

On the following day, then, the two remained shut up in the house again. And all day they heard a great clamour, chopping and hammering, and the sound of many voices, laughing, joking, and giving directions to one another. At night they went out, and saw new meat scaffolds in every direction as far as they could see. Then the two men came again, and told the children that the first drive would be made on the next day, and that a drive would be made on each day for four days. During this time, the children must remain inside; but each night some of the choicest meat would be placed at their door. Also there would be a white buffalo each day in the herd, and the skin would be placed each night at the door. The rest of the meat would be placed on the scaffolds. The two men said that all the birds were going to help them drive the buffalo into the corral.

For the next four days the children remained inside, as they had been told. Each day they heard a great noise of birds and the tramping and bellowing of the trapped herds; and each night choice pieces of meat were placed at the door, where they could reach them from within.

On the fifth day, the children came out of the lodge and found the scaffolds everywhere covered with meat, ready cut up and hung up out of reach the wolves. At their door they found the four white buffalo skins. They talked over for a long time what they should do with these skins. Finally they decided to save three of them to give to the chief of their people. The other one they gave to the old dog who had saved their lives, and had since been so faithful to them. They fixed up a nice soft bed of it for her.

Soon the two men came again to the children. They told No-Tongue that his people were starving, and that they were going to try to come to their old village on the river again. They told the children to prepare everything, and get ready to receive their people and divide the meat among them.

Meanwhile the people out on the prairie broke camp, and started to move back. They were nearly starved and had to travel very slowly on account of the old people, the women and the children, who were hardly able to walk. The chief decided to send a party ahead to try and find some food; so nine of the young men were picked, and they went on ahead as fast as they could. The young men came to the village after a long hard march. The two men had told the children of their coming, and the children had everything ready to receive them. The young men came to the edge of the bank, and saw the smoke from the children's houses. They wondered who it could be, living there in the woods. They feared it might be enemies; but they were so hungry that they decided to go and find out anyhow. So they started out, and soon came to the children's house. It was now night. The children invited them in; and gave them the food prepared. The two men had given No-Tongue full instructions as to what him should do and what was going to happen all the time.

On the following day; the children gave the young men what pemmican they could carry to take back to the rest of the people.

They travelled fast, and got the pemmican back to their people as quick as they could. All were nearly starved, yet the pemmican magically increased as it was used up, until every one was fully fed. After being thus refreshed, and having heard the young men's story of the abundance of food at the children's camp, the people pressed on rapidly.

The two men kept No-Tongue warned as to the movements of the people, and told him what to do when they came. So the two children, at the suggestion of the men, prepared a great pot of soup for their father, when he should come to their house. At last the people arrived and the children received them. Then No-Tongue divided the scaffolds of meat, giving an allotted portion to each household. To the chief he also gave the three white buffalo robes.

After this, the father came to the house of the children. To him they gave the soup, and kept urging him to eat, until he had finished it all. In his half-starved condition, the effects were deadly. The father began to be sick before he left their house, and he died before he could get back to the place where the people were camped.

For several days the people were busy taking care of their meat. Then they moved back to the old village on the bluff. The chief was very good to No-Tongue, and wished him to marry his daughter and take his own house, saying that he would build himself a new one. Shortly after the people moved back to the village, No-Tongue and his sister moved back also, taking with them the faithful old dog.

No-Tongue caused it to be announced that he wished to find out to whom the old dog belonged. Then he led her out into the open place in the village, and all the old women assembled there. They each took their turn, calling to the dog and talking to her; but she lay drowsing, and paid no attention to any of them. Finally all had tried, but one very poor old woman. She declared she did not believe that it could be her dog; for her dog was so old that it must have died long ago. However, her friends persuaded her to try. She went out and spoke to the dog from quite a distance, and the dog paid no attention. Then she approached nearer and called, and the dog roused up. Still nearer she went, and kept calling. The dog stood up, and, as the old woman approached, ran to her with every sign of gladness and recognition. So to this old woman, No-Tongue gave the white buffalo robe which had been allotted to the old dog.

CHAPTER 19

Mojave

Story of the Flood

One time there were people living under the earth. They send out one little bird, maybe in the upper world. The bird flew north, east, south, west. Not find anything. Then people make ladder of vines like grapevines leading up to upper world. Send bird up the ladder, and people followed the bird. After they reached the top, they heard a noise, and they went to the top of the ladder and looked down. There were big waters coming out of the hole.

Now they left Old Lady Frog down there. They thought she made water, and it covered the earth. Before the water became very high, they made a box, and put something to eat in it. They chose a girl, and put her in the box. They told her she would live when all the people were drowned. Then they told her when the box hit four times on the sky, she was to make a little hole. Then the water came, and all the people were drowned. The box floated on the water.

By and by the box struck the sky four times, and then it rested on the ground at Lake Montezuma (or maybe at Mount Montezuma Well, four miles east of Jerome, across the Verde River). The girl moved in the box. She opened the little hole or door, and came out from the box. She thought she would see the people, but she was all alone.

After some time she knew she was the only one, and she wanted to make a baby. She went to a waterfall and lay under it. In a few days she gave birth to a girl. Now there were two girls in the world; and when she grew up, her mother told her how conception had taken place, but they could find no waterfall at that time. They took a vessel of water and used that it the same matter as the waterfall. Soon the daughter gave birth to a boy, and called his name Jesus.

When the boy was four days old, the mother said to her daughter, 'Go out on the hills and get some fruit.' She went on the hills and gathered some guava seed. She heard an eagle coming in the sky, and the eagle came and carried her away to Montezuma Mountain on the very top, very high. The eagles killed her and ate her.

Little Baby Jesus stayed with his grandmother, and she gave him mescal to suck He grew older. When the boy was getting grown, he asked his grandmother where his mother was; what was his name besides 'grandson'. She told him that when he was four years old, eagles took her away and killed her.

Then the boy became a man and told the people he was going to kill the big steer. The steer was very big, and lay on the ground like a big root. The boy told a man to dig a hole for him, and the man finished the hole. It was toward the head of the steer, under his heart. The boy made a little fire, and got his knife red hot. He went down into the hole, and ran the knife into the heart of the steer. The steer struggled, and ran his horn so far into the ground he nearly killed the boy. He thought about the eagles, how they killed his mother. He wanted the blood and brains of the steer. He took the blood and smeared it all over himself and put the brains on his head and made handles of the hide. Now he was ready to go.

He went to top of Mountain of Montezuma, where the eagles lived, and lay on his back when he heard them coming. They carried him to their nest. They told their children, 'I have brought you something to eat.' They struck the boy with a rock. The steer's blood and brains came out. They told their young to eat, and they would hunt some more. Then they flew away and left the young with him. Both tried to eat meat.

Boy said, 'Sh–sh–sh!' Then he asked, 'Where does your mother sit?' They told him the rock where she usually sat. He took a lot of pine pitch and put it on top of the rock where she sat. Then, when she returned, she dropped on the rock, and her feet stuck so she could not get them out. Then the boy put the pitch on the rock where the father sat. He was hunting, and heard a great noise. It was the struggle between the boy and the eagles. He came flying, and was stuck to rock, so the boy took a stick and killed him. He took both young ones and threw them down the side of the mountain.

Now he did not know how he would get home. He tried to sing a medicine song. He put the medicine on his hands; and while he was singing, he pressed his head and hands down, and the rock began to go down the mountain. Halfway down he saw an old woman carrying a basket, and he called, 'Grandmother, come and get me!'

She asked, 'How did you get up there? No one can get up there. The eagles will kill you.'

He said, 'I killed all the eagles. Come and get me!'

The rocks were very sharp. The old lady turned herself into a bat, and began to climb by the rocks. She carried her basket by her head rope. She wanted to carry him down in the basket, but he thought the head rope was too slender. She told him to put a big blue rock in to test it. Then he took out the rock and climbed in himself. She told him, 'Sit in the basket. Do not open your eyes! If you do, the string will break and kill us.'

So he sat with his eyes tight closed. By and by he thought he would open his eyes and see if what she told him was true. He opened his eyes, the string broke, and they fell. The grandmother was hurt: legs, arms, wrists, and hands broken.

The boy says, 'I will cure you right away.' So the boy touched the broken places with the substance he gathered from his skin, and moisture from his tongue, and they were well at once.

Fire Myth

When Matyavela died, Mustan-ho, by his direction, started in to cremate him. The Coyote wanted to eat the corpse. At that time there was no Fire on earth. The Blue Fly put a star in the sky, 'Go over there, and get me some of that fire,' he said to the Coyote. The Coyote was fooled, and scampered off to bring in the star; he didn't know that the Blue Fly had learned the art of rubbing sticks together and making fire. While he was gone, the Blue Fly made a big fire and Matyavela was burnt up.

The Coyote happened to look back; he saw the ablaze and knew that something was up. He came back on the full run. All the animals were present at the funeral; they saw the Coyote returning, and formed a ring round the fire to keep him away from the corpse.

The Coyote ran round the ring until he came to the Badger, who was very short. The Coyote jumped over him, seized the heart of Matyavela, which was the only part not burnt up, and made off with it. He burnt his mouth in doing this and it's black to this day.

CHAPTER 20

Navajo

Origin of the People

The first (lowest) world was red, bare, barren ground, this was the earliest world. Etsehostin and Etseasun, his wife, existed there and they had nothing to eat till the fourth day, and on this day they began to think of eating. Hostjaishjine stood up and rubbed his belly and some skin was loosened which formed in a roll under his hands and he laid this roll of cuticle on the ground. The woman stood up and followed his example. Then they each trampled on the rolls. Etsehostin reached over his shoulder, down his back, and formed another roll and laid it on the ground. The two rolls that he had formed turned into a man with a mask. This new formed man stood up, and this is the origin of the first man. Etseasun again followed the Hosteen's (old man's) example and from the rolls which she formed a woman arose: this was the virgin called Djosdelhazhy (biting vagina). The Hosteen then reached under his left arm and formed another roll of skin which he laid on the ground, and it became a water monster called Teholtsody. The Hosteen then reached under his right arm and formed another roll of skin which, being laid upon the ground, became Usheenasun, Salt spirit, a woman who now lives at Nitco (Salt Lake South of Zuni).

Hosteen then took the end of his tongue between his fingers and spat out a little piece of it upon the ground before him, and it became a wing which he placed upon his ear. The wind would shake this wing and tell everything in his ear. Etseasun then took a roll of skin from her scalp and laid it on the ground and placed a little feather beside it and this became the Thunder (with wings). On the left side the feathers were black on top and white underneath, on the right side the feathers were white above and black below. Etsehostin then rubbed the sole of his right foot and the roll of skin became a large frog, Tcalc. He rubbed the sole of his left foot, and a crane, Teklaliale was formed. This makes altogether twelve personages up to this time.

Etsehostin began thinking, 'How can we get something to eat?'

Etseasun said, 'My husband, I know not.'

Hosteen looked back and saw Hostjaishjine and said to him, 'You understand these things, tell us how we are to get food.'

Hostjaishjine, who always looks stern and grim and angry, said, 'I do not know,' but he reached down on his neck and rolled a little skin in his hand and Wunushtcindy (locust) was produced. Then Etseasun looked far back and saw Nastjeasun and asked her how they could get something to eat. Nastjeasun rolled a little skin upon her breast and it became Ant, Nazozi, which was then buried in the ground for four days and at the end of that time many little red (yellow) ants came forth. Hostjaishjine then rolled some skin from his forehead and laid it on the ground when it turned into a horned toad, Ndshongbitcijy. Etsehostin built a house and lived there and the red (yellow) ants built all round this big house, and annoyed him and the others, so that they could find no rest day or night. Teholtsody thought he would go off and find some place to rest so he travelled to the east. The world was very small at this time, and Teholtsody soon came to its utmost limit and as he could go no farther, he built his house there. In like manner, the frog being troubled with the ants, he travelled to the south to the utmost limit of the world, and built there. Then Salt Woman went similarly to the west and built a house, and Tulthklahalle went to the north. Each of these houses was fashioned from east to west like a rainbow, and from south to north of Sun-rays. So when we build a house today we have four poles reaching from east to west and from south to north, and these meet at the apex.

After these four had left him, Etsehostin stayed in his own house. He said, 'I wish we could get some clouds, I want rain,' and he looked out of his house towards the east, where Teholtsody was and saw many clouds, for Teholtsody's house is of clouds. Etseasun then said, 'I wish we had some kind of rain,' and she looked to the south and saw a heavy fog, for this was the frog's house. Etsehostin wished that there was a mountain to stand on and look for rain, and he began to pray for rain; he looked west and saw a mirage like a person.

Etseasun now prayed on the north side, 'Send rain so that everything may be wet.' She saw a green scum on the water and made a house, of this. This makes four houses.

Etsehostin sent Thunder naked to the cloud house of Teholtsody in the east, telling Thunder to stand right in the doorway of Teholtsody's house. Thunder went there and stood in the doorway naked and Teholtsody gave him a mantle of feathers which is the sheet (quick) lightning. On his head is the heat lightning. He had a tail feather which is Hajillkish, sheet lightning. Etseasun told the monster Tehlin (horn horse) to go to the south to Frog's house of fog. He went and stood in the doorway. Salt Woman had gone west and Etsehostin told Thonainilly to stand just outside the doorway of her house and watch her. He was to be her guardian. An old woman sat on the north side of the world and she sent a fish (turtle) to watch outside the doorway of Tulthklahale's house and guard it. After Teholtsody went east he made a water vessel of white clay. Frog in the south made one of blue clay; the Usheenasun in the west made one of yellow clay. Tultklehale on the north made one of spotted clay. It had variegated surface of black, blue, yellow and white.

Etsehostin began to travel and he went to Teholtsody's house, and in the middle of it he found the pot Teholtsody had made and it was covered. He lifted the cover and found it full of water. He went home and told his wife that Teholtsody was growing wiser than they were. Etseasun then went south to Frog's house and saw his pot full of water, and she returned to her house and told her husband. Josdelhazhy said she also would travel and she went west and found that Salt Woman also had a pot full of water. She returned and told what she had seen. Hashjaishjine then went north and found a pot of water in the house of Tulthkalhale and he returned very angry. He said, 'They are all getting wiser than us. They are growing rich and we are still poor. We have nothing and cannot make anything.'

Etsehostin said, 'Why should you be angry? We will grow wise like them and have many things some day.' Then Etsehostin went to Teholtsody's house to get a little water, which he brought back to his own house. Etseasun went and brought some from the south. Next Hosteen borrowed some from the west and Asun borrowed from the north. Having brought water from each of these four places, Hosteen planted it all together in the ground. In a few days he saw a damp, green spot there. He returned to look at the place in a few more days and saw that bushes had grown there. He made a third visit and found jointed grass. He made a fourth visit and found the reed grass, but it had no pollen on the top, and there was a large spring also.

Hosteen again said, 'I wish we had something more,' and he went to the spring and found lookaitso growing right in the centre of it. Five different kinds of plants grew out of the spring and he pulled up some of each kind and took them home. One of these reeds had twelve joints and the wind came out of the other end and made music (a flageolet). The wind emerging from this reed whirled about on the ground all over the world and it went to the houses at the four quarters and caused them much trouble. The dweller at each house sent his guard out to trouble the wind. They took black clouds, fogs, and blue mould, also to each of them was given Thunder and Lightning and the guardians kept shooting at the little winds but these latter kept dodging about so that they could not be hit. But this only raised more wind and it rained heavily, then the guards stopped troubling the wind for they could not conquer it.

When the rain stopped Hosteen said to his wife, 'Everything looks beautiful, I wish we had something good to eat.' He looked in all directions and saw Hajillkish (Glow-light Heat-Lightning) at the four points where people lived. Then he prayed for some kind of grass, or fruit, or seeds to live upon. He went to the spring and saw something green that had come up out of the ground and it was corn. He then went east to Teholtsody and found the pumpkin and squash and returned. Asun went south and found that Frog had raised watermelon and tobacco. She returned. Then Hosteen went west to Salt Woman's house and found beans and cotton growing, then he returned home. Hosteen went north to Tulthkle's house and found muskmelon and gourds growing in great quantities. He then returned and said to Asun, 'We have wished for these things (i.e. we have everything we prayed for). Now we have many things. Let us pray for something more.' So he prayed and sang for more.

He went to the spring and saw a 'fruit' in the middle of the water. He went back for Spider Woman and told her to get this fruit out of the water. She got it and gave it to Hosteen who looked at it and saw it was Yolakaihatate, a big shell, big as a pan. He took this home and returned next day to the spring and found more fruit. Spider Woman again brought it out and it was Turquoise, Tedokiji. Hosteen then went east to Teholtsody's house and went in and found a big black bow and arrow, also eagle feathers. These Hosteen used as Thunder (the arrow for lightning, and the feathers to guide the arrows). Asun sent south to Frog's house, and Frog had stone knives. Spider Woman went to Salt Woman who had planted cotton and had been weaving it into cloth. Spider Woman got this and brought it home. Hashjaishjine went north to Tulthkle's house and found black cloth and fetched it home. On the first trip Hashjaishjine returned angry but this time he was in good humour. He said to Hosteen, 'The people at the four corners are growing rich.' Hosteen then prayed for more and went to the spring. The corn was growing ripe and each stalk carried twelve ears. Asun went over and gathered it and brought it home. They now had plenty of corn and much else besides. But those living at the four corners of the world had no corn so they came to Hosteen's house and begged him for some. He told them to provide for themselves, but finally he gave them some of the pollen; but none of the ear corn. He told them to plant the pollen. They did so and it grew up small, like onions, but no ears grew upon it. Then they begged Hosteen for some seed corn but he would not give them any.

Teholtsody said, 'When Hosteen came borrowing water we all gave him some, and enabled him to raise water of his own.'

Hosteen said, 'Surely you let me have water and when you begged for corn I gave it to you and taught you how to plant it as best I could.'

Teholtsody was very angry and thought how he could destroy Hosteen.

Teholtsody gave Thunder a bow and arrow and told him to go and kill Hosteen, 'For,' said he, 'we must have some of this corn.' Thunder went to try and burst Hosteen open with lightning, but Horned Toad was in the doorway of Hosteen's house and the wind warned Hosteen of his danger. Hosteen told Horned Toad to stand in front of him always, for as he was so rough-coated lightning could not hurt him. Frog was also angry and assaulted Hosteen. He sent his guardian Tehlinl (a water monster) to draw all the water away (to dry it up) from Hosteen's spring. But Spider Woman wove an impenetrable web around it so that Frog and his guardian were foiled. (Hostjaishkine was the most powerful). Salt Woman gave Tiinainilly a lump (double handful) of salt, and he also had some kind of lightning in his hands, and he came against Hosteen. Hostjaishjine saw him coming and knew his harmful intent. Hostjaishjine had a long stone knife with a wooden handle. He ran into the house and made a fire by twirling a spindle of wood. He made a small fire and scattered it all over Hosteen's house. Tiinainilly (a young man) came close in order to throw his lightning on to the house and his salt upon the fire, which exploded, but no harm ensued, so he went back to the west and the Salt Woman was powerless. Tulthklahale, in the north, sent Mud Turtle (Black-mud Fish) to harm Hosteen. Turtle had some kind of lightning of arrow, but could do no harm. Hastjaishjine made a big shirt of rawhide and gave it to Wunustcinde (locust) and this protected him against the lightning or arrows of the Turtle; no impression could be made on this shirt, and this is the origin of the shield. Hastjaishjini saw that all these people were jealous of the Hosteen and were trying to destroy him. (They were envious of his possessing corn, etc.). Hosteen then asked Hastjaishjini to do what he could against these people. Hashjaishjini's anger was roused against these people and he sallied forth to their houses. He went first to east, then south, then west, then north. He broke open their houses and successively broke the pot and spilled the water that was in them. The water that was in the pot in the east flowed to the south and the water that was in the pot in the north flowed toward the west, and all the waters met in the west and there was a great flood. Hosteen had corn, white shells, turquoise and everything he wanted. He had large hollow reeds which would float on the water so he did not care when the flood should reach him. But all these eight persons who were envious and at enmity with Hosteen were troubled and afraid of the flood. Hosteen and his people were not afraid as they had the means of floating on the water.

Hosteen and his family cut the great reeds and put all their corn and other possessions inside of these, and the whole world was gradually overflowed. Then Teholtsody and the others at the cardinal points began to wish that they could save themselves with Hosteen and his family. Teholtsody made a bow and arrow and gave them to Thunder and told him to go to Hosteen and give them to him and beg that there might be peace between them. Thunder went to Hosteen's house and said, 'Teholtsody sends you this bow and arrow and begs you to be his friend.'

Hosteen would not look at them and said, 'I have nothing to do with it. Go to Hostjaishjine. He is the one that broke the water vessels and brought on this flood.' So Thunder took them to Hostjaishjine and made the same offer.

Hostjaishjine would not listen to Thunder but said, 'Go to Wunustcinde' (locust).

Thunder went to him and he accepted the bow and arrow saying, 'This is just what I want.' There were two arrows and Wunustcinde thrust them into his breast, one at either side, and drew them completely through. You may see that this insect has the holes in its thorax to this day. Then he put them in his mouth and thrust them down his throat into his stomach and withdrew them again, and there was blood adhering to them.

Next Frog sent Teklin to Hosteen to say, 'My house is overflowed and I have lost everything except this tobacco bag which I wish you to accept that we may become friends.' The bag was made from the green scum of the water and was embroidered with beads, etc. Hosteen would not have it and referred him to Hostjaishjine who breathed upon it four times and there was some tobacco in it and he filled a clay pipe with it and smoked.

Next Salt Woman said, 'We shall be killed by the water, we cannot live here, let us go to Hosteen.' She had a cotton blanket and offered this through Tuneiini (Salt Woman's guard) to Hosteen. He would not have it, and said, 'Go to Spider Woman and give her the blanket.' She looked at it, put it around her waist, breathed from it four times and was satisfied. Next came Hakleale (Fish Guardian) who sent fish to Hosteen with a flint shirt and cap. He offered them, but Hosteen sent him to second man Naciuditcije (Horned Toad). He took the shirt and cap, put the shirt on and wore the cap, and therefore all four groups (eight people) were now on peaceable terms with Hosteen.

They were all friends. They stayed there a while but everything was flooded except on the east side. Little white mountains showed above the water. On the south side were little blue mountains; on the west side, little yellow mountains; on the north, little black mountains. All just barely showed their heads above water. Hosteen went east to White mountains and picked up a little earth and returned. Spider Woman wove a web on the surface of the water near each of the four mountains. Hosteen had a house of rainbow and sun rays in the form of a little mountain and he covered it with earth for a roof. The water had not yet covered the houses.

Spider Woman wove a web so that the spring could not overflow yet. Old Man (Hosteen) and Woman (Asun) went over to the spring and planted every growing thing, corn, melons, pumpkins, beans, all things, and they got all kinds of seeds and put them away. Those living in the various directions owned their water and had it with them. After the restoration of peace, Old Woman made new vessels for all these people in which they carried their water supply. When they made peace and were all united, the flood continued, so they put all their corn and property in the reeds and got inside themselves. All these people were inside the reeds and the water kept rising. Old Man and Woman went down to the spring. Old Man got on one side, Old Woman, on the other. He began to pray: 'We are going to leave the spring, we will never come back again, but wherever I go I will always live as I have done here, do everything as I have done here.'

When he finished praying, a young man came out of the spring and a little afterwards another. They did not look at the boys closely, but Old Woman took them in her arms and folded her blanket around them and went to the reeds. They made a hole in the reed in the side of the shaft and the people got inside and Old Man went in last, but Wunustcinde (locust) got up to the top of the reed and sat upon a leaf. As the reed began to move upward Wunustcinde began to make a noise through the holes in his thorax and as he did so the reed began to shake like wind. Black Wind shook it at the roots and made it move. The reed grew up higher and higher. The water now covered all the earth, everything except this reed which kept growing and Wunustcinde was always on the leaf at the top. As the reed grew, the water continued to rise; as Wunustcinde made his noise, the reed kept growing and Black Wind kept blowing at the roots and the people became aware that they were close to the roof of the world and did not know what to do as there was no space left for them between the surface of the water and the under side of this earth. Wunustcinde stopped his noise and Black Wind stopped blowing, and the reed stopped growing. They did not know what to do. Old Man then said to him of the north, 'You begged me to bring you along, now come with me to look around and see if there is any way to get out of this world.' But they could not find a hole anywhere nor any way to get out. They were frightened and thought they would all die there. But the Spider Woman wove a web on the surface of the water. It floated like a raft and all the people got out and sat upon it. They were puzzled what to do. Hostjaishjine picked up his Peshhath (stone knife) and began to bore a hole in the roof over them. It was of clay which dropped and crumbled and when he could go no farther he called Wunustcinde to try, who soon bored a small hole through and came out upon the new world, but the water coming up through the hole which he had made was like to flood the new world also, so he stopped the hole up with mud.

No one saw him there as yet. Then he saw the water rising up from east, south, west, and north. He made the noise with his thorax. He saw a swan on the south side making much noise and the water was all in motion. Wunustcinde made such noise that the swan from the east, also one from the north and one from the west came to him. All four came to him but did not know what to think of him. They asked him where he came from. He told them from the world below. They would not believe him so he told them how he had come. The swans told him that neither he nor his people should come to this new place for it belonged to the swans only, and they would not let anyone else live here. Wunustcinde had a hard time with the swans, and they fought him. Finally they said, 'If you want to stay here you must pay us.' So Wunustcinde returned to his people and told them all this. Wunustcinde had the red substance that causes the sun to set red when it is going to storm and he offered this to the swans for their land. They put it on their wings and were so much pleased with it they said, 'Well now, you can come and live here.' Wunustcinde said to them that some of his people could not live in the water, although some of them could. Then the swans said that after four days there would be some dry land. The swans had pots of clay and they placed one on the east side, one on the north side, one on the west side and in this way they carried off some of the water, and made some dry land. When the others came up to the new world they built little round houses again of the same red substance that had been given to the swans.

First Man made a man called Hosjelti and placed him on San Francisco Mountain; another called Hosjogwan who lives on Ute Mountains; another called Navesrhuni (Nagenezgruni) who lives on Navajo Mountain; another called Hokhjtshjine who lives on San Mateo Mountain. These four own all the game and other animals on these mountains. Old Man's people however lived close together. They took the earth gathered from the four mountains in the lower world and again they formed mountains as in lower world, at east, white; at south, blue; at west, yellow; at north, black. No one was allowed to see the boys who were found at the spring; they were left at the Ute Mountains when the people first came up. Old Man had brought seeds of all kinds with him and planted everything that grows, vegetables, plants, timber, sagebrush, flowers, everything. He found lots of people here who joined him. That was when bears, deer, antelope, rabbit, birds, all kinds of animals were people.

They made a white blanket for sunrise over Ute Mountains, east; a blue blanket for the south, sky, over San Mateo Mountain, south; a yellow blanket for sunset over San Francisco Mountain, west; a black blanket for Navajo Mountain, north. There had been neither day nor night in the lower world, only sufficient light for existence. Old Man now said, 'Let us arrange to have day and night, a time for work and a time for sleep,' and so we see it is today just before sunrise comes a white streak in the east. Then the yellow of sunset and the white of the east meet in the middle so as to give light enough to work. And when the blue and the black meet in the middle this way it makes night, the time for sleep.

Then Old Man and Old Woman said, 'We have nobody to talk to about ourselves (to worship us).' Old Man went off to the east to find people, for some as soon as they reached the upper world went toward the east. Old Man followed after these, and from east they brought back eagle feathers; from west, hawk feathers; from south, blue feathers; from north, speckled feathers (of whip-poor-will, night bird). When they got these altogether they laid them before them. Beside east feather they laid white corn and white shell; beside west feather, yellow corn and abalone shell; beside south feather, blue corn, and turquoise; beside north feather, all kinds of corn and shells and turquoise. All four were laid out together. Old Man arranged all these for singing and praying to these things as he did at the spring, singing and praying. He and Old Woman and all his people moved about walking over these things several times in ceremonial manner.

East feather was for the wolf. The feather and corn and shell were prayed over and Wolf was raised. They prayed over the west objects, and Mountain Lion was raised; they prayed over the south objects and Tabastin, Otter, was raised; they prayed over the north objects, Bud Beaver was raised. Old Man said, 'We need rulers,' and he made these four rulers over these several regions. He planted all vegetable things and sprinkled them with the earth of the four mountains to give them power. These mountains had much wild tobacco growing on them. The four animals were the rulers of all the land. They smoked and felt good and began to teach the people to be farmers, to plant corn, wheat, melons, pumpkins, beans, chile, etc. and how to irrigate and take care of their crops. All four (animals) taught the people to use all kinds of grasses, timber, etc.

Old Man and Old Woman again talked about how they should get some more people, and they worked hard and made people. Joshdelhashi assisted them. She rubbed down the skin on her arms, and put the roll of cuticle on the ground, and it became a man. (Repeat for various parts of the body, as in the first world, until twelve people are made).

They made six men and six women, and the offspring of these twelve people are all pueblo Indians, Moki, Oraibi, Zuni, etc. men who cut their hair across the front of the face. When the white streak of daylight, the white of the east, met the yellow of sunset in mid heavens, and after they had each returned to their place (as they do daily) the white of the east had offspring which was Coyote, and the yellow of the west a yellow fox. The blue and black met in mid heaven and returning had issue the blue, a blue fox, and the black, a badger. On the east side is Coyote; on the west, Yellow Fox; on the south, Blue Fox; on the north, Badger.

The Coyote of the east came where the people were and asked Old Man where he came from. Old Man told him from three worlds down below and also told Coyote how he came up, also saying 'If you (Coyote) are a clever man, I will teach you all we know about our religion, etc.' So he taught him everything. Coyote got to know a great deal, and he went off to the Ute Mountains and got on the summit and commenced howling and making all sorts of noises.

Old Man had Guardian Wind and Wind went to Coyote and asked him what he was yelling about, and Coyote said, 'It is none of your business.' Coyote said he belonged to Old Man and had learned how to do everything, and that no roaring of the wind could frighten him.

Wind said, 'Keep on then, see if Old Man will not make a living without (after) you.'

Coyote said, 'He will have to do more than he has been doing then.' Coyote went back to Old Man and told him lies about the wind.

Blue and Yellow Foxes went together to the pueblos and belong to them. Coyote and Badger belong to the Navajos, but Great Wolf was the chief (ruler) of the whole. He gets up at daybreak, stands in the midst of the people's dwellings and calls to the people to go to work in the fields. He advises them to get early to work planting corn, gardening and irrigating.

He had a very smart woman for a wife and they had two children. After a time this woman made herself three small sticks for gambling and would go off all day long and leave the children helpless. Late in the afternoon Wolf chief, the man, came home and saw the state of the hogan, untidy, and one of the children lying in the ashes of the fireplace. He did not try to clean up for he was very tired and lay down. At sunset his wife came back with her sticks but she had gambled away everything she had. Then the husband expostulated with her on her conduct. She replied tartly that he could stay and take care of the hogan and children as he had nothing to do. He said he provided food, etc. but she was quarrelsome and continued scolding (like the Navaho women today!). She told her husband she could take care of herself and so continued scolding, etc. until time for the Corn dance. She carried off the corn to grind and make mush for the dance although her own children were crying with hunger. Finally she told her husband to go off and she could easily find another. She said she could do without assistance. The husband avoided replying to her and said nothing. He lay still all night feeling bad about her. In the morning he did not know what to do. He took his bow and arrow and walked off. Shortly he found some meat in the woods on a tree and he took some and ate it raw. That is why Wolf eats raw meat. He stole this meat (for it belonged to the second chief) but it was by reason of the trouble with his wife and he was muddled. At sunset he returned, said not a word to his wife, nor to his people who came to see him. In the night all his people came to see him for they thought he was sick. On the second night he said nothing, and next morning he would say nothing.

The third chief came to see him, 'Come out and do some work,' said he. No answer. On the third night it was the same. On the fourth day the fourth chief called on him, still no result.

On the fifth night the three chiefs met together and said, 'Let us go to First Chief's house and speak to him.' So they went and said to him, 'We called the people to work but they idle and gamble in the fields. Come into the house (lodge) and examine each separately, and find out who has spoken a bad word of you, our Chief,' but they could find no one who had done so. Then they called in all the women to the lodge to find if any of them had given offence to the chief, still they found no one; by this time it was nearly daylight. Still the chief would say nothing. The women said there was none of them guilty. This was at daylight. 'Who is the man? No man nor woman caused his trouble but the woman he was living with.'

On the sixth night the chief said, 'I will speak a few words to you, and tomorrow I will go out to the fields.' He went out and saw the crops neglected and weeds growing. On the following night he called the men into his house and they all assembled. He said 'I am sorry. My wife alone is to blame, but every woman you have is liable to do the same as mine has done. Let them go and try to make a living for themselves and see how they like that. There is a wide, deep river, without a ford. Let us (men) find means to cross it, and leave all the women behind. Every man must leave his wife.'

Most of them felt sorry, and some said, 'What will we do in the case of a nursing boy baby, shall we take him away from his mother? How about Nutlys, berdaches? They also like to gamble with the women. Let us see what the berdaches say?' The berdaches were the last to come in. They scratched the ground with a stick a long time trying to make up their minds. They did not care to go with the women, and what could they do? Finally they said, 'We will go with the men.'

'Very well,' the men said, 'That is good, but you must take your own food with you.' The men asked them also, 'Have you your own grinding stones, pots, dippers, mush sticks, brushes, are all these your own?'

'Yes, by my own hands.'

'All right,' the men said, 'we will take one berdache with us to cook for us.'

The chief told the men to get ready to cross the river that day. They got ready to go. They had plenty of corn and all kinds of food, but he said, 'We must go without anything, only a few kernels for seed.' The berdache took along everything. Rafts were made and preparations completed. Best hunters crossed first so that if they should find any antelope with milk they might bring it back for the children. The berdache remained behind (at the camp after crossing the river) and ground some corn and made a little mush for the children, and the hunters were to come back in the middle of the day with meat and milk. The hunters brought back deer and antelope but many did not feel like eating as they had just parted from their wives. All the men sat up during the night to talk about their trouble.

Finally they said, 'Let us go to work,' and they began cutting trees for houses.

The women camped on the opposite river bank and held out their privates where the men could see them, calling out to them, 'How would you like to have some?' etc. trying to tantalise them and entice them back. The hunters went out again and some cleared the ground for planting. At that time they had only stone implements for axes and broad sticks for hoes. The second night they camped out again and some brought in deer and antelope and they were better off than before. The fourth night they were all contented, they had plenty of game and food. The little children began to be contented as they grew accustomed to their separation from their mothers. The women camped on the river bank, and ground corn constantly in sight of the men on the opposite bank. The houses were strung along as the mealing stones were arranged. They had some square houses too, but these belonged to the Pueblo Indians. The men became quite indifferent to the women, but the women were becoming restless with increasing amatory desires. Four years this separation continued, and as the men had left plenty of corn and food of all kinds with the women they did not suffer much until the end of this time. By that time however, the fields had become overgrown with sagebrush and cottonwood as the women had planted nothing. Then they had to gather up bones and boil them for all their possessions were exhausted and they suffered greatly. Badger (of the north) wanted to copulate with the women but he had a bad penis, crooked like a hook. The first one he tried was Joshdelhashi, then all the others. It made them crazy and they went wild with desire to copulate continually. Some of them took a corn cob wrapped with any soft substance and continually performed the sexual act artificially. Some tried to swim the river to get to the men but were drowned. Some died crazy with wild desire. This and lack of food caused the death of most of the women. Coyote, Blue Fox, Yellow Fox and Badger copulated with the women continually, and licked the women between the legs. That is why dogs and these animals lick each other that way.

On the other side of the river, the children had grown up so that all could work. They had plenty of food as there were no idlers to consume it. When they killed an antelope they cut out the liver and made a hole in it and artificially performed the sexual act. Some who could overtake a doe would copulate with it, but these lightning struck and burst open. Some in like manner with an antelope doe, and the rattlesnake bit and killed them. Another man would do likewise with mountain sheep and a bear killed him.

Kideztizi was out hunting till late and as he could not reach home he camped. He lay down before the fire with a piece of liver in his hand, warming his penis to cause an erection. Nastja (owl) lit on branch above him and hooting called 'Kideztizi, don't f— that liver,' and then flew away:

Another owl came from the same direction and lit crying 'You go on and do so if you wish.' He acted on the last suggestion and then went to sleep.

Very few women were left alive, but the men remained strong and well. The men came together one night and began to talk about the women and asked the chief what he thought ought to be done. Most of the men said, 'We are here without women and when we begin to die we shall disappear very fast as we have no increase.'

They talked four nights and then the chief said, 'One of you might go across the river and see how many of the women are left. Look for the woman who caused trouble and if she is dead, all will be well.' She was found alive but could hardly lift her head. Scarcely any flesh remained on her bones and she defecated where she lay. All the four chiefs went over to see her. As the head chief went into his old house where she had abused him, she seized him, but he jerked away from her, and then she began to talk to him. She wept with sorrow and repentance, and acknowledged that she was unable to live alone as she had once thought. All the women came and begged piteously. But the men would not touch them for they all smelled bad, like coyotes.

The chiefs all returned across the river to discuss the matter. Most of them thought that they might as well keep the few women remaining, or else the race would disappear. The men had one berdache among them and they decided to leave the question to his decision. He said he was content to have the women come across because he was tired of cooking for them all. He said, 'The best you can do is to bring these women over.' He made a lot of small boats (rafts) and brought the women across in two days. After the women were brought over the men would give them nothing to eat for they smelled bad, and they put them in the sweat houses and gave them herbs to make them vomit. Some of the women ate too much and it killed them. On the fourth night the sweating ceremonies were over, and the women were fed. They grew fat and healthy again. Those whose wives had died became jealous of those whose wives rejoined them. This jealousy spread, and it has always continued. At the end of four years the young girls had grown fit for wives and those who had none took these. At the end of these four years they came from the east and crossed the mountains.

A long time before this when Teholtsody left, he built a house under the water upon the bottom of the river, and no one had seen him since. At night the cries of a baby were heard from the water house and Coyote tried to get the baby but failed. He went to Old Man and told him, and Old Man said, 'Go to the Spider Woman.' Spider Woman spun a web which spread over the river to the place where the house was beneath the water, and she got the baby and hid it away so that Teholtsody could not find the child. He is sad to this day because of the loss of the child. He is everybody's friend. Spider Woman took the baby and wrapped it in the web and placed it under her left arm and no one can find it to this day. Teholtsody being unable to find the baby grew crazy and said he would keep on killing everyone he met until he found this child. Being very angry he opened the earth at four corners and let the waters loose, and the rise of the water brought the people together and they saw the waters come up and out of the earth like the clouds and they could not understand it. Then they prayed for the winds, and they came up.

White Wind being quick went to the east, Blue to the south, Yellow to west, and Black to the north, and they returned and said, 'You are going to be drowned, for great bodies of water are coming together.' Then one went to East Mountain to get some earth, one to San Francisco Mt, west; one to Navajo Mt, north; and one to San Mateo Mt, east. They brought earth from all these. When Old Man left the lower world, Old Woman brought the springs up with her under her arm.

Coyote Makes Songs for the Hills

Long ago Coyote said that the mountains had prayers and songs and that all the Indians ought to pray to the big peaks and the little peaks. That is why the Indians pray to the mountains, to mountains like San Francisco mountain. 'You must remember what I say,' said Coyote to the Indians, 'if you don't remember, something will happen to you.' So all the Indians prayed to the mountains and to the hills. Coyote made songs for the hills.

All this was not true, Coyote was just saying it, and he was just laughing at them. So they caught Coyote and hung him up. In the morning they turned Coyote loose in the house and he jumped through a little hole and ran off. They followed his tracks. Coyote ran into a rabbit hole where there were four rabbits. He caught them. The men who ran after him started to dig out the hole to get him. The men got tired digging and Coyote let one rabbit out from the hole and the people started to chase it. Then they came back to the hole to dig. Coyote let out another rabbit, and they started after it. Then Coyote jumped out of the hole and ran away. That's all.

Coyote Burns Up Her Children

Long ago Coyote was running through the forests and she met Deer and her little deers. Coyote said to Deer, 'What pretty little ones you have got. What makes your little deers so pretty?' she asked.

Deer said to her, 'I keep them in a hole, and I build a fire right beside the hole, and the fire scorches them and makes them pretty.' So Coyote went off and put her little coyotes into a hole and built a fire beside the hole. She thought she could make the little coyotes pretty by scorching them; but she burned up the little coyotes. That is all.

Mock Plea

One time Coyote wanted to catch Rabbit; but Rabbit was in the brush and Coyote did not know how he was going to catch him. Rabbit ran off, he found a hole through a rock and there he sat in the middle of the hole. Coyote said to him, 'I know how I am going to get you, Rabbit. I am going to get some green wood and build a fire, and the smoke will kill you,' Coyote said to Rabbit.

'That is just what I would like,' Rabbit said to Coyote.

'Well,' said Coyote, 'then I'll get some gum from pinon wood and build a fire in front of your hole and the smoke will kill you.'

'That is just what I would not like,' Rabbit said to Coyote. Then Coyote went and got some pinon gum and built a fire.

Rabbit peeked out and he saw that the gum was hot enough, and he said, 'Friend Coyote, blow it a little closer. I am about to die.' So Coyote blew it closer and Rabbit kicked the gum right into Coyote's face and Coyote's face and eyes were all burned. And Rabbit ran off.

Coyote at the River

Coyote was walking along, he was walking by the river. He saw scha (Chaparral Cock) in the wash, close to the water. Chaparral Cock was asleep. Coyote thought that he would carry him a long way off where there was no water. So on his back he carried Chaparral Cock a long way off to where there was no water. Then Coyote woke up Chaparral Cock and said to him, 'Nephew, I have never seen you this far from water before.'

Chaparral Cock was now awake and he said to Coyote, 'Nephew, please take me back to the water.'

Coyote said, 'No, I cannot take you back to the water, because I must go back to see my poor little children.' Then Coyote ran off, and poor Chaparral Cock crawled around trying to go back to the water. Finally he reached the water. After that he saw Coyote lying down beside the river. Chaparral Cock thought that he would carry Coyote way out into the river. Then he carried him far out into the middle of the river and there he threw him off into the water. He was right under Coyote. Coyote said to him, 'Please, Nephew, carry me out of the water.'

'No,' said Chaparral Cock to Coyote, 'You played a trick on me before.' So Coyote drowned.

Coyote Sets Fire to the Earth

Long ago Coyote was going along and he saw some children. While he was watching them, their mother went out. Coyote went up to the children and asked them where they got their matches to make their fire. He heard that they had a rock to make fire with. So he told the children that he wanted some matches. He told the children to cry so that their mother would come back, and to keep on crying out that Coyote wanted some matches. So the children began to cry, and their mother came back. She told them not to cry. But they kept on crying, saying that Coyote wanted some matches. So she gave some matches to Coyote. Then Coyote ran off and struck the rock on a big rock. There was a big spark. It started a fire, and the fire began to burn up the earth. Lots of people ran out crying; they ran out to the mountains. Coyote ran along and told people that they were in danger. Some of the people climbed the mountains and there they were safe. That is all.

Coyote Plays Dead

Long ago Coyote was walking along. The sun was hot and Coyote felt lazy as he walked along. He said to himself, 'I wish there was a little rain to wet my feet.' He said again, 'I wish the water would wet my belly as I walk along. I wish my arse would stick out as I walk along. I wish the water would carry me where there are lots of prairie dogs.' Then it rained and the water carried him where there were lots of prairie dogs. As he was lying there asleep, Wildcat came by and saw him and thought he was dead. Then Coyote woke up and said to Wildcat, 'My nephew, I want you to go and tell the prairie dogs that Coyote lies dead by the river.' So Wildcat went out into the field and hollered out that Coyote was lying dead over by the river. So the prairie dogs and the rabbits and the jack rabbits, lots of them, all assembled over where Coyote was lying. And they all danced around Coyote, saying that Coyote had died. Some of them danced on top of him.

Up jumped Coyote and killed lots of prairie dogs. And Coyote and Wildcat each got a stick and killed lots of rabbits and jack rabbits. Some jack rabbits escaped. Then Coyote and Wildcat dug a hole and built a fire and cooked the prairie dogs in the embers. After they were nearly cooked Coyote said to Wildcat, 'Nephew, I want you and me to have a race. The last to come in will have the smallest prairie dogs to eat.' Coyote told Wildcat to go on ahead, and Wildcat went on. He came to a big hole and went into it. Coyote was running behind him with a big smoke on the end of his tail. Coyote ran on, and Wildcat went back. Wildcat took out all the largest prairie dogs for himself and left only the smallest prairie dogs for Coyote. Then Wildcat carried the largest prairie dogs up a tree. Finally Coyote came back, he lay down in the shade and said to himself, 'Poor Nephew, I wonder where he is by now.' And he went to take out the prairie dogs; but there were only the smallest of the prairie dogs. Coyote was angry, he said, 'I know who took all of the biggest prairie dogs.' He found Wildcat's tracks and followed them up to the tree where Wildcat was eating the dogs. Coyote said to Wildcat, 'Please, Nephew, give me some prairie dogs. I have only the smallest ones.'

'No,' said Wildcat, 'I will not give you any of the big prairie dogs.' And he ate all the biggest, and Coyote ate all the smallest.

And Coyote kept on saying, 'Please, Nephew, give me some of the big prairie dogs.' He kept on begging for them, but he could not get any from Wildcat. Coyote thought he could fool Wildcat, but he himself was fooled.

Coyote Invites Wildcat to Eat

Long ago Coyote was up to lots of tricks. After Turtle killed Coyote, Coyote got up again. As he was going along he met Wildcat and Wildcat was asleep. While Wildcat was sleeping, Coyote cut out from Wildcat his lights, and made a fire and cooked Wildcat's lights. Then Coyote woke up Wildcat and invited him to eat. As Wildcat was eating, Coyote was laughing, he was just laughing. Finally he said to Wildcat, 'You have eaten your own lights,' Coyote said to him, and he ran off.

Wildcat was angry. He said to himself that he would do just the same to Coyote. So he followed Coyote. Coyote went way off into the hills and lay down, and he was asleep when Wildcat got there. While Coyote was sleeping, Wildcat cut out from him his lights. Besides Wildcat pulled Coyote's nose; that is why Coyote has a long nose. And Wildcat pulled Coyote's tail; that is why Coyote has a long tail. So Wildcat cut out the lights and made a fire and cooked, and then waked up Coyote and invited him to eat. 'You have eaten your own lights,' said Wildcat to Coyote. And Coyote was angry, and Wildcat ran away. That is all.

Coyote and Wildcat Scratch Each Other

Long ago Coyote and Wildcat were walking along together. Pretty soon they halted. Coyote had long claws and he showed them to Wildcat. Wildcat showed his paws to Coyote; but he drew in his claws. Coyote said to Wildcat, 'Let's scratch each other.'

'All right,' said Wildcat to Coyote.

Coyote said, 'Let me be the first to scratch.'

'All right,' said Wildcat. So he stood behind, for Coyote to scratch him. So Coyote scratched him, but he did not scratch him very hard. Then it was Wildcat's turn to scratch. Coyote stood behind Wildcat, and Wildcat scratched Coyote, he scratched off all the skin from Coyote. Coyote cried, and Wildcat ran off.

Coyote went on, and pretty soon he met a bird hopping along. Coyote was very hungry, he was trying to get something to eat, he was trying in every way he could to get something to eat. So there was this bird hopping along. Coyote said to himself that he would catch that bird. The bird hopped on to a bush, and he was sitting there. On one side of the bush there was a big hole filled with water. Coyote wanted very badly to catch that bird, so he jumped at him as high as he could. Up flew the bird and Coyote fell into the hole and was drowned. That was the end of him.

Origin of the Manygoats Clan

Alk'idaa' (A long time ago), there lived this family on the reservation. They lived in this valley with family members living close by. There was a young maiden about twelve years old. She arose in the morning and headed to the sheep corral to let the sheep out and then herd them down into the valley for grazing. As she opened the gate for the sheep to exit, she heard some horses galloping. She turned around and found herself face to face with a Ute war party. Not saying a word, she ran but was soon captured. They gagged her and tied her arms, tears filled her eyes as she watched her home fade into the far distance.

She was made a slave. The head warrior claimed her as a prize for the raid. She spent her days performing household chores, manual labour in the field, and tending to the sheep. She enjoyed caring for the flock because it reminded her of home. She had her attempts to escape, but the land was so foreign to her, considering that they blindfolded her after she left familiar territory. Her adjustment period went by, and she found her schedule keeping her mind off escaping. She was also put on watch.

So many years passed, and she grew into a young woman. Her duties always called on her, but she remained close to the flock. The local women of the band would make fun of her. They named her 'Manygoats girl.' She accepted the name without any retaliation and was dedicated to her work. Being close to the flock always kept that hope that she would return home where she belonged.

The years passed and the young lady blossomed into a beautiful woman. The women began to admire her and offered her things such as dresses and ornaments of Ute affiliation. She accepted the gifts, but she always dressed in Navajo attire, that of her mother. Just as she was attracting the attention from the female population, the eyes of eligible bachelors began to wander.

The man who took her as a slave through the years began to see her more as a family member. He had realised the attention she was receiving and decided to marry her off. She honoured his wishes and she soon found herself married. She found herself enjoying the next few years but always thought of her family back home.

She became pregnant and gave birth to a lovely daughter. At first there was some friction in what the daughter would grow to be. A Navajo? Or a Ute? But being that the Ute's were a matrilineal society, they decided that she belonged to her mother's people. As so she began to learn the ways of the Navajo People. With the passing of time, she had more children.

After a considerable amount of time, the grown woman wanted to return to her people. Out of the blue, she announced her decision. There was no intention of forcing her to stay and her husband was supporting her decision. And so, she left with her family and headed home.

Upon arriving home, she found that over the years only her mother had survived the years. She spent what time was left with her mother. Her children had some trouble with the adjustments of being half Navajo and half Ute. The Utes were still considered to be enemies of the Navajo People. They received constant badgering from other Navajo children and life wasn't easy for them. But with the following years, they found their place and dwelled in the valley their mother grew up in.

Many years went by and the woman carried the name that the Ute's bestowed upon her. Her family automatically inherited the version the 'Manygoats clan'. And so, that is how the Manygoats came to be.

CHAPTER 21

Ojibwa

An Adventure of Wenabuzu

Wenabuzu was living with his grandmother. While hunting in the woods for his grandmother, he thought about his mother, so he concluded to ask his grandmother. When he returned home from hunting, after he had eaten his supper of venison, he asked his grandmother, 'Where is my mother? Whatever became of my mother?'

'My grandson, some enemy came and took your mother away, and murdered her. This enemy lives far off. He lives on an island in a great big lake. It is almost impossible to reach him. Eventually he will murder you if you ever reach him. I therefore advise you not to go.'

So when Wenabuzu went out hunting again the next day he thought over the matter of going to war with this man. He was now getting to manhood. He was quite a young man. He therefore asked his grandmother how to reach this enemy. So his grandmother gave him instructions how to reach this place. 'The first thing to do is to make a canoe of birch bark, and sew it with cedar roots, and pitch it with pine pitch. And then go on the lake. Get some fish that have a lot of oil in them.'

Well, he went according to the directions of his grandmother. The grandmother made oil from this fish. So he started with this oil in his canoe. When he had gone quite a ways off, and reached the island where the enemy lived, then the water began to turn into pitch while he was paddling. So he took his oil. He began to oil his paddle and his canoe. Finally he got through this pitchy water.

When he got to the shore, there were a lot of birds there, and squirrels. All the birds and animals which he saw on the island belonged to this man, the enemy. They were already to make known to the man that an enemy had come on shore. Wenabuzu prevailed on them; for Wenabuzu had power to talk to those animals, those birds. So he went up to the wigwam. It just happened that the man was not at home. In the meanwhile, while he was waiting for him, he took his pipe and began to smoke; and he examined the wigwam inside. He found his enemy's bows. These were twelve in number. He noticed there was a little bird there. It was a chickadee. Wenabuzu asked the chickadee which was the best bow in the whole lot. The chickadee showed him three or four bows, telling him that these bows were used for war. 'If you battle with him, he will be bound to get one of those bows.'

As a reward to the chickadee Wenabuzu painted him. Then the man came; the enemy came. Wenabuzu got up, introduced himself, telling him he came on a friendly visit. Then they smoked their pipes, telling stories to one another. Wenabuzu, during the absence of his enemy, made arrangements with the owl to come hooting around there in the morning, promising the owl, 'If I succeed in beating him, I will liberate you all, so you can go anywhere you wish.'

Just at daybreak in the morning, the owl came hooting there. Wenabuzu jumped up with his arrows, ran out. His enemy followed right after him. Wenabuzu turned around and shot his enemy. The enemy returned the shot. They had a battle all day. Wenabuzu shot this man all over, endeavouring to find out where the seat of his life was. Just at sundown he shot him on one of the braids of his hair (this man had very long hair). He killed him instantly. After he killed this man, he looked all over the house, the wigwam. Then he found the scalp of his mother. After he liberated all the animals that had been kept there, then he returned back to his grandmother. Then the old grandmother prepared a feast. They had a dance, which they call a scalp dance, because he had brought a scalp to his grandmother. This was Wenabuzu's first war path.

CHAPTER 22

Papago

Montezuma

Long ago, so it is said, another people lived in this country, whose chief was named Montezuma. At that time all people spoke the same language; in fact, everything was able to speak, and Elder Brother caused the rain to fall, and fed all the people. He planted some food plants, chia and flax seed and choya, many different kinds of seeds. And Chief Montezuma always took good care of his people.

But there came a time when he treated them badly and killed them. The chief sent pain upon them, with which he killed his people. When they learned that it was Montezuma who had done this, they all set out, and went to his house and killed him. Then they returned to their homes. Four days later one of them went again to Montezuma's house, and was astounded to see him sitting there. He found that Montezuma had come to life again. So he returned home, and told his people that Montezuma had revived. 'He is sitting right there,' he told them. Then the old leader told his people that they must go and kill Montezuma again. Again they set out, and came to Montezuma's house, and were surprised to see him sitting there. Again they killed him. They cut up his body, and mixed his flesh with earth. They pounded it all to bits, and his bones they likewise pounded up, and mixed with earth and scattered. Then they left him and went home.

Four days passed, and again one of the people went to Montezuma's house. And there he sat! He had revived again. Again the man went home, and told the people that Montezuma had come to life again. Then said the leader, 'We must again prepare, and go and kill him again.' So they got ready, and again went to Montezuma's house. There, indeed, he was sitting. Surprised as they were, they again killed him, and cut him up; but this time they cooked the flesh until it fell to pieces. They took it out and tore it into little bits, and scattered them far and wide. Then again they went home.

Again four days passed, and someone happened to go by Montezuma's house. And there he sat! Astounded at the sight, he returned home, and told the people that Montezuma had revived again. Then said the chief, 'What can we do to kill him so that he will not come to life again?'

Then the people from all parts held a great council, and debated the matter. 'How can we kill this Montezuma so that he will never again come to life? By what means shall we kill him so that he will not revive?'

'You must immediately take council with one another, and possibly you will find some way by which we can kill this Montezuma so that he will never again come to life.' Thus said the old chief.

Then said some of the people, 'We will tell Yellow Buzzard, who has the iron bow. Possibly, if he kills him with that, he will not revive.'

'All right!' said the chief. 'It may be true, that, if he is killed with the iron bow, he will not come to life again.' So said the chief.

And the people also said, 'It is well that we should tell the one up there.' This they all agreed.

And the chief said, 'Go, one of you, and tell him to come here to my house, that I may smoke with him. Thus will you tell Yellow Buzzard.' So one of them ran and told him that the chief had sent for him.

Then said Yellow Buzzard, 'All right! I'll go there. Run ahead!' Thus said Yellow Buzzard. So the man ran home to his house, and told the chief that he would come.

Then said the chief, 'All right! I'll wait for him.' At last Yellow Buzzard arrived there, and the people all smoked together. Then the chief said, 'I will tell you why we have sent for you, Yellow Buzzard.' Thus said the chief.

'I did so because Montezuma is killing us off. And you, Yellow Buzzard, have the iron bow, with which you may kill him so that he will never again come to life. For that reason I sent for you.'

Then said Yellow Buzzard, 'All right! I will do as you have said.' Thus said Yellow Buzzard. Then the chief said, 'Four days from now you must be ready, and come here. And then you will go and kill Montezuma.'

Then said Yellow Buzzard, 'I will come on the day that you name. On that day look for me, and I will come.' Thus spoke Yellow Buzzard.

'Good!' said the chief. 'You people must also all be ready when Yellow Buzzard arrives.' Thus did he say to the people. Then Yellow Buzzard went back to his home.

Four days passed, and Yellow Buzzard arrived. The people also sat ready, and they went over to Montezuma's house. And when they came to it, there he sat! Then Yellow Buzzard sat down and seized his iron bow. Carefully he took aim, and shot and killed Montezuma. Then they all went home. Then said Yellow Buzzard, 'Now I have killed Montezuma! Four days from now one of us will go there to look at him. Perhaps he will not come to life, as before; but if he should revive again, come up and tell me, and I will kill him again.'

Thus spoke Yellow-Buzzard. 'It is well,' said he, and Yellow Buzzard went home. And when four days had gone one of the people went to the house of Montezuma. He was surprised to see that Montezuma had not revived, as before. There he still lay. So he returned home, and told the chief that Montezuma had not come to life, but still lay there. Thus did he tell the Chief.

Then said the chief, 'It is well; possibly he will never revive as before.' And truly he did not come to life for four years.

For four years Montezuma lay there dead, though before he would have come to life the next day; but after four years he rose again, and ascended, and travelled with the sun, for he was offended at his people. He decided to send sickness upon them, and kill them all. Four years he remained with the sun; and during that time he gathered every feather which he found, eagle feathers and all other kinds. When he had collected a great bundle of them, he burned them, and kept the ashes. Then he roasted a little corn, and ground it on the metate with the ashes. He filled a little basket with the feather pinole. Then he made a man; and when it was noon, he sent him down with the pinole to a large village, instructing him what to do when he met the inhabitants.

The man whom Montezuma had made came down from the sun, and took his stand by the pond where the people of the village got their water. Soon some women came to get water. 'Are all the men at home?' he asked them, and they replied that they were. 'Send one of them over to see me,' he said. 'I wish to talk with one before I go back.' The women then went back, and told one of the men that they had met a stranger at the pond who was anxious to return, and wanted someone to go and talk with him immediately. So the man went over, and saw Montezuma's man sitting at the edge of the pond. 'Before I talk to you,' said the latter, 'I'll mix you some pinole, so that you may drink first.' He then mixed some of the pinole, and gave it to the man to drink. And when he had drunk it, he felt a pain in his stomach, and a desire to shake himself; but when he did so, little spots broke out all over his body. 'I'll mix you some more,' said Montezuma's man; and when the other had drunk the second time, he shook himself again, and feathers began to come out all over his body. A third time he did the same, and the feathers came out a little stronger. The fourth time the remainder of the pinole was mixed; and when he had drunk it and shaken himself, the feathers grew out long over his entire body. Then Montezuma's man said, 'That is what I came here for, to give you this pinole,' and he rose up and went off. Going to the same place where he had reached earth, he ascended again to the sun.

The man who had drunk the pinole was left alone at the side of the pond; and every once in a while he shook himself, and the feathers came out more strongly. He was ashamed to return home and see the people. In the village all the men were waiting for him to return, and tell them what the stranger had said. One of the chiefs climbed up on his house top, and told all the people to come out and hear what he would report. 'After he reports,' he said, 'we are all going out to hunt rabbits.'

Now it was getting late, nearing noon; and the chief said, 'I wonder why he doesn't come! It is getting very late, and we won't kill any rabbits!' So he sent out a man to see what was keeping the other so long by the pond; but when the messenger neared the pond, he saw only a great eagle standing by the shore, shaking his wings. So he went back to the chief, and said to him, 'There is something strange at the pond, so I didn't go over there to see about the man.'

But the chief said to the people, 'It isn't true! This man is just lying.' And he sent another man. But when the second man neared the pond, he also saw the eagle sitting at the edge; and he likewise returned, and told the chief that there was a large bird at the pond, so he didn't go closer, but came back. Four times the chief sent different men; and each time they returned, and told him that it was true that something strange was at the pond.

Then said the chief, 'Well, if it is true, get ready, all of you, and we will go out and kill this strange thing.' Then all the people started out with their weapons, and came close to the pond. 'Some of you go to this side, and some to that,' said the chief, 'so that we may be sure of killing it.' But when they came close to him, the eagle rose up, flying so low, that the people ran along under him, and tried to shoot him with their bows and arrows. But the eagle at last left them behind, and came to a big tree, where he thought he would rest a while. But the tree broke down with his weight, and he had to rest on the ground; and while he was resting, the people came up again, and began to shoot at him. Again he flew away, so swiftly that the people lost sight of him, and ceased the pursuit; but they still tried to find out where he had gone. He flew away to a steep mountain which had perpendicular sides, like a mesa. When he first rested on it, it shook for a little while, but finally quieted. Here he made his nest. Every morning he would sally forth in pursuit of game – deer, antelope, rabbits, or anything he could kill.

Now, at this time Montezuma was not alive. It was his spirit which had ascended to the sun, but his bones were still lying where Yellow Buzzard had killed him. And every day the children played with them. One morning they went out to play near his bones, and were terrified to see him sitting up alive. So he lived among his people again, and they treated him well; but they feared him because of his powerful magic, with which he could work them much harm. When he came around visiting, they were much afraid of him, and did not like to have him go among the houses.

Now the great eagle which Montezuma's spirit had sent down was killing all the animals, and exterminating the deer and rabbits, and it was very difficult for one to get any food. So Montezuma thought it would be a good plan to let the eagle kill some of the people, so that he might then rid them of the monster and earn their confidence and gratitude, so they would no longer fear him. So at last the eagle could find nothing more to eat, and went to the village, and, catching a man, carried him to his cave and ate him. Then the people were greatly disturbed; and the chief called a council, and said, 'What are we going to do? This eagle will eat us all up!'

And someone said, 'We had better consult Montezuma about it; he may have some means of killing the eagle.'

So the chief sent a man to call Montezuma to the meeting; and when the messenger came to his house, he said to Montezuma, 'The chief wants you to go down to the meeting and hear him speak about a certain matter.'

'Very well,' said Montezuma, 'I'll be down there in about four days.' So the chief told all the people to gather at the council in four days to hear what Montezuma would propose. When the four days had passed, all the men gathered at the chief's house in the evening; and they sat up all night waiting for Montezuma, who never came. So in the morning the chief sent another man to his house, but Montezuma told him the same as he had told the first one; but he did not mean days, he meant years. 'After four years I'll be down there.' So the chief kept on sending men, but Montezuma always replied the same. And all the time the great eagle was continuing to eat the people, one or two every day. He even took a girl, but did not kill her; he kept her for his wife.

At last the four years had passed, and Montezuma went down to the chief's council. 'Please do all you can to kill the eagle,' said the chief, 'or else he'll eat us all up.'

And Montezuma replied, 'Very well, I'll do all I can to kill him.' He asked the people to gather him some reeds, and with these and his great machete he started off. He came to the foot of the steep mountain, and sang a song. Then he stuck one of the reeds in the side of the mountain, where it remained. Pulling himself up by means of this, he stuck in another; and after repeating the process ten times, he reached the top of the rock. The eagle was out hunting; so Montezuma went into the cave, and saw there the wife with a year-old baby. When she saw Montezuma standing at the door, she asked, 'How did you get here? I didn't think that anyone could come here alive, because the eagle is killing everyone.'

Then Montezuma replied, 'I came up some way to ask you when the eagle will be back.'

'He'll be back in the middle of the day,' she said. Then Montezuma told her that he had come there to kill the eagle, and asked her, 'What does he do when he comes home at noon?'

'When he comes home,' she replied, 'I give him his dinner; and when he is through, he lies down, and I pick the lice from his head. Then he goes to sleep, and the baby also goes to sleep, and I lay it by his side.'

So Montezuma told her to do the same as she had been in the custom of doing to the eagle. 'Come along!' he said. 'I'll tell you where I'll be hiding, so that, when they are asleep, you can come and let me know.' So they went over to the place where the eagle kept the dead persons' bodies; there was a great pile of them. 'I'll make myself into a green fly, and hide deep down under the mass of dead,' Montezuma told her, 'but when you come to call me, call in a low voice, not loud.' So he did as he told her, and went down under the pile of dead.

Soon it was noon, and Montezuma heard something coming roaring like the wind; and when it came closer, he heard a person groaning. The eagle flew down, carrying a great many people; but when he arrived at the cave, he was excited, and looked all over the cave, smelling and sniffing. 'I believe some live man has come here to our cave,' he told his wife; but she replied, 'No, no one has come here; you had better come and eat your dinner which I have prepared. No one would be able to come here; you merely smell the live men you have just brought in.'

But the little baby looked up at his father, and tried to speak, saying, 'Apatcuvi!' the meaning of which is unknown.

'Someone must have come here!' exclaimed the eagle. 'Listen to what the baby is crying to tell me!'

'Oh, come in and eat!' she replied. 'That's the way babies always do when they are beginning to talk; he doesn't know what he's saying!'

Then the eagle went over to the pile of dead, and began to turn them over and inspect them. And when he came to the one on the bottom, he exclaimed, 'Phew! This one is getting rotten; I'd better throw it away.'

'No, don't!' said his wife, coming out; 'for someday you'll have had bad luck and not kill anything, and the baby will be hungry. Then we'll eat it, anyway.' The eagle still wanted to throw it away; but the woman induced him not to do so, for she knew that Montezuma was inside of that body. So he took his wife's advice at last, and put the body back, and laid the others over it. He went back into the cave and ate his dinner; and when he had finished, his wife began to louse him, and he went to sleep. He lay on the ground with the pillow under his neck, and his head hanging down; and the baby slept beside him in the same position.

Then the woman went to the pile of dead, and told Montezuma that the eagle was sleeping. At that he came out and resumed his natural shape. 'Go inside the cave and make yourself a firm seat,' he told her, 'because the mountain will tremble when I kill the eagle, and you might fall off.' Then he took out his great knife, went into the cave, and cut off the heads of the eagle and the baby. The heads he threw to the north. Then he cut off their breasts, and threw them to the east, the bellies to the south, and the legs to the west. Firmly he clung to the rock, while the great mountain began to shake. It trembled for a short while, and then came to rest. Montezuma told the woman to warm some water; and when he had washed all the dead persons with this, they revived. All climbed down the way that he had mounted, and went to the village. Montezuma asked them if they all recognised their houses, and all did but two who were the most rotten. These he told to go with the others.

Now Montezuma thought that he had done a great service to his people, and that they would no longer be afraid of him; but whenever he came to the village, after he left and returned home, the chief would call his medicine men together and ask them if he had done anything to make the people sick. Montezuma knew what they doing, and became angry again because the people were still afraid of him and thought him an evil medicine man.

So he planned to do some more things to establish his station among them.

One morning early he started east toward the sunrise, and met the sun as he was coming up. He made another man, and painted him, and gave him a kicking-ball.

'Go with the sun,' he told him, 'and when he gets to the middle of the heavens, come down to the village, where all the people are living.' So, when the sun had reached the zenith, the man descended to the village, and began to kick his ball around. He kicked it toward the village; and when he came near it, he saw some women sitting outside of one of the houses, making a mat. Coming a little closer, he kicked his ball to where they were sitting. One of them took it, looked at it, and hid it in her dress. When the man came up and asked for his ball, she replied, 'Your ball never came this way; I haven't seen it; you must have kicked it somewhere else; I never look around when I'm working.'

'No, you've got my ball!'

'I never saw your ball.'

'Well, you can keep the ball if you want to, but I know you won't take as good care of it as I. I've taken great care of it, and used it as it ought to be used.' So he went back to the sun again. After he had gone, the woman thought she would look at the ball; so she arose and looked all around, but could not find it; so she went to work again. But the ball entered her body, and she became pregnant. When the baby was born, it had long finger nails like a bear, and the parents wanted to kill it, but the mother refused. This monster was known as hooke; it was neither man nor woman.

When the child grew up and played with the boys, she scratched them when angry, so the people who had children did not like her. And when she grew up, she fought with the boys. But one day her mother tied her to a post, and whipped her so hard, that she became furiously angry and ran away. She went south, and found a cave across the Mexican line, where she lived on deer and rabbits. She would hang around villages; and when a child began to cry, she would come up, and say, 'Why don't you make my grandchild stop crying? Let me quiet it!' Then she would take the child and rip out its entrails, and carry them home, where she would grind them in her mortar and eat them. So there were no children growing up.

Then the chief called a council of the people, and said to them, 'What are we going to do? This hooke is eating all our children! We had better send for Montezuma again, and ask him to kill the hooke.' So he sent a man to Montezuma's cave to ask him to come and hear what the chief wished to say to him. 'I'll be there after four days,' replied Montezuma, and he really meant four days this time. So after four days he came to the meeting, and they decided to go to Pozo Verde. He told the people to sing for four nights and four days, so that the hooke would be sleepy and go home. So, when evening came, Montezuma began the singing, and sent a man to invite the hooke to come over.

'I'll be down there in a little while,' replied the monster. Soon she came down, and the dance had already begun. She entered the group in which Montezuma was, and began to dance with him. At this all the people shouted, which pleased the hooke immensely. All night she danced with Montezuma. For four nights and four days this continued, and the last night the monster went to sleep.

Then Montezuma took her on his shoulders and carried her home, singing and dancing. Before this, many of the people had been at the cave, gathering dry sticks. They laid her on the bed in the cave, and filled it with dry wood and set fire to it. When the fire reached her, she sprang up, and cried, 'Why are you doing this to me? I have been enjoying your hospitality, and now you are treating me ill!' So hard she sprang up, that she hit her head against the top of the cave, so that the rock split. But Montezuma ran above the cave and put his foot on the crack to close it. The footprint is still to be seen there. When four days had passed, the fire had ceased, and the cave was cool. The people entered, and took the body out. They cut it up into little pieces, and the people of each village took a piece and went home.

Montezuma was sure that now the people would think well of him, because he had done so much for them; but they suspected him just as before, and he found no friends among his own people. He considered other plans by which he might make his people like him.

Away to the south was another chief whom he knew; and he went to him, and asked him to find a plan by which he could make himself popular with his people. 'I can't do anything for you,' said the southern chief. 'It is too difficult.'

He then went to a chief in the north, who also declined, but sent him to a chief in the west. 'I can't help you,' said the western chief; 'but go and see the chief in the east, possibly he can do something for you.'

But the eastern chief also could do nothing to help him. 'Go to the chief under the ground,' he said, 'he may be able to aid you.'

So Montezuma sank into the ground, and came to the village of the chief there. To him he told all his troubles – all the services that he had done to his people on the earth – but the people still feared him. 'There is no way by which your people can be brought to respect you,' said the under-ground chief. 'The only thing to do is to kill them off, and let my people take their place. If you say so, I'll take my people up there, and we'll kill them off and take the land.'

'Very well,' said Montezuma. 'I'll take you at your word. That's what I came here for, to find out what I should do.'

The chief of the underworld then instructed his people to make a great enclosure, so that they might all hold a council inside and hear what he had to say to them. The enclosure was made, and in four days all the people gathered there. Then he stood up among them, and told them that Montezuma had come there for help, that his people had not treated him kindly. 'I know that all my people are fighting men,' he said, 'so I told him we would help him. Now get ready, all of you, and we will decide what day we will go up and fight the people on the other side. And you medicine men also, prepare to use your influence when we begin fighting with them.'

Then Montezuma also stood up and encouraged them, saying that the people on the outside were unable to do anything. 'We'll kill them all off and take the land,' he told them. 'After four days we'll be out on the other side. So I want you all to get your bows and arrows ready; and if there is anything you medicine men need, get it ready.'

Then the chief of the underworld stood up again, and told the people to have the women prepare food, for no one was to be left below – all were to go to the other side and fight.

When the four days had passed, all the people were ready, and Montezuma and the chief led the way. They went a little distance away from the village, and Montezuma tried to make a way for them to get through to the surface of the earth, but was unable to do so. Then the chief tried and failed, and then all the medicine men. Finally a medicine woman stood up and made the way, and all climbed up on the outside. When all had reached the surface, the hole closed up again.

At that time the woman's carrying basket (kiho) was able to walk alone, carrying its load. But the coyote laughed at it, saying, 'What's that walking around over there?' Then the kiho stopped, and never walked again. Since that time it has always been carried around by the women.

The people came out of the earth somewhere in the east. There they spent the first night; and the chief said to them, 'In the morning we will divide into many groups, so we can occupy the entire earth. Some of you will go to the sea, and others to the north and the west. Kill everything you see – people, birds, deer, and everything. We must kill everything off.' So in the morning they divided as the chief had instructed, and set out. All over the country they travelled, killing all the people. When food gave out, they settled in a place for a year or so, and raised corn and beans for food and provisions; and on they came again, fighting the former inhabitants. And when the latter heard that they were coming, they prepared to meet them and to fight against them to protect their lands. Whenever they came to a village, Montezuma's medicine men would make them sleep, and blinded them so that they could come into the villages and kill the inhabitants without resistance. It was while the country was thus being conquered that the incident of the buried children occurred among the earlier population.

The people were hungry. There was no water, and no rain fell. One day a man went out to hunt hares. He saw no hares; but he saw a badger, and thought he would kill it. So he ran after it, but the badger ran into a hole. Then he decided to dig it out and kill it: so he commenced to dig where the badger had gone in. Very deep he dug until he came to a big hole with water in it. Out of this hole the wind came. Then the man went home. The people heard the wind roar, and said, 'Where is that roaring?' And they told the medicine man to try to find out where it was. He decided that the roaring was where the badger had gone in, and he told the people so. Then all the people went over there and saw it.

Then the chief spoke, and said, 'You medicine men, try to do something to stop that wind from blowing so!'

That is what he said to the medicine men; and they replied, 'Very well, we'll try to do something.' So they tried their best, but were unable to stop it. And they told the people so. Then said the chief, 'Let everyone come to our meeting!' and they all came. And he said, 'If anyone owns anything valuable, let him bring it. If anyone has any beads, bring them, so we can stop the wind with them.' Thus said the chief. So all the people brought their beads; and the chief took them, and walked over and left them near where the wind was blowing. 'Cease blowing!' he told the wind, but it never stopped. Still it blew. They could do nothing, and went home.

For four days the wind blew, and then came the water. Then the people gathered again in council to debate about what they should do. 'It will drown us all,' they said. So they asked the shamans to try again, but they replied that they were unable to do anything. Then one man who was not a medicine man – just a wise man – said, 'Let us put some children in the hole; possibly then the water will stop pouring out.' Thus said that intelligent man.

Then the chief said, 'Good! All you who have children, bring them, so that we may do as he says.' And all the people agreed to put their children in. 'We will put four children into the hole,' said the chief. 'Two of them shall be boys, and two girls; so there will be four.' They told some of the children that they would be put into the hole, and the children replied that it would be all right. 'It is well that you put us into the hole,' said the children; 'for possibly then the water will cease.' That is what they said.

'We will meet again to put in the children,' said the chief, 'or the water will increase.' So they all assembled again, and brought four children. The water was pouring out. So they threw the children in, and the water ceased.

Then the medicine men said, 'Find a large jar, and let us put it somewhere and place the beads in it!' So they all hunted around, found a large jar, and took it to the shamans, who carried it a little farther down.

And when they had found a good place, they stopped, and said, 'Here will be a good spot for the jar to be placed. So bring your beads and put them into it.' And all the people brought their beads and put them in. The medicine men buried the great jar, and said to the people, 'Hereafter, whenever anyone comes to this place, he must give whatever he has with him as an offering to the jar, as long as the world shall last.'

For many years no rain came in the country. This was owing to the magic of the invading medicine men, who thus made the former population hungry and unable to fight. And the people here heard about those who were coming from the east, and they built the Casa Grande so that they might have better protection from them. The largest villages were along the Gila. At Casa Grande there was a man named Sivanyi, who was the most powerful shaman of all the people around there. He was able to sink into the ground, and come out at some other place. But one of the medicine women of the invaders changed herself into lightning; and when Sivanyi endeavoured to sink into the earth, she struck him and killed him. All along the river they fought until they came to Va'ahlu, a place between Gila Crossing and Sacaton. There they encountered a powerful hostile medicine man, and were unable to get the better of him. He was stronger than they. So one of the medicine women changed herself into a dark red snake. She coiled herself around the building, and squeezed and cut it in two, so that the top fell in, and killed all the people within. Then they went ahead fighting their way, but found no more powerful opponents.

As far as the sea they went; and here the shamans and the medicine women caused the sea to divide, so that they crossed on the dry bottom, and conquered the people on the other side of the sea. Then they crossed the sea again, and returned. But as they were beginning to cross back, a boy about eleven years old became obstinate, and cried and rolled on the ground when his mother tried to carry him across. So his parents were delayed; and the seas came together again, and left them on the other side. And so there are still some of the same people living on the other side of the sea. Then they came back again to this valley, and settled here; and Montezuma told them to spread over the entire country. 'Each village will talk a little differently,' he told them, 'but you will all understand each other.' Then he divided the Apaches from the rest, and sent them to the northeast; and he said to the others, 'These people will fight against you just so as to keep you active and good runners and good fighters.' And he told the Apaches of certain things they must eat, and certain which they might not eat. And he told the Apaches to come here and fight. Having done this, he went back to his old cave.

Some time after this, two men came from the south, from heaven, looking for Montezuma. They passed through here on their way to Tuaki. And the chief at Vaaki sent out men to tell Montezuma to come to the council. When Montezuma came, the two men told him that they had come to get him, and to take him to the chief of the place from where they had come, who wanted to speak to him. Montezuma did not want to go, but finally agreed, and set out. But after they had gone halfway, Montezuma stopped, and said he would not go any farther. 'I also am a chief here,' he said to them; 'and if any other chief wants to talk to me, he'll have to come halfway and meet me.'

Then the two men tried to compel him to go with them, but he would not go farther. 'It is better for me to stay right here,' he told them.

'Very well,' said the two men; and they dug a hole and made him an underground house, and sealed him in. The house has four doorways, and is somewhere just over the line in Mexico. And there is Montezuma locked up.

Some of Coyote's Adventures

A short time after Coyote married, he became careless about his appearance, and grew sleepy, lazy, and indifferent. There came a time when he had to provide for four children. To hunt deer was hard work, so he and his wife went about visiting relatives. When they were given food, they always called the children, so that they could eat too. The women said many ugly things about them, and these finally reached the ears of his wife. One night she became enraged at what was told her. She ordered Coyote to hunt. She refused to continue begging, and said unless he decided to provide for her and the children, she would return to her father. Coyote's pride was touched at being ordered about by a woman, and being spoken to in such harsh terms.

In the morning he went out. He said, 'I will not chase deer all day. I will kill birds or little beasts, for any meat is sweet when one is hungry. I will play my tricks and catch game.'

He walked along and soon came within sight of a flock of quail. He commenced singing a song something like-

'Little quail, what are you thinking about, flying away so quickly?'

This song he repeated until all but one quail had flown. He stopped singing then, and said, 'That is good; one is left. I shall catch it and make a meal of it.'

He set about his self-imposed task, caught and devoured the bird, well satisfied with a good meal.

For a time he rested, and then went leisurely along until he came to a grassy valley. There he came on a gathering, and sang a song, as follows:

'Little rats, little rats,
There you are running,
One stumbles and falls,
It is crippled and cannot run.'

In this way Coyote is enabled to catch a rat. But not satisfied with one as a meal, he repeats the luring chant three times more, and each time successfully catches food. On four rats he has fed this time, satisfied his hunger, and goes on.

CHAPTER 23

Piegan

The Woman Who Turned into a Bear

A woman had seven brothers and one younger sister; that made eight beside herself. The seven brothers went to war. The woman was in a tepee in a big camp. One evening she told her mother, 'I must take a walk.' Every evening she told her mother; 'I am going to take a walk.' The old lady said to her younger daughter, 'You must follow your sister next time she takes a walk.' So the younger girl followed her sister that evening when she took a walk. Her sister went into a thick woody brush. The younger sister crawled up to her. She saw a large bear playing with her. The younger girl became frightened and ran home. She said to her mother, 'O mamma! What did I see down there? I saw a big bear.' The old woman told her husband, 'Your daughter has been with a bear down in the timber.'

The old man said, 'We will go down there and kill him the next time our daughter goes down there.'

The girl took a walk again that evening. The old man got a lot of young men to get their guns. They all followed the young girl down to the brush. They sneaked up. When they looked, the bear was playing with her. The girl just started home when they shot at the bear. The elder sister went home, crying, with her younger sister. She sent the younger sister back. 'Here, you go back; get me the bear's paw; don't let anyone see you.' So the younger girl went back and got a paw. When the Indians were cutting the bear in pieces, the girl sneaked up and got one of the paws. She went back with it. 'Here you are, sister!' The elder sister was glad to get that, because the bear was her sweetheart, you know.

That evening she sat down crying. The younger sister said, 'What are you crying about?'

'I was lonesome for my sweetheart; she said. 'Tomorrow get all the boys and girls together. We'll go down to the brush, and I'll play bear.'

So the younger one gathered all the boys and girls, and they went down to the brush. The elder girl, who lay in the brush, said to the girls, 'You must take little arrows and tickle me.' The boys and girls came up and tickled her. She jumped up and cried out like a bear. The boys pretended to shoot at her. She went into the brush again. The girls tickled her again. She called to her younger sister, 'Don't tickle me on the hips; you can tickle me any place else; you must all look out.'

The younger girl went to the boys and girls. 'What did your sister say?'

'My sister says you must not tickle her on her hips.' The youngest said, 'She can't do anything; let's tickle her there.' So they all sneaked up; and the youngest one tickled her on the thighs. So the elder girl turned into a bear. She ate them all up except her younger sister, and her seven brothers who were at war. The bear ran into the tepees and ate everybody. She went into her mother's lodge and turned into a woman again. She called her younger sister. 'You must come. I shall not kill you.' So the younger sister came out from the brush. The elder sister said, 'Here, sister, you're my servant.'

'All right! I'll wait on you, and do anything you want.' So she cut wood, got meals, and did everything a girl can do.

One morning the younger one went after water. Somebody called her. 'Sister!' She looked all around. It was the seven brothers who had come back. 'Come over here! We want to see you,' they said to her. 'What has become of all the people?'

'Don't talk loud! Sister will hear you. Our sister turned into a bear and killed off all the people.'

'You go ask your sister what will kill her.' The girl went back. When she came in, her elder sister sniffed around, and said, 'It smells as if a person were around.'

'Don't say that! There's nobody around.'

'Come up here!' the elder one said. 'Look on my head and put me to sleep.'

The younger sister said, 'All right!' So she looked on her head, and felt around her face. 'Poor sister!' she said, 'I love you! I'll be an orphan if anyone comes along and kills you.

'Oh, don't be frightened about that, sister. Nobody can kill me with a gun, nor can a fire burn me, nor can I get drowned; I'm a medicine-woman.'

'What can kill you, sister''

'Where I walk on my paws, an awl will kill me there.'

'Is that so? I didn't know that.' So she put her elder sister to sleep, and went after water again. Her brothers called her again. 'What did your sister say was going to kill her?'

'Oh, yes! She'll die by an awl, brothers. You go around the camp and pick up all the awls.' They did so.

The next day they went down to the river when the younger sister went to the water. 'You take these awls,' they said to their sister. 'Here's a rabbit for you. You cook it when you get home. Don't give her any, even if she asks for it. Stick all the awls close to the tepee.'

So the girl went and hid the awls outside, and went into the tepee. She said to her elder sister, 'I've got a rabbit for you.'

'Cook for yourself alone,' the elder sister said. So the younger one started cooking the rabbit. Her sister said, 'Look on my head! Put me to sleep again.' So she did so. Then she went out and put awls around the tent, near the door and all around. The girl went back to the lodge. The rabbit was done, but she didn't eat it; she was waiting for her sister to wake up. She woke up. The younger sister said, 'The rabbit's done; do you want a piece of it?'

'No! Eat it alone. Go ahead and eat it. It smells like persons. Somebody must be around.'

'No, there's nobody around.' So the younger started to eat the rabbit, but hid half of it. 'I guess my sister must have eaten all that rabbit,' the elder one said, 'I had none of it.'

'No, I've got some more here for you'.

'Eat it all up; don't save any for me' said the elder sister. The younger was putting away the dishes. 'Did you eat it all up?' said the elder sister, 'Yes; I don't care; I ate it up.'

'I'll eat you up,' the elder, said. 'I don't care; you may eat me up,' the younger said as she ran out of the lodge. The elder sister turned into a bear again and chased her.

When she jumped out, she stepped on one of the awls and could go no farther. Her brothers shot and stabbed her; and made a fire, and pulled her into it. So the bear was nearly dead. 'Let's make a bigger one, so that she will burn up well!' said the brothers. Then, she burned to death. Then all left. At the time a little piece of her finger blew to one side. So she came together again. When the brothers and sister looked back, the bear was coming at them again. The oldest one told the middle one, 'What do you think? Do you know of anything?'

'I'll save all of you. I'm stronger than sister. I'm medicine,' he said. He took out a little feather. He blew it up into the sky. All seven brothers went up into the sky. They became the seven stars [the dipper]. 'You run to that rock over there! they cried to their sister. She ran there. Old Man sat there making arrows. 'Save me, save me! My sister is coming to kill me! She's a bear:' Old Man raised the rock up. 'Sit under there!' She crawled under. He shut the rock down on her. He sat there making arrows. The bear came. 'Where is my sister?' Old Man said nothing, but kept on making his arrows. 'Where's my sister, before I swallow you?'

'Get out!' he said. He took a butcher-knife, cut off her ears and tail. 'I'm not going to kill you, just make you suffer,' said he. 'You're going to look like that.' He opened the rock again. 'Come out and be happy!' he said to the younger sister. That's the end of it.

Old Man and the Geese

Old Man saw some Geese. He went to them crying. They asked him what the matter was. 'So and so, the chief of the geese is dead.'

'We never heard of him.'

'Well, to think that you don't know about your own chief, while a stranger does. All the geese know about him.' They became interested. He got them to agree to smoke a pipe with their eyes shut. He took a curved stick and killed several by hitting them over the head. The rest peeped and flew away. Old Man cried out, 'What fools you were to think there was a chief of the geese!'

How the Beaver Bundle Was Introduced

A boy was an orphan, and his grandmother reared him. He was very poor, very ragged. He had sore eyes, and was very dirty. After he was washed, he was a very decent-looking fellow.

In those days the Piegans had no horses, but only dogs, with which to travel about the country. The head chief then had three wives; the youngest was a girl.

In those days Piegans were not jealous of their wives. The women had a dance society, and at those dances they would imitate the dress of their lovers. So it appears, now and then the head chief's youngest wife had had connection with this boy.

The women started to have one of these dances. They began to dress up as they were going to the dance. So the head chief said to his wives, 'Some one of you must have a lover. Why don't you dress up and go to the dance?' For a long time none of them got ready. Finally the youngest began to fix up, asked her husband if he had any coyote skin. So the old chief began to dress her up as her lover looked. Her lover was very fond of carrying coyote skin around his arms and legs and on his head. So she dressed just as he used to dress. He always wore the bottom of his robe round in front, so she cut her robe round in front. As soon as the chief saw how she was dressed, he knew who her lover was; and it made him ashamed that she had had connection with such a poor fellow with sore eyes, and so dirty; but he said nothing. So after the girl went to the dance, all who were in the dance knew whom she was imitating.

So when they commenced dancing, this young fellow told his chum between times, 'I've been having something to do with the chief's youngest wife.' His chum didn't believe him. He laughed at him.

'Well, partner, I don't think that girl would have anything to do with you.'

'Chum, let's go down to where they are dancing, and see who is there!' So they went down there. When they arrived there, he saw the girl dressed just as he was; and his partner saw her too. So his partner believed him, and said, 'You're right, partner, you have had something to do with her; she's dressed just like you.'

They were dancing at the time; so the girl spoke out after she had finished dancing, and told the people, 'When the river gets warm, I'll float to the shore.'

So it made the fellow ashamed to see her dressed as he was, because everybody knew then that he had had connection with her. They walked away, this fellow and his partner. He said to his partner after they had walked away, 'Partner, come with me! I am going to some of these lakes to search for a dream, so that I may be a medicine-man. You will know where I am, then you may go home.' His partner went with him to the side of a lake where there was a beaver dam. He said to his partner, 'In four days come back after me.' So his partner went home and left him there.

He lay there four days, but didn't get his dream. He got up and left the place, and his partner came back in four days. He searched diligently everywhere for him, but could not find him anywhere. He went home. He thought his chum had been killed by the enemies. The fellow that was searching for a dream went to the river and lay on a high cliff. He lay there crying, and acted in such a way as inspire pity. He looked, and saw a boy near him. This boy said him, 'Partner, my father wants you to come down to his lodge. Shut your eyes.' He shut them. When he looked up, he found himself in a beaver's lodge. He looked around. He saw the old man and old woman, who were beavers. The old beaver said, 'My, my, what are you sleeping around here for?'

'I'm sleeping around here to find a dream to lead me through life.'

The old beaver said, 'My son, that's not very hard to do. Some day you will be a head chief of your tribe, but you have to stay here all winter with me.' The old beaver said to him, 'What do you eat?'

The young fellow said, 'Well, I eat meat, and I eat pemmican.'

So the old beaver said to his own son, 'You go out and get me some buffalo dung.' The young boy went out and fetched a lot of buffalo dung. The old beaver went through his performance of medicine man, and covered this manure. When he took the cover off this manure, it was all pemmican.

The young fellow lived on pemmican that winter. All around the inside of the lodge, the old beaver had different medicines tied up: beaver, weasel-skin shirts, and other medicine shirts. At the rear, there was around pool of water. In that pool of water there was a stick floating. That was supposed to be the old beaver's son, but had turned into a stick. The old man said to the young fellow, 'Son, when the river goes out three times, you may go home.'

Every moon the old man sent his own son out to see if spring had come; and every moon the old man sent his own son up and down the river to invite all the beavers on the river and creeks; and every moon all the beavers used to come and sing beaver songs. At last the old man went out himself. He came back. He said to the young fellow, 'The river's breaking up; in four days you may go home.' He said to his own son, 'You go and invite all the beavers you can find to come. I want them to sing for your brother here, so he can take the songs to his tribe.' So the boy invited all the beavers; and all the beavers came, and sang for four days and four nights for the young fellow. They taught him the songs.

The morning after the fourth night the old man said to the young fellow, 'Well, my son, you may go home today.'

The next morning the old man and old woman went outside. When they went out, the old beaver's son told the young fellow, 'You see all these medicines which are hung up around here? When my father comes in, he is going to ask you, "Now, my son, look around all through these medicines here, and pick out what you want to take along with you;" and don't you take any of them. When he asks you, you tell him that you want the stick in the water here. The stick that's in the water, that's the chief of his medicines. He is going to ask you that four times. Don't you pick out anything but that stick. When he asks you that the fourth time, he will let you have it. He will try to put you off and get you to take something else; but don't you take anything else. When he sees he can't put you off, then he will give it to you.'

The old man came in. Well, the old man sat down. 'Now, my son, you're going home today. You see all these medicines hanging around my lodge. They are all strong medicines. Pick out your choice, anything you want to take home with you.'

The young fellow said, 'I don't want any of them. I want that stick in the water.' The old beaver said, 'Well, my son, that stick won't do you any good; there are all these other medicines hanging around here. They are better than that stick; you will get some benefit from them.' The young fellow said again, 'No, I don't care for any of them; I'd rather have that stick.'

'Well, my son, you're very foolish. That stick will do you no good. You'd better take something else hanging around here.'

'No, I'd rather have that stick in the water.'

The old man said, 'Why, my son, that's foolish; there are other medicines here; they're better than that stick; they'll be of some benefit to you.'

The young fellow said, 'No, I don't want anything else, only that stick.'

Well, the old man thought long before he said anything more. Finally he gave a grunt, 'Anhahan' (this means it was against his will; he didn't wish to part with that stick). The old man said, 'All right! Take your brother, then, take your brother and look out for your ears. Do not leave him down; always wear him around your shoulders. If you leave him down, that's the last you'll see of him. That stick there is your youngest brother.' Then he gave him a bone whistle. 'Now, when you are on your way home, you will meet this big river here. When you cross it, it is going to be pretty deep; you can't wade it. Just put your stick down and sing one song. That stick will turn into a beaver. He'll cut some trees down for you, so you can make a raft to cross with.'

Meanwhile he was fixing up the young man's face, and made a good looking man of him. He cured his sore eyes, and everything like that. He made a fine looking young man of him.

Well, the boy started out for home, bade him good-by, and kissed him.

When he came to the river, he couldn't wade it; it was high water. He put his stick down, sang a little song, and the stick turned into a Beaver. The Beaver walked off and chawed on a tree for him with his teeth. The young man threw the tree into the water. They got in, the Beaver and the young man, and they got across. The Beaver turned into a stick again.

The young man walked and walked; and, as luck had it, when he got to the top of a big hill, he saw a big camp-circle, a camp of Piegans.

He stayed on that hill all night. Next morning, when it was early, the Piegans were searching for their horses all over. A Piegan saw the fellow sitting on the hill. This Piegan thought he was an enemy. He rode over to see who it was. He said to the young fellow, 'Who are you?'

The young fellow said, 'Well, I'm so and so.' He called his name. 'Are any of my people still living? – my sister, grandmother, my brother-in-law, and my chum?'

This Piegan said, 'Yes, they're alive yet. They were looking very pitiful. They camp outside the circle there. We thought you were dead, that you had been killed. They're mourning for you. Their hair is cut off, and their legs are gashed. They're mourning for you.'

The young fellow said, 'Will you tell my chum and my sister and my brother-in-law to make four sweat houses just as soon as they can. When they get the sweat houses finished, send someone after me.'

So the fellow went back to camp and notified the people to build four sweat houses just as soon as they could; and he notified them to invite several old men to be sitting there when he (the young man who had been with the beavers) came.

The sweat houses were finished, and the young man was sent for. The young fellow came up and went into the first sweat house. He invited the old men to take a sweat with him.. He said to the old. men, 'I'm going to sing you songs that you never heard in your life, beaver songs.' He started in with his medicine beaver songs in this sweat house, and these old men were very much surprised. They had never heard these songs in all their lives. They went from the first sweat house into the second, and went through the same performance. When he went from one sweat house to the next one, he always left a pile of sand where he had been sitting until he went into the fourth sweat house, and then the sand was all out of him.

From the sweat lodge, he went home to his lodge where his brother-in-law was; and all his people came there to see him. They kissed him. They were all glad to see him.

Next day after he had got home in the morning, a war party was starting out. He said to his partner, 'We don't want to keep where the bunch are; we'll keep to one side, just the two of us together.'

After they started for war, he began to tell his chum what a medicine man he was, and his dreams, and all that was given to him when he wintered with the beavers.

When they had been out two days, they saw the enemy. They walked up to the river. The enemy were on one side of the river, and they were on the other. The enemy were the Cheyenne. The river was so broad and high that they couldn't get at one another to fight. The Cheyenne's chief would come down to the water, and would go up on the hill again. He was talking to his own people, but the Piegans did not understand what he was saying to his people.

The young fellow said to his chum, 'Partner, I am going to play at beaver; I'm going to swim across under the water; and I am going to kill yon Cheyenne chief. You watch me when I get across. When I kill him, I'll dive down stream. But don't go away from here. When the Piegans all rush down stream, I'll come up here. We'll divide his scalp between us two.' That's what he told his chum.

The young man jumped under the bank to make his medicine. He started in with a beaver song . When he was about to cross, his partner saw his head above the water. When the Cheyenne chief saw him jump in the water, he ran to the river. He jumped down the bank. He had a big spear. When the young fellow came out of the water to his waist, the Cheyenne chief waded in after him to strike him with his spear. When the Cheyenne chief waded in, the young fellow walked backwards to coax the Cheyenne to come in a little farther. The Cheyenne struck at him with his spear. The young fellow threw up his stick, and the spear struck the centre of the stick, and did not strike the young man at all . As the Cheyenne struck the stick with the spear, the young man grunted 'Anan!' He took the spear away from the Cheyenne and killed the Cheyenne with his own spear. He took the Cheyenne and dove down the creek with him. The Piegans saw him dive down the creek. They all rushed down the creek. He dove up stream to where his partner was sitting when he was halfway across. He pulled the enemy out to his partner, scalped the fellow, and divided the scalp with his partner, and took all that was on the Cheyenne, and divided that with his partner. When the Piegans rushed up again, they had taken everything the fellow had on.

Well, he and his partner led the way back then. They were chiefs. When they got pretty near home, the Piegans saw the war party coming over the hill, singing scalp songs. Some of the leaders of the camp began to cry out, 'The war party is coming back! You had better go out and meet your relatives. There are two fellows in the lead. I don't know who they are. They must have done something wonderful; that's the reason they're so far in the lead.' When they got a little closer, then the Piegans saw who it was. The leaders cried out again, 'It's so and so and so and so. They're leaders; they must have done something wonderful; their relatives had better go and meet them.'

When the head chief heard it was so and so, he said to his wife, 'Where's the girl?'

Her sister looked for her, and found her in the brush, picking rosebuds, and told her, 'There comes your lover; you'd better go change your clothes and go to meet him.' She spilled her rosebuds right there on the ground and started running home.

The girl changed her clothes, ran back to her lover, met her lover with a kiss. Her lover gave her that spear and that scalp, and told her, 'Give that to my partner.' [You see, when one has connection with another's wife, they call him 'partner'.]

So when the girl went home with this spear and scalp, she told her husband, 'This is what your partner gives you;' and the old chief was very well satisfied.

The old chief said to his oldest wife, 'Go ahead and cook some grub; I want to invite my partner over here to supper.'

When supper was ready, he cried out for his partner to come over eat with him. When his partner, the young man, came in, the old chief said to him, 'I'm the head chief of the Piegan tribe here, but I'm going to give away my chiefship; you shall be the head chief now. That's our wife (pointing to the girl); I give her to you. You shall have her for good. And this lodge, I give you this lodge; and I'll move out. There's my roll of beavers, I give that to you. I have four dogs and four travois; I'll give you two dogs and two travois to haul you around. And now you're the leader of the Piegans. You're head chief now.'

CHAPTER 24

San Luisenos

Creation Myth

In the beginning Tucomish (night) and Tanowish (earth) sat crouching, brooding, silent. Then Tucomish said, 'I am older than you.'

Tanowish said, 'No, I am stronger than you.' So they disputed. Then Tucomish caused Tanowish to go to sleep. When she woke she knew that something had happened, and that she was to be the Mother. She said, 'What have you done?'

'Nothing. You have slept.'

'No,' she said. 'I told you that I am stronger (morally) than you.'

Soon within her grew all things and she sat erect and round. Wyot was her first born, the father (in a care-taking sense) of all things. The grasses, trees, birds, all things were born of Tanowish.

Then Evil, Towish, wished to be born. He tried to escape by the ears, eyes, and nose, but at last passed from the mouth with a tsiz (hissing noise). He is nothing but spirit. He has no form whatsoever.

Taquish is a ball of light, and is a witch. He was the third son.

The frog was beautifully made, white and red, with great eyes. Wyot said, 'Oh, my daughter, you are so beautiful.' But her lower limbs were thin and ugly. When she saw men walk she was jealous, and hated Wyot, cursing him with terrible words.

Then Wyot said, 'In ten months I shall die. When the great star rises and the grass is high, I shall go.' Wyot said to his people, 'You have never killed anything; now you may kill the deer. Make an awl, gather shoots of bushes and grasses and make a basket to contain my ashes.' Then he taught them how to make baskets, redas, ollas, and all their arts. He died in the spring, May.

They burned his body, but his spirit became the moon. His ashes were placed in a long basket, and for this reason they pass the basket in front of the chief dancer and mourn. They sing 'Wyot, Wyot,' nine times, then 'Neyonga (My head) Nechaya, tomve.'

The dances were to please the moon and prevent his waning.

CHAPTER 25

Shasta

Origin of Death

People grew in this world in the beginning. There were many people here and there. They became numerous. Then one died. Cricket's child died. The people were talking about it. 'What shall we do?' said they. All the people gathered together. They did not know what to do. Some said, 'Let us have people come to life again. Let us not bury them!'

'Stop!' said others. 'Go and tell Coyote. He does not know what happened.' So someone went to tell him. Coyote came. 'What do you think?' said they, 'We were saying that the dead should come back again.'

'Why are you saying that?' Said Coyote. 'Bury him. He is dead. If people come back, they will fill up everything. Around this world there is water. They will fill the world up and push us into the water.' So they buried Cricket's child and cried.

Now, five days after this they finished the sweating. They felt sad. They thought, 'Would that Coyote's child might die.'

So it died, and Coyote cried. He said, 'My child is dead. Let us have people come back to life.'

'No!' they said. 'If he should come back to life, my child that died before would not smell good. He has decayed. You said we must bury people. You said that the dead would otherwise fill up the world.' So he buried him and cried. That is the way the first people died. That was the first death.

The Dead Brought Back from the Other World

A man had a wife called Woodpecker. She fell into the fire and was burned, so that she died. He thought he saw her ghost go up toward the sky and went out back of the house, where he found her trail. He followed this and reached the sky. She went along the Milky Way; and her husband, following on, was only able to catch up with her at night as she camped along this trail. In this way – catching up with her at night, and losing her in the day – he finally came to the other world where all the dead were dancing and having a fine time. For along time he watched them, and then asked the fire tender if he might get his wife back. He was told he could not. After a while he fell asleep; and when he woke, it was daytime, and the dead were all asleep. They lay like patches of soft white ashes on the ground. The fire tender gave the husband a poker, and told him to poke the various sleeping ghosts, saying at the one that got up and sneezed when he did so, would she be his wife. Following this advice, he found his wife, and picked her up and started home with her. At first she weighed nothing, but she grew heavier as they approached the earth and his house. Before he got back, he dropped his burden, and the ghost ran back to the other world. He followed her again, and the next time got within a very short distance of his door, when he dropped her, and again she ran back. For the third time he returned to the land of the dead, but was told that he might not try again. He was told to return home, and that in a short time he would be allowed to come and live with his wife. He followed these instructions, returned home, and went to sleep. He died, and as a ghost then returned to the other world for good.

Urutsmaxig

There was a trail which went up the river on the other side. There was a ford; and a house stood on this side, just below the ford. People coming up river had to wade across to this side at the ford. Just as they were in the middle, the man who lived in the house would jump out, go down towards the bank, take a hooked pole, and catch the traveller. Then he would drown him. That was the way it was formerly, and the people who had been thus drowned were piled up in heaps along the bank.

A traveller came along the trail. He said, 'I will go and buy a wife.' He came to the place where the evil being lived, and saw the piles of drowned persons scattered along the shore. He had heard people say that if one waded across, he was tripped up and drowned; that all were so drowned that the evil being saw. The man wondered where the crossing was, as he went on. Then he saw the house opposite; the door was open. Then the trail led down into the river. 'This is the place,' he thought. 'This is the place they speak of. Here is where everyone is drowned who crosses.' He went on, and thought what he should do. He started to wade over; he got halfway across. Then the evil being in the house looked out.

'Who is that?' he said, and jumped out through the door. He ran down to the river bank and picked up the hooked pole. He reached out and caught the traveller by the leg; but he kept on wading over. The one with the hook pulled hard to trip him up, but not at all could he trip him. So the traveller came across.

'What are you trying to do to me?' he said. Then he reached out, and seized the evil being who tripped people up, and took away from him the hooked pole. He broke it to pieces, and threw them into the river. The evil being who tripped people up stood very still. He was surprised that the other should take the pole and break it up. Then the traveller seized the evil being, lifted him up, and threw him into the river. 'I am a supernatural being, but you are not. You will be a newt, not a supernatural person.' So he killed him at last, and he was drowned.

The name of the traveller was Urutsmaxig. He went on up the river. He had concealed with him Maiyaho (one name for the Cottontail Rabbit), who gave him advice. He saw a house on the opposite side of the river. 'I wonder who lives there!' he said. When he came opposite the house, he saw piles of dead persons lying by the trail.

'What is the trouble with them, I wonder!' he said. 'What could have killed them all!' He noticed that the door of the house on the other side was open.

Now, while he thought this, the people in the house said to the person living there, 'There is a chief passing along over there. Do not look across at him.' But the person got up anyhow to look across, and the people seized him to prevent his looking. 'It is a chief who is passing,' they said.

The evil person tried to pull loose from them, and said, 'What is a chief? I am a supernatural person myself.' Then he got loose, and went to the door, and looked across. He winked, opening and shutting his eyes, for in this way he killed people. But Urutsmaxig still went on. Again the evil being winked, opening and shutting his eyes, and still Urutsmaxig went on. Then Urutsmaxig put his hand into his sack, and took out a bundle of flints. The evil being kept winking, winked repeatedly and long, but Urutsmaxig went on just the same. Then he tossed a handful of flints across, threw them into the evil being's eyes, and at once he fell over backward into the house. His head fell into the fire.

The people seized him. 'I told you not to look,' they said. Then they pulled him out of the fire, and rubbed the fire out, rubbing off his hair and much of his skin too.

When Urutsmaxig threw the flints across, he said, 'You will be Buzzard, not a supernatural person.'

The people said, 'We told you not to look across. We said it was a chief who was passing.' Then the person sat still there, with his back to the fire.

Now, Urutsmaxig went on, to buy his wife. He arrived at the place. He came to where an old woman lived who had two daughters. He stayed there for a few days; and then the old woman said, 'M-m-m-m! My son-in-law, I wish you would go and stand there, where the deer run. I will go and rattle deer bones, and drive them toward you.'

'All right!' he said, and got ready and went. The old woman went with him, and showed him where to stand.

'Stand there,' she said, 'and I will drive the deer to you. Don't miss them, for I am hungry for meat.' So he went there, and stood. When he was out of sight, the old woman went back to the house. She went to the place where she kept things hidden, and took out her gambling sticks. She gambled, and thought she had killed her son-in-law. Urutsmaxig stood where she had told him. Below was a great rattlesnake. The old woman had told him to stand there for that reason. It was so that the rattlesnake might swallow him. That was why she gambled, she was happy, and she thought, 'Now by this time the rattlesnake has swallowed him.'

Urutsmaxig stood there, and thought, 'Where is the old woman going to drive?' and while he thought this, while he wondered where she was driving, the rattlesnake breathed in. Now, where Urutsmaxig stood there were many trees; and when the rattlesnake opened its mouth, they all leaned toward it, drawn by the wind.

Urutsmasig was drawn along. He seized the trees, but they were pulled up by the roots. He was drawn down towards the rattlesnake's mouth. He thought, 'I am going to die.' Then he braced himself, but his feet slipped; he was sunk into the ground up to his knees, but could not hold. Then he thought of the spare flint flakes he had tied up in his quiver. He reached in, took them out, and just as the rattlesnake was swallowing him, he threw the flints into the open mouth. So he killed the rattlesnake; and cut off the head, and took it away.

He returned to the house, and put down his game at the door. This made a noise. The old woman was gambling as he walked in, and she quickly threw her gambling sticks over her back toward the wall. 'It is outside,' he said.

'Yes,' said she, 'I'll eat outside.' Then she went out. Urutsmaxig had killed one of the old woman's relatives. She had said she would eat outside, but she wailed and cried. Then she buried it, and came back again after a time.

By and by she said, 'Son-in-law, go down to the river! There is a salmon trap there, inherited from one who is dead. I want some fish, any kind of fish.' So he went down. There were many fish in the trap, and he reached down to take some out. Then rattlesnakes stuck their heads out of the water, and he nearly was bitten. Then he killed them with his arrow flaker, and tied them up in bunches, and took them off.

As soon as he had left, the old woman had begun to gamble. When she heard Urutsmaxig at the door, she threw her gambling sticks away. 'I have brought them, old woman!' said Urutsmaxig.

Then she said, 'Yes, I'll eat outside.' So she went out and cried. By and by she said, 'Son-in-law, I wish you would go there and climb up to that eagle's nest. It is on a tree. Take the young birds. They will soon be flying.'

'All right!' said he. So he went. 'Where is this man?' he thought. After awhile he saw a juniper. It was bushy, and there was an eagle's nest in it. He climbed up after the nest, and kept on climbing. As he climbed, the tree grew up with him, until it reached the sky. Finally he reached the nest, and looked over the edge into it. And there were rattlesnakes in it. They coiled and struck at him, and almost bit him. He took out his arrow flaker, and struck them on the head, and killed them. He tied them in a bunch, and stood on the top of the tree. He pressed it down with his foot, then he climbed down again, and went back to the house, carrying the game.

The old woman had been gambling ever since Urutsmaxig had gone. She thought, 'By now he is killed, in spite of his coming back before.' Then, just as she was thinking this, he came in.

'I left it outside, old woman!' he said.

'Yes,' said she, 'I'll pluck them outside.' So she went out. She wailed and cried, and then buried them. He was killing those who had been her relatives.

After a time she said, 'Son-in-law, I want to eat spawning salmon.'

'All right!' said he.

She told him which one she wanted. 'Spear the one that floats down blue in colour. Do not take the one that is red; but the one that floats down blue.'

So he went, and took with him Maiyaho, the little one. He arrived at the place where the old woman had told him to go. He undressed. He had a skin about his waist only. He tied his hair up in a bunch on top of his head, and put eagle-down on it. He took out his spear, tipped with black obsidian and with red and black obsidian, a two-pronged spear. He put on the points. Then he told Maiyaho what to do. 'Do not cry,' he said, 'if I am pulled into the water, I will stick this arrow flaker in the bank. Do not touch it. If it falls, you may cry; and then after ten days you come here.' So he stood watching. Now, the red salmon floated down, but he did not spear it. Then a blue one floated down, and he speared it under the arm. It jumped and roared in the water. When it jumped and flopped about, it nearly pulled Urutsmaxig into the stream. He pulled the salmon out, and then it pulled him into the stream, pulled him wholly in, until he was out of sight; even the eagle down did not come up.

Then Maiyaho cried, he whom Urutsmaxig had told not to cry. He did not return until after dark to the house. Next morning he went away right after breakfast, and did not come back until night. For all the ten days he did this. He watched the arrow flaker; but still it stood up, and did not fall. Urutsmaxig had said that unless it fell, he was not to cry; yet he cried every day. The tenth day came, and Maiyaho watched. It was the same time that Urutsmaxig had been pulled in. The water rippled from an unseen cause.

Maiyaho wiped the tears from his eyes, and thought, 'I wonder if I did not see something!' Again he saw it. Then the eagle down appeared above the water; then Urutsmaxig came up out of the water as far as his shoulders; then he came fully out. He pulled out the thing he had speared. It was worth looking at, for it had a person's body and a fish's tail. Urutsmaxig carried it off. He said to Maiyaho, 'I told you not to cry until the arrow flaker should fall.'

Then they went back with the head. Maiyaho told him, 'The old woman has been gambling all the time. She did not even eat.' When they got back, they made a noise at the door, and the old woman threw her gambling sticks over her back to the wall. They came in.

'I have come back with the fish,' said Urutsmaxig.

'Yes, I'll cut it up outside,' said she. Instead of this she buried it; for it was the head of the old woman's daughter he had brought. It was that she buried.

Now she could do nothing to him. She thought, 'What way can I kill him?' Then she said, 'Son-in-law, don't you feel like playing?'

'Yes,' said he, 'I don't care what the game is. Let us go!' So they went. So they got to the place where people swing and sway on a tree. The tree stuck out far over the water of a lake. It was a fearful sight. Now they walked out on the tree to play. They bent it down by standing on the end of it. Then the old woman jumped off. It sprang up until it struck the sky, then bent back and, sunk deep under the water. By and by it came up, and Urutsmasig was still standing there on the end. 'Now, old woman, it is your turn,'. he said. So he bent it down for her, and jumped off. Just as before, the pole sprang up to the sky, then sprang back under the water; and, when it came up again, the old woman was gone.

'Where is she?' thought Urutsmaxig.

Then far up in the sky she laughed, 'He; he, he! You did good to me, my son-in-law. I shall see what people do at night. If they steal anything, I shall be the one who sees.' So she became the moon. And Urutsmaxig went onto his home. It was that way that he did in the olden times, they say.

The Race with Thunder

Thunder and Silver Fox lived side by side. They bet with each other, saying, 'Let's run a race!' So they ran, and Silver Fox was beaten. Then Thunder bet again, with another, with Red Fox, and won. There were ten brothers of them; and next Black Fox ran, and was beaten. Then they talked together, and said, 'Whom can we hire?'

'Whom else than Wolf?' said one. 'Yes,' said they. So one went at night to tell Wolf to come that night.

He arrived. 'Ha!' said he, 'what is the trouble?'

Then Silver Fox said to him, 'Take pity on me! Thunder has won all I have. They are racing now, and three have been beaten.'

'Well,' said Wolf, 'what can I do to win? I think I will go and look on, at any rate.' So they went at dawn. They hid Wolf, and as it grew light they told him about things. 'This is what he does to us, this is how he beats us. He almost kills us. He runs in front of us, and tears up the ground. That is the reason he wins.' So they told him about it.

'Ah!' said Wolf, 'what can I do? I will try, anyway.'

Now, the sun was just rising. It rose; it rose higher, and now they began to race. Wolf prayed for luck while he was running. They started; and soon Thunder tore up the ground, he tore open trees, he ploughed up the earth ahead of Wolf. Wolf kept praying silently. He was running behind Thunder, and he turned in and ran directly in line behind him. He pulled a Pain from his tongue, and threw it ahead, so as to strike the ground where Thunder was to run. When Thunder came to the spot, it seemed as if he stood still, so fast did Wolf pass him, and win. So they won back all that Thunder had won away from them. That was the way they raced. That Wolf was the only one who could beat him. No others could do it. That is how they did when Thunder bet and won.

The Captive of the 'Little Men'

There were many Indians living at Seiad long ago. A man went out to hunt, and the 'little-men' took him prisoner while he was hunting in the mountains. They took him to their house.

The house seemed to be full of dried deer-meat, of service-berries and other things, packed in baskets along the wall. They gave him meat to eat, they gave him berries.

Now at home they worried about him. They said, 'This man is lost,' and many were sent to hunt for him. But they could not find him anywhere. 'Where is he now?' said his wife, crying. She was crying herself to death.

The little children cried also. Yet all the time he was only a prisoner, and he stayed there with those 'little-men'. The people gave up trying to find him. 'Where can anyone find him?' they said. So they gave up.

Now, it came on winter. He had been lost in summer. It came on spring, the early spring. Then the 'little-men' said to him, 'Now go back to your home.' So he went. They loaded him down with deer and berries. Now, another man was going along in that same direction. The man who had been lost was dressed in feathers, and carried a huge load. The other man spoke to him. So he was found, the man who had been lost the year before. That is the way the man was captured by the 'little-men' long ago.

Coyote and the Rogue-River People

People were gambling, and the Rogue-River people won everything. An old woman lived in a house with many children. Below, farther down the river, were two women. Coyote arrived where the old woman lived. She was his aunt; and he came without any bed, carrying his gambling sticks. She gave him some supper; then she said, 'Where are you going?'

'I am going to gamble,' said he.

'You are always clever. Where is your wager?' said the old woman. Then he took out of his sack some beads. 'You are always wishing to do something,' she said, and broke up his gambling sticks, and threw them into the fire. He saved one, however. Then she made his bed for him.

'You can't strike me with anything,' said the old woman. Then she put her rattles on her wrists and rattled them. She placed a basket of water near. 'Sprinkle me with that,' she said, 'and I shall come to life again.'

Then she gave him some 'poison', and told him to sit on the opposite side. Then she sang, 'I am going to dance in this direction. You thought I was going that way.' So he threw at her, and 'pak!' he hit her. He forgot what to do. Then he remembered and splashed her with the water, and she breathed and sat up.

'Now you do the same,' said the old woman to Coyote. So he got ready, and did just as the old woman had done; he sang her song. He made a feint to go in one direction. He was afraid. 'Dodge about in every direction,' said she to Coyote. 'Look out!' Then she threw this direction, and he jumped up straight, and escaped. 'You take this,' said she. 'Down river are two fine women. You can wager them.'

'Very well,' said he, and went on. He went in a canoe, and had all kinds of blankets and shell beads.

'See a chief is coming,' the people said. He married the two women, and went on down the river.

He came now to where the people were gambling. He said to his wives, 'You must not tell who I am. I will talk the Klamath language.'

'What did you come for?' the people said.

'I came to gamble,' said Coyote.

'What is your wager?' they asked.

'Here is some money,' said Coyote.

'No; that will not do! We do differently. We wager people.'

Then Coyote said, 'We do not wager people. By and by, it will be different; there will be another people. I will wager bead money.'

'No,' said they.

'I will measure so much: three fathoms of beads you shall have if you win, four fathoms.'

'No!' said the people, 'we bet persons.'

'Well, all right! I will wager my body and my two wives. Where are your gambling sticks?' said Coyote.

'Where are yours?' said they.

Now they were ready. A little bird was concealed in Coyote's hair just behind his ear. 'We will throw at you first,' said they.

'Very well!' said Coyote, so he sang.

'They are going to make a feint,' said the little bird. They threw to knock Coyote over; but he jumped straight upwards, and they missed.

'Now it is your turn,' said Coyote to them.

Then the bird said to him, 'Throw on that side! They will dodge in that direction.' He threw, and knocked them down.

'Pa–pa–pa,' said Coyote. So he won. He kept on knocking them down. For five days he won, and won back all his people.

Then the Rogue-River people, said 'Let us climb for eagles. There are some a little ways over there.'

'Very well,' said Coyote. So they ran and came to a tree. Coyote climbed up, and as he climbed, the tree stretched up to the sky, and became ice – became so slippery, Coyote could not climb down. He threw down the young eagles. 'I don't know how I shall get back,' he said. Then he took some moss and floated down on that. He ran back, and came to the place where he had gambled. So again he won.

'My friend, let us go and fish at that weir,' said they.

'Very well,' said Coyote. So they ran thither. There was a rattlesnake in the weir. He took it out with his spear. Everyone ran away. Then he killed it.

It was a Rogue-River person. Coyote then ran back to his gambling and again he had won.

'My friend, let us dive for dead salmon!' said they.

'All right!' said Coyote.

'Take your arrow flaker with you,' said the little bird to Coyote. They went to the river and dove. Coyote was almost out of wind; he could not hold his breath any longer; but he got the salmon, and rose with it. Then he hit his head against the ice, for the people had caused the river to freeze. So with his arrow flaker he made a hole in the ice, and came out. 'An-an-an,' said he. 'Here is your dead salmon to cook.' So he won again.

'My friend, let us stop!' said they. 'Let us sweat!'

'Take a flute with you,' said the bird to Coyote. Inside the stones cracked with the heat; but Coyote made a hole with his flute, and ran through it and got out. So he won again.

Now Coyote went off. 'Let us stop here!' said he. 'I'll sleep here. I want to rest.' So he slept. By and by, it got dark. 'We must go back to my house,' said he to his wives, and they went. Then he took three rotten logs, and laid them side by side, and covered them with a blanket. He then went off, and leaned against a tree near by. Pretty soon some Rogue-River people came. They had big stone knives. They mashed and struck the rotten logs.

'What can this be?' said they. 'Long ago I said we ought to kill him, ought to catch him and kill him,' said they.

'You cannot catch or kill me, An-an-an!' said Coyote, and ran away.

They followed him, and were close behind. Coyote jumped into a clump of bushes. 'Let me become an old woman! I must be an old woman,' said he; and he became one.

'Hit him! That is the one!' said the pursuers.

'M–m–m!' the old woman sobbed. 'The one you follow passed by here running. I bore your mother long ago, I am your grandmother. He passed by here running and panting hard.'

Coyote came to a small creek. He jumped in, and said, 'Let me be a salmon.'

'That is the one! Spear it!' said the ones who followed.

'No! We must follow him,' said one. 'We can spear it coming back.'

'An-an-an! You will spear it coming back,' said Coyote and jumped out. Again they ran after him. 'Let me become a sedge!' said he.

'Pull that up, cut it!' said they.

Then Coyote said, 'An–an–an! You people are going to gather basket materials.' So he jumped up again, and again they followed him. 'Let me a fog!' said he. Then it rained and hailed. That is all.

CHAPTER 26

Shawnee

Huron Legend of the Snake Clan

An old woman and her granddaughter lived in a lodge in the pine woods. From the best hunters and greatest warriors of the tribe the young woman had offers of marriage. She was haughty, and would speak to none of her people. These women were of the Deer Clan. So it seems she (the young woman) was wandering about her lodge in the wilderness of the pine woods. She saw in the distance a fine-looking young man. He approached her with insinuating addresses. She desired him much. He carried her away to his own lodge. They lived there for some time. His mother lived in their lodge.

One day she went into the woods. She left him lying down. She came back to the lodge and looked among the skins where he was lying. There was a great heap of snakes. When she looked again, there was one snake – a big snake. She cried aloud and was terrified. His mother said to him, 'Why did you do this?' (i.e. turn into a snake).

She turned about, and fled for life towards the seacoast. When she reached the coast, she found a man in a canoe, who told her to jump on board. When she had done so, he paddled at lightning speed to the other shore.

When the man and the young woman in the canoe had gone some distance, they heard the snake man coming in pursuit, calling to his wife, and entreating her to return. He came to the water and waded in a way, in his effort to follow her, always crying out to her to return. When the snake man went into the water in pursuit, the black cloud rolled across the sky, and Heh-noh slew him with a fiery dart.

The man with whom she embarked conveyed her safely to the other shore. Upon her arrival there, she saw a man, who said, 'Follow me.' He took her to a medicine man. Her children were called snakes; and from these is descended the Snake Clan.

Legendary Origin of the Kickapoos

In the early days, ten Shawnees went on a bear hunt and were gone many days. When the hunt was finished, they made, as was their custom, a bear's foot feast. With the Indian the bear's feet, and especially the forefeet, are a great delicacy. When Indians went on a hunt, the feet of the bears killed were carefully saved for the feast at the termination of the hunt. On the occasion of which I am telling, the feet, as was the custom, were put in a kettle and hung over the fire to cook. It took quite a time for them to cook, as it does hogs' feet. While they were cooking, the hunters lay down to sleep – three on one side of the fire, and seven on the other. Some time in the night one of the seven men awoke and examined the feet to see if they were cooked enough to eat, but, finding they were not, lay down again and went to sleep. After some time one of the three awoke and examined the feet to see if they were sufficiently done; and he found that they were. He roused his two companions, and they ate all they wanted, and again lay down and went to sleep. Not long after that, one of the seven examined the feet; and when he found them ready to be eaten, he woke his friends, and then the three on the opposite side of the fire, and told them to get up and they would have their feast. The three told them they had had what they wanted, and that the seven could have what was left. So they began to eat, but soon discovered that their companions had eaten the forefeet, and had left only the small hind-feet for them. This made the seven so angry that they drove the others from camp, forbidding them ever to return to the Shawnee tribe. So they went off for themselves, and from them originated the Kickapoo tribe.

CHAPTER 27

Shoshone

Cosmology

Our own Father made us. First of all, he made the moose, then the elk, then the buffalo, then the deer, the mountain-sheep, the antelope, the crane, the chief of the birds, the big black eagle, the white-tailed bald eagle, the chicken-hawk and the homara, the owl, tire crow, the magpie, and the dogoaruka (snake-eater). Our Father made everything; he made us.

Our Father sent the crow, who was sitting on a high mountain, to bring earth. 'Get earth! I will once more create the drowned people.' Then the crow flew away, and, after a while came back to the creator. 'You must have been eating the drowned people. You stink. Go back! Now, you, little Chickadee, bring dirt! Then I'll create all the people again.' When the chickadee returned with dirt, our Father made the earth and sky. We now walk on the ground he made. He said, 'Now, my children, pray to me; then I will listen to you, and take pity on you.'

The whole earth was covered with water. Only on a high mountain there was a dry spot. Our Father sent the crow to get earth in order to make our land. Then the crow came back stinking. 'You are crazy,' said the Father; 'you have eaten the drowned people. Now, go back, and go around homeless. You will eat whatever anyone has killed. Go, now! You will be black.' Then he said to the small birds, 'Come, I will now hear which one of you has a good heart and good sense.' He found that the chickadee was the only one that had any sense and was good-hearted. Then he bade it bring earth. It brought it. Our Father made the earth out of it. 'It will be small,' he said, 'for little hands brought it. You will have six moons. You will not lose track of tongues. You have good thoughts.'

The Star Husband

Once two young girls were lying outside their lodge and counting the stars. They said, 'Would that those stars would come to us!'

The next morning their people broke camp. The two girls were continually losing their belongings and fell behind the rest of the people.

They lost their paint bags and went back for them. They found them and followed the trail. Looking back, they beheld two men who soon caught up to them, and asked, 'Do you two know us?'

'No,' said the girls.

Then the young men said, 'We are those two stars you wished to come to you last night.' Then the girls recognised them. The stars said, 'We will take you above with us.'

The girls consented. Then all went up above. The stars married them.

Once, after a long time, one of the women said to her husband, 'I am going with the others to dig roots.'

The star said, 'Yes, but be sure not to dig up a big one.'

The woman went. While she was digging, she thought to herself, 'I wonder why he forbade my digging up a big one.' She dug up a big root. Looking down, she saw all her people. She came home crying.

Her husband, knowing what she had done, said, 'I told you not to look.'

The woman said, 'I am going home.' Her husband consented to let her go. The next morning all the people went hunting. They killed lots of buffalo. The next day they cut the skin into strips of rope.

The woman's husband said to her, 'Well, attach your child firmly; tomorrow they will let you down. When you get back home, you must tell your brothers not to look at your baby.' In the morning they tied up the child and let down the woman with it.

One of her brothers lying in his lodge saw her descending. 'What is that falling from above?' The rest of the people looked for what he had seen, but could not detect it.

'Something is the matter with your eyes,' they said. He insisted he had seen something. After a while he again told them about it. Then they could see it. While they were gazing at the woman, she dropped to the ground. They untied the child.

She said to them, 'You must not see this child of mine.' She lived with them for a long time. One day she went out to fetch wood, leaving her child at home. While she was gone, a sore-eyed brother of hers thought, 'I wonder why she always said we must not see it.' He arose and looked at it. She had said it was a baby, but he only found buckskin bundled up. Unwrapping it, he took some for a breech-clout. His sister returned. She cried when she found her child gone. Then she declared to her parents and her brothers, 'I am going to follow my child's tracks.' She went and touched the sky rope, tied herself to it, and was pulled up to the sky. Her relatives all cried. They seized her youngest brother, the sore-eyed one, and threw him into the fire.

Weasels and Owl

Two weasels went hunting. They killed some game and dried the meat. The older brother said to the younger, 'It is not good to eat at night. If anyone builds a fire at night in this place, a bad owl will carry him away. You had best cook meat now, then you will not have to build a fire at night.' The younger man cooked plenty of meat, lay down, and ate in bed. He ate up all he had cooked. During the night he rose and built a fire. 'Oh, don't build a fire!' said the older man.

His brother answered, 'Oh, don't make believe it is bad. I will beat it to death.' He laid a bone among the food. He ate and sang. After a while a loud sound was heard. He took the bone and sat listening. The owl came near and sat down. He struck at him with the bone, knocking him down. Owl seized the man and carried him to his island home. Two young men were there and one old woman.

The young men told the newcomer, 'Tomorrow he will eat one of us.'

He replied, 'In the morning we will kill him.' Next day Owl killed one of the young men, ate part of him, and went hunting. While he was gone, the two surviving young men dug a hole and put a flint on the blood of the slain victim, sticking it through his flesh. Owl returned, ate of the corpse, and was killed by the flint. The two youths went into the hole, took the bird's wing, and made a boat of it. As they were starving, they ate the old woman. Then they returned home.

The Eye-Juggler

Coyote was eating rose-berries. He heard some yubaciduno (a species of birds) crying, 'Eyes, eyes!' He said, 'Oh, I hear my brothers!' and ran toward them. They came up to him. 'Hallo, my brothers! What were you eating? Tell me, and I will go with you.'

'We are eating yampas (wild carrots).'

'How do you eat them?'

'We just throw our eyes on the brush, then the yampas fall down to us, together with our eyes. Throw your eyes on the brush now, crying, "Eyes; eyes." '

Then Coyote threw his eyes up, and the yampas fell down to him. He ate them. 'Oh, they are good!' he said, 'This is a fine trick. Let us go around together now and practise it.' He went with them, and they all fed on yampas.

After a while Coyote said, 'My brothers, I can do this by myself, too.' He left them. He threw his eyes on a big brush, and the yampas fell down. He ate them. 'This is good,' he said. 'I will always continue to do this.' Again he threw his eyes on a big tree crying, 'Eyes, eyes!' His eyes did not come back to him. He repeatedly tried to get them back, but failed. Giving up hope, he went away.

Coyote got to the bank of a river, and sat down. On the other side he heard the jingling of bells. 'What kind of girls are you two?' he cried.

'We two are Yayaru girls. What kind of a man are you?'

'I am a Yayaru man,' he replied.

They said, 'Come over to our side.'

'No, you two cross over here.'

The girls came over to him, and offered to build a shade-lodge. They went upstream and erected it.

Coyote sat down inside. After a while he went out at one side of the entrance. When returning, he again missed the door. The girls said, 'Why do you never use the entrance?'

'Don't try to tell me,' he answered; 'if we went out by the entrance, the enemy might charge upon us.' They told him there were some buffalo resting on the hill. Coyote offered to kill one for them. He packed his quiver, and left, scenting for the buffalo-tracks. At last he got close to them, and repeatedly shot at them. By accident he hit one buffalo, and tried to locate it by its odour. The girls came running to him. 'Oh, what are you looking for?'

'I am looking for my arrows.'

'Why, you are standing on one of them.'

'Well, I see it, but I won't pick it up before I find another one.' At last he begged the girls to look for his arrows, and they began to search. In the meantime he had found the slain buffalo, and skinned it, but split the skin in the wrong place.

The girls returned with the arrows. 'Oh, what are you doing?'

'What have I done?'

'Why, you cut the skin in the wrong place.'

He answered, 'No, the larger piece is meant for the bigger one of you, and the other one is for the smaller one.' Then they helped him, and they got through skinning. They carried the game home, and roasted the ribs. As they were sitting there, one of the girls said, 'Something on the other side has a bad smell.'

'It is the buffalo I killed.'

After the meal, Coyote said, 'I wish one of you to louse me.' He rested his feet on one girl's lap, and the other began to pick his lice. The girl sitting at his feet happened to look into his face, and cried, 'Why, there is a worm coming out of his eyes!' Then both examined his eyes, and found them full of worms. They went out, brought in a rotten log, and laid his head on it while they placed his feet on a rock. Then they took their belongings, hung his quiver on a tree, and fled.

When Coyote woke up, he said, 'Oh, louse me!' His head bumped against the log. He found that the women were gone. He tried to find them, but in vain. He also failed to discover his quiver. At last, by smelling around, he found it, and by scenting also found the girls' tracks. He ran along, and caught up to them. When he was close, they threw their bells down a cliff. Coyote heard the bells drop, and tumbled after them. The women laughed at him. 'What is the sightless Coyote doing down there?'

He said, 'You are just talking. I have killed a big mountain-sheep, and am eating its marrow.' The girls went home and told about him.

Coyote's older brother went to look for him. Finally he found him and brought him back. For a while he was sick, then he recovered. One day Coyote played at nahanid. His brother bet on his success. Coyote missed the mark, and his side lost. After Coyote had gone to bed and was asleep, his brother looked at his eyes, and found that he was blind. 'He's blind, that is why we were beaten.' Early in the morning, while Coyote was still sleeping, his brother took a yearling buffalo's eyes and inserted them in the sleeping Coyote's sockets. Then he roused his younger brother. Coyote saw well. He repeatedly defeated the people at the game. This is how Coyote came to have a yearling buffalo's eyes.

CHAPTER 28

Sioux

Ben Kindle's Winter Count

1759 Wicablecaha Wani yetu
They are broken apart / year.
When the tribes scattered.

1760 Hokuwa Wicaktepi
Fishermen / they are killed. (While engaged in fishing, they are killed.)
Two Sioux boys went fishing in the creek and the enemy killed them.

1761 Wablikuwa Wicaktepi
Eagle, trappers / they are killed.
Two Shoshone were trapping eagles and some Sioux killed them.

1762 Pte Anuwapi
Buffalo / they swim out for them.
Hunters chased buffalos into the Missouri river and killed them there, then dragged them to land.

1763 Tuki milayapi
Shell / they use for knives.
The Indians had no knives, hence they brought shells from the Missouri and Platt rivers to use as knives.

1764 Tazuskala ktepi
'Little ant' / they kill him.
A Sioux called 'Little Ant' was killed.

1765 Wazikute ahiktepi
'He shoots at the pine' / coming they kill him.
The Sioux Indians attack the Crow and a Sioux named Shooting Pine is killed.

1766 Walagala ktepi

'Pouch' (made out of the rough lining of the first stomach) / he is killed.

A Sioux called 'Pouch' is killed.

1767 Anuk op iyayapi

Both sides / in company with / they go off.

The Crow Indians are at peace with the Sioux and the two live together, also the Sioux are at peace with the Pawnee and they live together. When the Crow and Pawnee fight together, they find that there are Sioux on both sides and so they make peace.

1768 Iyeska kicizapi

White or clear speakers (those whose language is understandable, i.e., those in the same tribe) / they fight against each other.

The first civil war among the Sioux Indians: The Standing Rock Indians and the Cheyenne fight against the Oglala and Rosebud.

1769 Itehakitula ktepi

'He (little one) wears a mask' / they kill him (or, he is killed).

A Sioux named 'Mask On' is killed. The mask is made out of buckskin fastened to a willow hoop with eyes cut for a mask.

1770 Wakataka iha bla wiya wa gnaskiya

God / to see in vision, or dream of in sleep / woman / a / she goes crazy.

A woman has been accustomed to go to lonely places for visions and then come back and tell the people where to go for buffalo and when the enemy is coming. One morning she can not speak, she does not know anything and soon she dies.

1771 Miwatani oguwicayapi

Mandans / they are burned out.

Hostile Indians dig a trench down by the creek and the Sioux are unable to drive them away. So they build fires all about the trench and the enemy have to escape in the night.

CHAPTER 29

Tahltan

The Man with the Toothed Penis

An old man had a penis that could reach a long distance. The end of it was provided with teeth which chewed like mice. It could cross water like a snake and go underground like mice and moles. When it met any obstructions, such as the roots of trees, it gnawed through them and went on. The man could distend or project it at will. When he thought he was observed, he drew it back, and it assumed ordinary proportions. It would attack women when they were asleep. They were not rendered pregnant, as the penis simply fed on them. When they awoke, they felt sick, but the feeling soon wore off. Once two young girls were sleeping together. The elder girl woke up feeling sick and thought she had felt something touching her. She found that her breeches had been gnawed as if by mice. She put on breeches of thicker skin and watched. The penis came and began to chew them. She seized it and held on. The old man tried to pull it back, but he could not do so. The girl called for her knife, which was made of an animal's rib. It would not cut. She asked for a sharper knife. The men came and cut off the end of the penis. The girl told them her story, and said that she thought the penis must belong to the old man who slept at the end of the lodge, for he was moving about. The next morning the old man was sick. He told the people that he was going to die. He said, 'I am very sick and am going to die. I cannot eat any food, for I have lost my teeth. I don't mind telling you everything, for you have found me out. Women's privates are my food. If you give me back the piece that you have cut off, I may live some years longer, but I do not care very much.' The people let the old man die. If they had given him back the end of his penis, *then men at the present day would have had small teeth there; but as they withheld, it has its present form now.*

The Three Sister Rocks

There were three large rocks in the Stikine River between Glenora and Telegraph Creek, known to the whites as 'Three Sister Rocks'. The Tahltan tell the following story of their origin. Once a long time ago in the Tahltan county, a number of people were living together. A girl of one family was discovered to have had connection with a dog, and this made her relatives and the other people so ashamed that they deserted her. After they had gone, she and the dog lived together as husband and wife. After a time she gave birth to three pups – two males and a female. When they had grown to be big, the mother suspected the boys of having connection with their sister, and to make certain of this she smeared gum on the girl's hands at bedtime. Next morning she discovered the marks of their sister's hands on the backs of both the boys. This confirmed her suspicions. She then left home with her husband and children and journeyed north. Reaching the Stikine River, she crossed over to the north side and then asked the children to follow. They crossed one above another in the stream, all holding hands. The father stayed on the south bank of the river and watched them. The youngest boy was downstream, his elder brother farthest upstream, their sister being between them. When they were in the middle of the river, their mother called to them to let go the youngest. They did as directed, the current taking him downstream. At the same time the other two disjoined hands; and immediately the whole group, including the parents, were transformed into stone. The dog children now form the rocks in the river known as 'The Three Sisters'. The smallest rock is more detached and farther downstream. The rocks on each side of the river opposite are the dog and the woman.

Story of Dcandui

Dcandui was a celebrated hunter who killed and trapped all kinds of game. Once he went trapping marmots, but could not catch any because his traps were sprung. Although he watched, he could not find out what sprung them. He fasted three days, and then made his deadfalls heavier. Again he fasted three days, and this time he caught somebody by the hand. The man begged him to spare him, and told him that he would go to his camp with him and help him. Dcandui agreed; and the man, who was Wolverine, accompanied him. Wolverine told Dcandui to fast for three more days and to save all the urine. Dcandui wondered what he wanted to do with the urine and watched through a hole in his blanket. When it was nearly daylight, he saw Wolverine get up and wash himself in the urine and then dry himself. That day they both set traps. Next day Wolverine had a marmot in each of this traps, while Dcandui had none. Wolverine now told Dcandui that he must not eat the small bone at the back of the knees of marmots. He wondered why Wolverine had told him that, and one day he ate one. Then came a spell of rain, snow, wind, and bad weather. All the marmots stayed in their holes, and they could not catch any. Wolverine charged Dcandui with having eaten the forbidden bone, but he denied it. Then Wolverine went and examined his excrement and found it. He said to Dcandui, 'You lied about not eating the bone, but I found it.' He wrapped it in feathers and burned it, saying, 'Tomorrow good weather will come.' After this they caught many marmots in their traps, and they soon had the camp full of meat.

When Dcandui was ready to go home, Wolverine said he would carry the meat for him. Dcandui made up a pack for Wolverine of about the same size and weight as he himself could carry. Wolverine said it was too light, so Dcandui added more to it. Wolverine said, 'I can carry more,' so he added more. At last all the meat was in Wolverine's pack, and he walked off with it as a man does with an ordinary load. When they arrived on the outskirts of the village, Wolverine put down his load and returned. He told Dcandui not to tell anyone that he had helped him. When Dcandui arrived home, the people asked him what luck he had had. He answered, 'Poor luck. I have a very small pack of meat. I left it some little distance away.' He told a man to go out and bring it in. The man could not move it, so he came back and told all the people to go and see it. They went out, and it took all of them to carry it in. They thought Dcandui must be a very strong man. *This is why Wolverines can carry such heavy loads now, and also why the Indians never eat the small bones at the backs of marmots' knees.*

Story of Gonexhataca, The Snail

Many people were living at a place called Cite. Among them was a little girl of the Raven phratry who found a snail and made a pet of it. She wrapped it up, nursed it, and played with it, just as little girls do with dolls. It grew in size. When the girl grew up, she dug a hole under her seat and kept the snail there. She always talked to it just as one speaks to a baby; and, as a mother does, she put it to her breasts. At last it drew milk, and grew rapidly in length and bulk. The hole became too small for it; and it bored underground with its sharp tail. It bored underneath her parents' house, and up through a vessel holding olachen oil, and drank all the oil. Now it grew to an enormous size. With great rapidity it bored from one house to another, until it reached the last house of the village. In every house it bored a hole upwards, and drank all the oil that was stored there. When the people went to their oil vessels, they found them empty, and wondered what had taken their oil. The snail lay with its head in the hole below the girl's bed. Whenever the girl went into her room, she at once opened the hole, called it pet names, fondled it, and called it 'my little boy' and by other endearing terms. She also sang cradle songs to it, and composed songs out of love for it. Sometimes her mother asked her what she was doing; and she answered, 'I am just fooling, and playing with a doll I have.'

Towards the end of the period of her puberty training, she went from house to house doing work for people – sewing, and making robes and moccasins. Her mother became suspicious. One day, when the girl was absent, she went to her daughter's bed and examined the place. She found below the bed a pit like a cellar. On opening it, the snail opened its mouth wide. She closed the pit quickly, ran out, and told her husband and sons. On the following day they sent the girl to the farthest house of the village. Then they prepared to attack the snail with spears and knives. The snail, when attacked, wriggled so much, that the ground burst in a number of places. At these places they cut through its body. After a while they killed it, and then covered up the places where the ground had been rent. The girl heard the commotion, and surmised that something had happened. However, the people of the house in which she was said nothing, and did not appear to be alarmed. When she reached home, she hurried to the hole where her pet was, and saw that it was dead. She reproached her brothers, saying, 'Why did you kill your nephew? I was rearing something for you to make you powerful and strong.' She wept much, singing, 'Oh, my little boy! Oh, his little feet! Oh, his little eyes, his little teeth, his ears, his nose, his moustache, his little hands!' She cried long, and would not be comforted. At last her mother broke down, and gave vent to her grief; then her brothers became affected, and joined in the crying; then her father, and finally all the people. The girl sang her cradle songs while weeping. She cut her hair, and all the people did the same; and thus they mourned for their dear dead relative the snail. *Because the girl suckled the snail, the women of the Raven phratry now have large breasts. Because the girl cried and sang, people now sing mourning songs when a relative dies. Because the girl cut her hair, the people followed her example, and now cut their hair when a relative dies.*

The Sisters Who Married Stars

Two adolescent sisters who were living together were staying apart from the other people. One evening when about to retire, they were playing and joking with each other. Happening to look up at the stars, one of them said, 'Do you see that nice star? That is my husband. I wish he would come here and take me!'

The other sister looked around among the stars, and picked out one which seemed very beautiful. She said, 'That one is my husband. I wish he would come for me!' Soon after this the girls fell asleep. In the morning they found themselves in the sky. The stars they had chosen had taken them up during the night. They lived with these men as their husbands. The star men were great hunters, and always killed an abundance of game. The women had to carry home all the meat and skins. After a while they discovered a hole in the sky, and they used to watch the people moving on the earth below. They thought by what means they might be able to descend to earth, and, according to the elder sister's suggestion, they secretly cut up skins and made a long rope. They told their husbands that some animal was eating the skins.

When they thought the rope was long enough, the elder sister said, 'I will go down first. If you feel me shake the rope, you will know that I have reached the ground. If I do not shake it, and all the rope is out, you will know that it is too short, and you must pull me up again. If you follow me, tie the end of the rope to the cross-stick over the hole, pull it up, and come down yourself.' Their husbands were out hunting. Both sisters reached the earth in safety. The rope was not quite long enough, but they alighted on top of a tall tree.

The younger woman had just got clear of the rope when the star men arrived, and finding that their wives had descended, but the upper end of the rope, which fell down had lopped off all the side branches of the tree. The women could not descend, and sat in the top of the tree, where a few branches were left. They called for help on the various animals that passed near the tree; but some passed without paying any heed, and others promised to help on their return.

At last Wolverine came along, and they called to him. He said to them, 'Yes, I can carry you down.' He climbed the tree and began to play with the girls.

The elder girl said to her sister, 'Keep him off until after he has carried us down.' She said to Wolverine, 'You must carry us down first.' He carried the elder one down, and wanted to lay with her, but she would not let him until he had carried down her sister.

When he came to her, he wanted to do likewise; but she said, 'You must carry me down first.' When he brought her down, he asked for his reward; and the sisters said, 'We are hungry; you must get us meat first.' He brought the meat, and asked them again. They said, 'Let us eat first.' When they had finished, he asked again; and they said, 'We are thirsty; bring us water first.' Wolverine was not getting tired, so he brought the water. They said to him, 'Take us up to the top of yonder steep bluff, and then we shall really give you what you want.' He took them there, and the women prepared a bed to sleep in. Wolverine wanted to sleep farthest from the steep bluff, but they made him take the place over the precipice. He lay down next to the younger sister, and immediately the elder one pushed him off. He fell over the cliff and was killed. Now the sisters left, and looked for the camp of their people. One night Bush-Tailed Rat entered their camp and killed and ate one of them. The other escaped and reached the people, who had given the women up for dead. The surviving sister told the people of her adventures and how the stars were fine-looking people.

Because of this story the Indians believe that *it is dangerous to wish for the stars;* for they may come and take you away, as they did the sisters in the story. Because Wolverine carried these women on his back, *the wolverine at the present day can carry meat on his back.*

The Man Who Fooled the Cannibal Giant

Some men were disputing as to the powers of cannibals and giants. One of them maintained that giants were not clever. They had mosquito brains; therefore, they could easily be deceived. He claimed that giants and cannibals and mosquitoes were all related, parts of the same flesh. They all had the same instinctive desire to attack, kill, and eat people; but nevertheless they were all foolish. This man said he would show the others how foolish giants really were. He would try them. He stripped off all his clothes, and stood naked near a trail that giants frequented, in an open place, where people could see a long way. A giant saw him, and came stealthily towards him. The man stood perfectly rigid and motionless. The giant came up and felt of him, saying to himself, 'He is just like game.' He smelled of his mouth, privates, and anus. He smelled of him all over. He lifted his eyelids, and opened his mouth. He said again, 'He is just like game, but he does not act like game. It is funny that he should be here now. Not long ago there was nothing standing here.' He wondered. He went away some distance and watched the man, but the man never moved. He went farther away and watched. Then he came back and examined the man again. At last he made up his mind that the object could not be game, and departed. When the giant was out of sight, the man put on his clothes and went home. *This is why, if a hunter sees game at a distance lying or standing and motionless, he is sometimes deceived, and mistakes the game for something else.* When one does this, other people joke him or make fun of him by saying, 'You are just the same as a giant,' or 'You have mosquito brains.'

Story of the War between the Tahltan and the Taku

A desultory warfare between the Tahltan and the Taku had continued for several years. A number of people on both sides had been killed. The Taku had almost exterminated a large camp of Tahltan at the mouth of Salmon

Creek, and the Tahltan had on one expedition killed many Taku on the Taku River. The nearest village of the Taku was at the mouth of the Nakina, and the village of the Tahltan closest to it was Tagoon on the Nahlin River. It was springtime, and the people of Tagoon were short of food. Four men from Tagoon went down to within the confines of the Taku country to catch spring salmon. They said to their friends, 'If we do not return within three or four days, you may assume that the Taku have killed us.'

These men discovered a fishing place of the Taku. Signs of people were still fresh; and fishing utensils, such as poles and spears, were lying about. They helped themselves to these, and began to fish. One of the men fished right at this spot; and his three companions, on the stream a little above. While they were thus engaged, a large party of Taku observed them. They went down to the stream and surrounded the men. Some of them crept unobserved to a rock overlooking the place where the lone man was fishing, and threw rocks into the water all around him. When he ran away, the party amused themselves by throwing stones at him from all directions, before they finally seized him. His companions also took flight, but were intercepted; and, seeing themselves surrounded on all sides by many people, they considered it useless to resist, so they threw away their arms, and allowed themselves to be taken. The four captives were tied each with a squirrel skin rope around his neck and waist. A man held the end of each rope, and they were marched down to the Nakina village, where the party was going to take their canoe to go down the Taku River. Some of them belonged to the lower part of the river, and others to the interior.

The party held a consultation as to how they should deal with their prisoners. Some said, 'Let us kill them at once.'

Others said, 'Let us take them to the place where the Tahltan massacred so many Taku, and let us kill them there. They will be a sacrifice to our dead.'

Still others said, 'Let us take them to the coast and make slaves of them.' The chief decided to take them down the river. The day they were to embark they were led to the canoes in the same fashion as before; but the people, while preparing for leaving, did not watch them closely. One young man who was being brought down behind the others, and was being led to the canoe, managed to loosen the squirrel skin ropes attached to his neck and waist. Suddenly he disengaged himself and ran off at top speed. The Taku chased him, but he was too swift footed and enduring for them, and got away by running uphill. In vain they fired arrows at him.

The other captives were taken in the chief's canoe, and were closely watched on the way down the river. On reaching their destination, they were allowed the liberty of walking around where they chose, for it was considered impossible for them to escape to their tribe from that distant place, and through such a difficult country, without being overtaken or dying on the way. They were also given plenty to eat, for a well-fed slave was of more value than one half famished and miserable looking. Their clothes were taken from them, and each was furnished with a goat wool blanket, their only clothing. They were not supplied with any moccasins, for fear that they might try to make their escape.

The Taku held another consultation, and it was decided that at a certain time when the people were ready, the captives should be taken up the river, and killed at the exact spot where the Taku had been slaughtered by the Tahltan three or four years previously. They were to be offered as sacrifices at this place with much ceremony, and many Taku were intending to witness their deaths. An old man and an old women had given the prisoners this information, so they made up their minds to escape at the first possible chance. They commenced to cache all the old moccasins that they found. One woman who took pity on them cached moccasins, knives, and flint and steel for them in different places, and told them where to find them.

One night they ran away, and in the morning met an old man who had been friendly to them returning from a hunt. He hailed them, and offered them meat and other assistance; but they were afraid, and hurried on without heeding him. The men had made their escape just when the Taku were about to ascend the river to execute them.

The Taku were much disappointed, and a large party followed the fugitives for several days without being able to overtake them. For five days the three men travelled without eating and without stopping. On the fifth day they came to a place where beaver were numerous. They caught four, and, after eating, they continued their flight.

On arriving opposite Tagoon, they found the people of that place all away. Before leaving, they had destroyed the bridge across the river. They went farther up to other places, but no one was to be seen. All the Tahltan of Nahlin and Chesley Rivers had gone east and south for fear of the Taku, and had destroyed the bridges across these rivers. The men proceeded up the north side of the main streams, and, crossing at a shallow place, went up on Level Mountain. Here, from a eminence, they saw smokes of camps in various directions.

Approaching the nearest one, they came upon a woman wailing, and lamenting the loss of her husband. It happened that this was the camp of the wives of these three men. Believing themselves widows, they had come up here together to snare ground squirrels for winter use. The husband of the woman approached her. He was naked excepting a piece of goat wool robe around his shoulders. The men had from necessity cut up their robes for use on their feet, and each now had only enough left to make a kind of cape. When the woman saw her husband, she believed him to be a ghost, and she excitedly called to the other women. When they realised that these were really their husbands, they were overjoyed and made a signal fire to call the people together. They came, and, after listening to their story, agreed that they would go on an expedition against the Taku.

The following spring, when the snow was well crusted and snowshoe walking good, the Tahltan assembled, and, with the four men as guides, went on the warpath against the Taku. While still within the confines of the Tahltan country, they met two caribou chased by two Taku men. They killed these men on the spot. On the fourth day the Tahltan reached the place where the Taku had camped the previous night. The Taku had broken camp when the hunters did not return, fearing an attack by the Tahltan.

The next day they had difficulty in following them, as the Taku had all separated in twos and threes, going in different directions. They found, however, that all met again at night, and camped together. After following them for three days, they found them encamped. The Taku evidently thought they had travelled far enough away to be safe, and had constructed a large sweat house in which all the adult men were now sweating, the rest of the party being in the camp nearby. The men had all their weapons hanging in a bush near the sweat house, their clothes and some tools being scattered around. Unperceived the Tahltan surrounded them. A boy who was playing around shooting arrows fired an arrow, which fell among the Tahltan. When he came forward to pick it up, he noticed the enemies in hiding. He made no cry, however, but, seizing his arrow, was about to run back with it, when a Tahltan clubbed him.

The Tahltan ran to the sweat house, threw it down, and dispatched all the inmates excepting one man who seized a fire drill and managed to get away. While the Tahltan were slaughtering the men who were sweat bathing, a Taku woman who was nearby seized a spear from the bush, attacked the Tahltan from behind, and killed two of them before they could dispatch her. Some of them pursued the man who had escaped, and soon overtook him on the ice of a lake, and killed him. He had no chance to make his escape, as he was naked, and without snowshoes could make no headway in the deep snow. They killed the whole Taku party, including the children, and spared only four young women, whom they told to seek out their tribe and relate the fate of their friends. They spared them because the four Tahltan men had been well treated and helped to escape by a woman. From this place the Tahltan party returned.

As soon as the ground was free of snow, a large party of Taku, including a few women, invaded the Tahltan country, bent on revenge. The Tahltan made signal fires all over the country, and assembled a party equally as large as that of the invaders. The latter crossed Chesley River at the ford near the mouth of Salmon Creek, and the two parties met on an open flat near the crossing. The Tahltan party had women with them, who were prepared for battle also. The parties talked to each other from a distance; and the chief of each, armed only with a knife, went forward, and they met halfway. The Tahltan chief was the father of the present chief, who is now a very old man. The people of each party held their weapons in hand, ready to attack each other. The chiefs sat down, and, taking sticks, counted the numbers slain on each side since the war began. The chiefs sometimes brandished their knives, and several times nearly fell a-fighting before a satisfactory arrangement was reached. During the war a larger number of Taku had been killed than of Tahltan; and since the life of each man, woman, and child on both sides was reckoned at a certain price, the Tahltan had to pay a considerable amount to the Taku. On the conclusion of the agreement, the Tahltan feasted the enemy, and each of the parties gave a dance.

When they parted, one important man of each party went with the other to stay for one year as hostage. At the appointed time the following year the two tribes met again at the same place and exchanged hostages. Each side feasted the other and exchanged a large number of presents. The Tahltan paid the blood money they owed, and a peace was consummated between the two tribes which has lasted to the present day.

The Woman Stolen by the Ducine

A Ducine man stole a woman, and took her to his country. After travelling many days, they came to a canyon, through which they passed. The Ducine people had their home at the other end. No strangers ever went through this canyon and returned, for the Ducine killed them. The woman bore two children. Both of them came to live among the people, whom they told all about the country and habits of their father's people. Their mother never returned from the Ducine country. After this marriage the Ducine did not kill any more people; and any who travelled into the canyon near their country were turned back, and not killed. The Ducine kept watchers at the canyon to prevent people going through.

The Story of Tcizqa; or The Hunter Who Could Not Kill Game

A number of young men were living together in a camp or lodge such as young men use at the age of puberty. Nearly everyday they went hunting. One of them never killed any game, and the others laughed at him. In the same place lived a wealthy man who had a young marriageable daughter. He thought it was time for her to marry; and one day he said to her, 'Carry a dish of food to the young men's lodge. Give it to the best hunter, and then sit down beside him and become his wife. You will be able to tell the best hunter by examining the young men's hands. The one who has the darkest mark at the base of the thumbs is the best hunter.' The young man who was an indifferent hunter happened to overhear these instructions. He went to the campfire and blackened the front part of his thumbs with charcoal. Then he sat down among the other young men and exposed his thumbs, that the girl might see them. In the evening the girl came, peered in through the brush of the lodge, and looked at the hands of the young men. She noticed that Tcixqa's thumbs were much darker than any of the others; therefore she entered the lodge, gave him the food, and sat down beside him. On the following day all the young men went hunting. They stayed out two days; but, as usual, Tcixqa had no game. They all laughed at him, and said that marrying had not changed his luck. After his marriage he left the young men's camp and went to live with his wife and father-in-law. He went hunting with the latter, but never killed anything. His father-in-law thought this was strange for a man chosen as the best hunter of all the young men. He resolved to watch him, to learn why the youth did not kill any game. He saw him going after a caribou. He just ran a short distance, then stopped and walked on with long strides, to make people believe by his track that he had been running. The father-in-law went home, and said to his daughter, 'Now I see what your husband does. He is no good. He cannot run, and therefore he never gets any game.' At last Tcixqa felt bad because he could get no game. He cut his anus and pulled out about a yard of his intestines, cut them off, and put them in a bag. Then he plugged the hole with moss and went home. When he reached there, he threw down the bag beside his wife, and told her to cook the contents.

His wife said, 'He has killed game at last,' and hurried to cook it.

Her father stopped her, saying, 'It smells bad. Let him cook it himself! There is something wrong.' He hung the intestines on a stick above the fire to cook. When he reached up, the plug fell out of his anus, followed by his entrails and blood, and he died right there. *This is why today women always fancy the best hunters,* but some choose and marry men who are very poor hunters. Also *this is why lichens (Cladonia bellidiflora) have red tips,* for the man used them as a plug. The red are the bloodstains.

The Deserted Woman

A long time ago an old woman was deserted by her people, who were short of food, and had to leave to look for game. As she was too weak to keep up with them, they left her behind in the old camp, with a fire. After the people had gone, she hunted around and found some scraps of sinew, with which she made a string for a rabbit snare. Many rabbits came to the deserted camp, as they love to do, and she caught some with her snare. She made many snares of the rabbit sinews. She caught many rabbits, and had plenty of food. She also made rabbit skin robes to wear and to sleep in. The people did not find much game where they had gone. After some time they sent two girls back to see if the old woman was alive and if there were signs of game near the old camp. They found the old woman with plenty of food, and well clad. They returned and told the people, who now moved back. As they approached, the old woman went out to meet them dressed in a large rabbit skin robe, and danced, and sang –

'You thought I would starve.
What did you think I would eat?
I am dancing now.
I wear a rabbit skin robe.'

The Cannibal Women Who Lured Men

A cannibal woman and her daughter lived on an island. When men landed on the island, they were lured by the mother to make love to her daughter. The daughter induced the men to lie underneath her; and then she slit their throats with her forearm, which was as sharp as a knife. The two women then ate the men's bodies.

A man who lived on the mainland nearby had noticed that no one who went to the island ever came back, and he wondered what became of them. He watched, and saw that they entered a house and never came out. He hid a sharp knife in his clothes and went to the island to investigate. He was called by someone who had a sweet, attractive voice. He followed the sound to the house. There he was met by the old woman, who invited him in, saying, 'Come in and see my daughter! I have a fine daughter of great beauty.' He went in, and noticed the old woman sitting some distance away, partly concealed. Presently a very fine-looking young woman came in from the other side of the partition, arrayed in fine garments and nicely painted and combed. She asked him if he cared to lie with her, and he nodded his assent. She told him to follow her to the other room. She asked him to take the lower position.

He said, 'No, I will not do that, in my country the man always is on the top.'

The old woman thought they were taking a long time. She became anxious, and called, 'Are you not ready yet?'

The young woman answered, 'No, he wants to be on the top; he will not go underneath.'

Her mother said to her, 'It does not matter, you can cut him just the same.' The young woman then agreed, and they lay down. The man quickly cut her throat, and covered her mouth with his other hand, so that she could not make a noise.

The old woman asked again, 'Are you not through yet?' and the man answered,

'No, pretty soon.' When he was sure that the woman was dead, he withdrew his hand and quickly ran out of the house. The old woman was surprised to see him run out, and went to see her daughter. When she found her lying dead in a pool of blood, she gave chase. The man ran to a strong fort in the forest. The old woman, who was in a great hurry, ran straight through the forest, cutting a wide swathe of trees and bushes with the large knives on her forearms. When she reached the log fort, she attacked it with her arms, the knives cutting slices out of the logs. As she kept on cutting, she became more and more tired, and the knives more and more dull. When the house was almost cut through, she became so tired and the knives so dull, that she could hardly cut any more. The man then ran out and killed her with his knife.

Big-Man and the Boy

Two brothers were out hunting, and came to a porcupine hole. While they were trying to get the porcupine, Big-Man overtook them. He had been following their tracks. When they saw him, they were much afraid, and crawled into the porcupine hole. Big-Man asked them to come out. He asked them many times; but they were afraid, for they thought he was a cannibal and would eat them. At last he told them that, if they did not come out, he would defecate in front of the hole, and then they would never be able to get out. The younger brother said to the other, 'I shall go out. He may eat me. Then perhaps he will leave you, and will not defecate in front of the hole.' He went out; and Big-Man patted him, and told him he would not hurt him. The boy said to his brother, 'Come out! This is a good man, and he will not harm us. He is not a cannibal.' The brother, however, refused. He said, 'He is treating you well just to deceive us. When he gets me out, then he will eat us both.' Big-Man became angry and defecated in front of the hole, and his excrements turned into rock. The boy could not get out; but Porcupine made a new hole to get out in another place, and thus liberated the boy, who went back to the camp and told his people how his brother had been taken by a giant.

Big-Man carried the boy he taken in a bag. He saw some caribou, and said, 'See the rabbits!' He killed three of them and slipped the carcasses in his belt, carrying them much more easily than a man could carry rabbits.

After a while he saw a moose, and said, 'See the caribou!' He shot the moose, and carried it in the same way. At night he camped, started a fire, cooked the moose and three caribou, and fed the boy. He was very much amused at the small quantity of meat the boy ate, and laughed heartily. He said, 'You are a light eater.' He finished all of the rest of the caribou and moose himself. Soon he said, 'Let us go to sleep!' and he lay down on the ground, occupying the whole of a large open place. When he spread out his arms and legs, he knocked down all the trees in the way, just as a person might do with grass. He put the boy in his armpit to sleep; but the boy crawled out, and lay by the fire. The lad grew rapidly, and soon became a man. They came to a lake where there was a large beaver house. Big-Man said, 'See the beaver! Get a pole to open their house.' The boy cut a pole about four inches through, such as is used by Indians for breaking open beaver houses. Big-Man laughed, and said, 'That is no good, it is too small.' He got the boy to cut larger and larger ones, until he was hardly able to carry the last one. Big-Man said they were all too small, and that he would now help him. He pulled up a large tree by the roots, struck the top of the beaver house with it, broke it down, and thus killed all the beavers. He picked out the carcasses and cooked them. He ate the meat, but threw the tails into the lake. The boy took one of the tails and ate it. Big-Man said, 'Don't eat that! It is poison, and will kill you. In my country we never eat beaver tails. We are afraid of them' The boy continued eating the tail, so Big-Man thought he would taste it. He said, 'Oh, my! It is very sweet!' and he sent the boy to gather up all the tails that he had thrown away. He ate them all. Big-Man asked the boy how he knew that beaver tails were such nice food; and he answered, 'They always eat them in my country.'

He stayed with Big-Man a year, and by that time was a full grown man. Big-Man treated him well all the time. Now they came to the end of Lower Iskut Lake. The lad said he saw something dark moving near the other end of the lake. He thought it must be wind or a storm cloud. Big-Man looked, and said, 'A bad man lives there. He is a large fierce cannibal. His children are swinging there.' When they came near, they saw two large trees moving backwards and forwards. The hammock of the cannibal giant's baby was attached to them. The baby was asleep, and the mother was there swinging it. Big-Man told the lad not to be afraid when they entered the camp. Big-Man asked the giantess where her husband was, and she answered that he was out hunting. The giant himself then killed the woman by means of his membrum, which was so long that it pierced her heart. They then killed the baby and departed, leaving both bodies where they were. Big-Man said to the lad, 'Her husband will pursue us, but do not be afraid. If you run away, he will eat you.' Big-Man always carried a bag which contained four heads – two of old and two of young beavers. These were his helpers. He said to the lad, 'When the cannibal giant attacks me, and seems about to overcome me, I shall call on you. You will then bring the heads of the oldest two beavers and place them against his legs. If I call a second time, bring the heads of the young beavers.' Soon the cannibal arrived at the other end of the lake. He cried when he discovered the bodies of his wife and baby. He tracked Big-Man, who waited for him. When he reached them, he said to Big-Man,

'You killed my wife and child.' Big-Man acknowledged it. Then they fought and wrestled almost all day. Towards evening Big-Man called out that he was getting weak. The lad took the heads of the oldest two beavers out of Big-Man's medicine bag, which was in his charge, and placed them one against each leg of the giant. They chewed the giant's legs; but their teeth were dull, and they were too old to chew very fast. Before long Big-Man called again, and the lad set the heads of the young beavers at the giant's legs. Their teeth were sharp, and they cut quickly. The beavers chewed through the giant's legs; and he became helpless, and was about to fall. Big-Man held him up, and called to the lad to run to the top of the neighbouring mountain. The lad ran up a considerable distance, and called, 'Grandfather, am I far enough?'

Big-Man answered, 'No, go farther!' The lad climbed again. Thus several times he asked Big-Man, and then went higher, until at last he reached the top. Big-Man then lifted up the giant's body and threw it into the lake, and the splash of the water almost reached the place where the boy was standing. The remains of his body may be seen there now as island in the lake.

After this event Big-Man found the lad crying one day, and asked him the reason of his sadness. He said he wanted to see his parents. Big-Man said, 'All right! You shall see them.' The lad thought he might lose his way if he attempted to return alone. Big-man said, 'No, you will not get lost.' He cut a stick, and peeled the bark off the lower end, leaving a little bark and the stumps of the limbs at the upper end. He said, 'Plant this stick at your camp every night before you go to bed, and in the morning you will find it on the ground pointing in the direction you have to go. At night sing the word "TatsEstuhe!" and game will appear, which you may kill and eat. Sing "EkukEmze!" when you want fat, and it will be there for you to eat; but always leave a little, never eat it all.' The lad bade Big-Man goodbye, and started on his journey. The first night he sang the game song Big-Man had given him, and immediately a lynx appeared above him on a tree. He killed it and ate his fill. The second night he sang the fat song, and a white thing appeared. This was fat. He ate what he required, and left a little. Thus he used the guiding stick and the two songs as Big-Man had directed; and each morning he knew which way to go, and each night he had plenty to eat. At last he came to the crossing of two winter trails made by the people. He camped here, as he had been directed by Big-Man; and in the morning, by the direction in which the stick lay, he knew which trail to take. At last he reached the lodge of his people. He stuck up outside in the snow the stick Big-Man had given him, as he had been directed. In the morning it was gone. He kept the fat for a long time. He ate it whenever he wanted, but always left a morsel. In the morning the piece of fat was always as large as before. He kept it in a sack. Once when he was out hunting, his brother looked in the sack, and, seeing a little fat, ate it all. The fat expanded in his stomach, and he swelled out and burst.

The Bad Man and His Son-in-Law

A man who had married a girl, the daughter of a man of evil disposition, was hated by his father-in-law, who had made up his mind to kill him. One day he told the man to go hunting at a place where a gigantic cannibal toad lived. When the man approached the toad's abode, he knew by the power of his protectors that he was in danger, and called on them for assistance. His four protectors – the grizzly bear, black bear, wolf, and lynx – appeared at once. The toad came out to fight the man, and opened its great mouth to bite him. Grizzly Bear, who was foremost, immediately jumped down its throat before it could bring its jaws together, and the others followed him. Then the four tore its entrails, and the man shot and killed it. The animals ate their way out, leaving four great holes in its body. When the man returned, his father-in-law was much disappointed because he had not been killed.

The following day he asked him to go hunting on a high mountain at a place where snow-slides always came down and killed people. When he reached this place, he changed himself into something so tiny that the snow-slide could not crush it. The avalanche came and carried him down, but failed to harm him. When he arrived at the bottom, he resumed his natural form and went home. His father-in-law could hardly suppress his disappointment and anger.

He said to his daughter, 'I will change you into a grizzly bear. Go out on yonder side hill and act and feed like a bear.' He put a bearskin on her, and told her to tear her husband. Then he pointed out the bear to his son-in-law, who went to kill it. When he came near and was about to shoot, his wife called out, 'Don't shoot! Save me! I am your wife.' He never heeded, and kept on shooting until he had killed her. His father-in-law was now very angry, and pursued him. The man threw down part of the inside of the bear; and this formed a deep chasm between them, stopping for a time the advance of his pursuer. The latter caught up again; and the man threw something behind him, which again formed an obstacle and delayed his pursuer. Thus he threw down several things, which became canyons, lakes, etc., behind him. His father-in-law managed to pass them all, and again caught up. He had only one thing left that he could throw. This was a stick, which turned into fire. His pursuer ran right into the fire, and was burned to death.

CHAPTER 30

Tewa

Water Jar Boy

The people were living at Sikyatki. There was a fine looking girl who refused to get married. Her mother made water jars all the time. One day as she was using her foot to mix some clay, she told her daughter to go on with this while she went for water. The girl tried to mix the clay on a flat stone by stepping on it. Somehow some of it entered her. This made her pregnant, and after a time she gave birth. The mother was angry about this, but when she looked she saw it was not a baby that had been born, but a little jar. When the mother asked where it came from the girl just cried. Then the father came in. He said he was very glad his daughter had a baby. When he found out that it was a water jar, he became very fond of it.

He watched it and saw it move. It grew, and in twenty days it had become big. It could go about with the other children and was able to talk. The children also became fond of it. They found out from his talk that he was Water Jar Boy. His mother cried, because he had no legs or arms or eyes. But they were able to feed him through the jar mouth.

When snow came the boy begged his grandfather to take him along with the men to hunt rabbits. 'My poor grandson, you can't hunt rabbits; you have no arms or legs.'

'Take me anyway,' said the boy. 'You are so old, you can't kill anything.' His grandfather took him down under the mesa where he rolled along. Pretty soon he saw a rabbit track and followed it. Then a rabbit ran out, and he began to chase it. He hit himself against a rock. The jar broke, and up jumped a boy.

He was very glad his skin had been broken and that he was a big boy. He had lots of beads around his neck, earstrings of turquoise, a dance kilt and moccasins, and a buckskin shirt. He was fine looking and handsomely dressed. He killed four jackrabbits before sunset, because he was a good runner.

His grandfather was waiting for him at the foot of the mesa, but did not know him. He asked the fine looking boy, 'Did you see my grandson anywhere?'

'No, I did not see him.'

'That's too bad; he's late.'

'I didn't see anyone anywhere,' said the boy. Then he said, 'I am your grandson.' He said this because his grandfather looked so disappointed.

'No, you are not my grandson.'

'Yes, I am.'

'You are only teasing me. My grandson is a round jar and has no arms and legs.'

Then the boy said, 'I am telling you the truth. I am your grandson. This morning you carried me down here. I looked for rabbits and chased one, just rolling along. Pretty soon I hit myself on a rock. My skin was broken, and I came out of it. I am the very one who is your grandson. You must believe me.' Then the old man believed him, and they went home together.

When the grandfather came to the house with a fine looking man, the girl was ashamed, thinking the man was a suitor. The old man said, 'This is Water Jar Boy, my grandson.' The grandmother then asked how the water jar became a boy, and the two men told her. Finally, the women were convinced.

The boy went about with the other boys of the village. One day he said to his mother, 'Who is my father?'

'I don't know,' she replied. He kept on asking, but it just made her cry.

Finally he said, 'I am going to find my father, tomorrow.'

'You can't find him. I have never been with any man so there is no place for you to look for a father,' she said.

'But I know I have one,' the boy said. 'I know where he lives. I am going to see him.'

The mother begged him not to go, but he insisted. The next day she fixed food for him, and he went off toward the southwest to a place called Horse Mesa Point. There was a spring at this place. As he approached he saw a man walking a little way from the spring. He said to the boy, 'Where are you going?'

'To the spring,' the boy answered.

'Why are you going there?'

'I want to see my father.'

'Who is your father?'

'He lives in this spring.'

'Well, you will never find your father,' said the man.

'Well, I want to go to the spring. My father is living in it.' said the boy.

'Who is your father?' asked the man again.

'Well, I think you are my father.'

'How do you know that?'

'I just know, that's all.'

Then the man stared hard at the boy, trying to scare him. The boy just kept on saying, 'You are my father.'

At last the man said, 'Yes, I am your father. I came out of the spring to meet you.' He put his arms around the boy's neck. He was very glad his boy had come, and he took him down to the spring.

There were many people living there. The women and the girls ran up to the boy and put their arms around him, because they were glad he had come. This way he found his father and his father's relatives. He stayed there one night. The next day he went to his own home and told his mother he had found his father.

Soon his mother got sick and died. The boy thought to himself, 'It's no use for me to stay with these people,' so he went to the spring. There he found his mother among the other women. He learned that his father was Red Water Snake. He told his boy that he could not live over at Sikyatki, so he had made the boy's mother sick so she would die and come to live with him. After that they all lived together.

Tewa Goat

Once upon a time there lived at Tewa a goat who was a great gadabout. He had a very firm friend in a chicken cock. The sheep and goats had decided at a council of their chiefs, that, if they wanted to live to a good old age, they must cease eating of anything that would make fat. So Goat, knowing man better than his sheepish companions, concluded that the best way to do was to hunt for rabbits, and bring them to the village to trade, as the Navaho did. He asked Cock to go hunting with him. He said to Cock, 'But what are you going to do, my friend, for something to eat? I can eat grass, but you need corn.'

'Oh, no!' said Cock, 'I will fill my pouch with corn, which will last a long while; whereas you must have water, which I can do without.'

'Don't let that trouble you!' said Goat. 'I know where a spring runs cool and refreshing water.' They started, each wondering what the other would kill. At dark they reached the buttes, and at a place where a single cedar was growing they camped. Just after they had settled down for the night, a man came along and went to sleep under the tree. So Cock emptied his bowels, and the droppings struck the face of the sleeping man. He woke up, and he cried out that it was strange that in this country it should rain when there were no clouds in sight. Then Goat shed his filling; and again the man cried out that it was a strange country, for it hailed when no storm clouds were in the skies. When it became day, he saw the goat, but it ran away. Then he saw the chicken in the tree. He shot at the chicken, and killed it and ate it. From that day to this, the Castillia has been eating chicken. That is all.

CHAPTER 31

Ute

Nowintc's Adventures with the Bird Girls and Their People

Nowintc was wandering alone about the country. He thought how he would like to have a home, a tepee, and many babies. Then he came to a hill where there plenty of service berries, and he ate some. He spied a deer, and crouched down behind the bushes. He was just going to shoot, when the deer saw him and cried, 'Hold on! Don't shoot me, and I'll tell you something. I saw two girls over there swimming in the lake. It is a fine lake, and many people swim there. The water is neither cold nor hot, but just right. All the girls swim there. It is just over the hill, with a fringe of willows all around it. Go and look through the brush, and maybe you will see something.'

So Nowintc went on till he came to the lake. He went close and peeped through the willows, and saw two girls swimming. They looked something like birds – one yellow, the other green. He looked around till he found their dresses, and took them a little distance off. Then the girls noticed him, and said to each other, 'Why has he taken our dresses?' And they cried, 'Bring our dresses here!'

Nowintc then came up to them, and said, 'Well, if you like me, then I'll give them to you.'

One of the girls said, 'Why should we like you? Give me my dress.'

'We'll talk about that pretty soon,' said Nowintc.

Then she said, 'Well, I like you,' and Nowintc gave her her dress. The other girl said nothing. Then the girls talked together so that Nowintc did not hear. They talked about some fine ear ornaments they had left under their dresses when they undressed. They prized the ornaments very much. Nowintc had not seen the ear ornaments; but if he had taken them, the girls would have said they liked him very quickly. Then one girl got dressed and put on her ear ornament without Nowintc's knowledge.

The other girl then said, 'All right, I like you,' and Nowintc gave her her dress. When she had put on her ear ornaments, she told him that if he had taken the ornaments, they would have married him, but since he had overlooked them, they would not.

Then Nowintc told them about the service berry bushes, and they all went and ate some, and also some choke cherries. The girls had brought some bread and meat along to eat. Now it was night, and Nowintc was sleepy. He said, 'Let us sleep here tonight and go home tomorrow!'

'Our home is a long ways off,' said the girls. They thought, 'He would like to sleep with us.' So they all lay down to sleep. The two girls tickled and played with Nowintc, and he liked it. Now it was midnight. Nowintc was sound asleep, but the girls only pretended to sleep. Then they got up and ran away.

At daylight he woke up and looked around. 'Where are my girls?' he cried, for he liked them very much. He resolved not to go back, but to hunt for them, so he followed their tracks. They led up to the top of a hill and then disappeared, just as if the girls had flown away. Then Nowintc walked back to the lake again. It was now noon, and there were three boys swimming in the lake.

He lay down in the willows for a while. Now it was afternoon, and he went down to the lake shore. 'Hallo, Nowintc!' cried the boys. 'What are you doing here?'

'Oh!' said he, 'I came over to take a swim.'

'Do you swim here?' they said. 'We never saw you here before.'

'What people have you seen here?' asked Nowintc.

'Oh! We see everybody here; we've seen many girls swim here, three or four kinds.'

'What colour girls?' asked Nowintc.

'Oh! all colours,' they replied. 'We've seen black ones, white ones, sometimes one a little red, sometimes a little white, sometimes red, sometimes yellow and green ones.'

'They are the ones,' said Nowintc. 'Where are they from? What tepee?'

'Oh! their tepee is very far off,' said the boys. Then they told him all about the girls. 'They have nice ear ornaments, green ones for the green girl, and yellow ones for the yellow girl. When they come to swim, they put the ear ornaments under their dresses. Maybe Nowintc will come along, and like the girls. If he takes the dress and ornaments that's the best way to catch the girls. If he keeps the ornaments, but gives them the dresses, then the girls will say, "Let's go home to mother and make everything right!" Then he will be married.' Then the boys said to him, 'You don't know much! If you do that, then you'll be married.' Then they said, 'Maybe you are Nowintc. We think so. You took only their dresses. You don't know much.'

'Yes,' said Nowintc, 'but where do the girls live?'

'Far to the east,' answered the boys. 'You go about a hundred miles, and then you come to a big mountain. From there you can see another big mountain about a hundred miles farther on. You go straight to this mountain, and from its top you can see a little house, about fifty miles away. Here one of the girls lives.'

Nowintc thanked the boys and started off. He travelled very fast; and when he had gone halfway to the mountain, he rested awhile on a high hill. Then he continued on to the mountain, where he slept for a night. In the morning he started off for the next mountain; but he felt rather tired, and soon sat down for a rest. Then he went on a long distance through a river bottom, and soon he saw two boys playing on a little hill. He went up to them. 'Hallo, boys!' he said.

'Hallo, man!' they answered. 'Where have you come from?'

'Oh, I came along the trail,' he answered. 'I don't know the trails about here. Where does this one lead to?'

'It goes to the big mountain a long ways off,' they replied. 'But why are you coming this way?'

'I am hunting for my girls,' he replied.

'What girls?' they asked.

'Two of them, one green and one yellow.'

'What kind of ear ornaments had they?' asked the boys.

'Green and yellow ornaments and dresses,' he said.

'Yes,' answered the boys, 'we saw them. They are very far off yet, a long distance past the big mountain. Maybe you won't be able to walk there. It is very far.'

Now the boys had some fine large eagle feathers with them. 'What do you do with those feathers?' asked Nowintc.

'Oh, we just use them to fan ourselves when we are tired,' replied the boys.

'No,' said Nowintc, 'now tell me the truth.'

'Well,' they answered, 'we use the feathers to fly.''

'How do you use them?' asked Nowintc.

'We hold some feathers in each hand and cry, "Fly, fly!" and then we go.'

'Let me see them!' said Nowintc, and he took the feathers in his hands. Then he noticed a veil on each boy's arm. 'How do you use the veils?' asked he.

'We spread them over ourselves, and then no one can see us,' they answered.

'Let me see them also!' said he, and they gave them to him. Then he spread out his arms with the eagle feathers in his hands, and cried, 'Fly, fly!' He rose into the air and flew rapidly over the big mountain. He looked behind, but the boys could not come after him. Soon he stopped safely in front of the house he sought. Nowintc then spread the veil over himself and walked around the house. In the door sat an old woman, and inside the room an old man. In the other room he heard a girl singing. Then he walked slowly in the door. He looked at the old couple, but neither of them saw him.

Then he looked into the other room and saw the green girl cooking meat. She put the meat down, and Nowintc ate it all up, for he was hungry. Then the girl turned around and saw that the meat was gone. She cried, 'Where's my meat? Who took it?' Then she went out to the old woman and said, 'Mother, did you eat my meat?'

'No,' her mother answered, 'I guess you ate it yourself. Maybe you are joking.' Then the girl came back into the room. Nowintc took off his veil, and the girl saw him. He put his hand over his mouth as a signal to be quiet.

Then she shut the door and greeted him, saying, 'How did you come here?'

'Right through the door,' he answered.

'Didn't my father and mother see you?'

'No.'

'Are you hungry?'

'Yes, very.'

'Well, come here tonight. My father is harsh, and maybe he will bother and scold you, but after supper he will go to sleep.'

Nowintc said, 'All right!' Then he put on the veil and went noiselessly out of the door. He went out a little ways to a hill, where he lay down and slept, for he was very tired.

When he awoke, it was nearly nightfall. Near him he saw some people who had not observed him. He crawled up close, and saw a man with two girls. The girls, who were all black, said, 'We saw a man called Nowintc over at the lake far back there.'

'Well,' said the man with a conceited air, 'is he a much better-looking man than I?' Then he stood up and posed. 'Do you like that man Nowintc?' he asked.

'No,' they replied, 'that Nowintc is a nice man, but do you see that green girl over there? She likes him. He caught her and the yellow girl at the lake, and now they want him all the time.'

Then the man said, 'What's the reason they don't like me? Why do they like him? What tribe does he belong to? I'm a good man.' Then he posed again.

But the black girls smiled, and said, 'No, the girls like Nowintc.'

The man said, 'Why don't they like me? I'm a good man. I'm going down to see them tonight.'

Now it was nightfall. The old father ate his supper; and then his daughter said to him, 'You'd better go to sleep, old man; you're pretty old.'

So he went to bed. Now Nowintc came in and sat down, and she gave him plenty to eat.

Then Nowintc said, 'Another fellow is coming to sleep with you tonight.'

'What kind of a fellow is he?' asked the girl.

'He was with some black girls,' explained Nowintc.

'Oh,' said the girl, 'I don't like him, and my father and mother don't like him, either.'

Nowintc said, 'Then let him come in.' Soon there was a knock at the door. Nowintc put on his veil, and the green girl opened the door.

'Why do you come here?' she asked. 'You had better go home.'

'Oh, I have come to sleep with you,' said the man.

'No,' replied she, 'I'll tell my mother.'

'What's the reason you don't like me?' he asked.

'You'd better go home,' she replied.

'Do you like somebody else?'

'No.'

'What's the matter with me?' he asked, as he strutted with pride. 'I'm a good man. Look me over.'

'No,' she said, 'you are not. You haven't any nice ring. I'll tell my mother if you don't go home.'

'All right,' said he, 'I'll go,' and he went.

Then the girl made the bed, and they spent the night together. She said to him, 'Maybe my father won't like you, and will tell all the people around here. They are bad people and may kill you.'

In the morning the green girl got up and got the breakfast for the old couple. Then she said to Nowintc, 'Come and get your breakfast.'

The old man looked at him and said, 'What is this man doing here?'

'I met him a long ways off at the swimming lake,' replied the girl. 'He took our dresses and gave them back again. That's the reason he comes here to see me.'

'Well,' said the man, 'I'll go out and see my friends about it.' So he went out and told everyone he met, 'A man came and slept with my girl. What shall I do?'

'Let's kill him!' said all the people, so they told a number of boys to go and get him. Then they made a great fire, and put a big pot full of water over it. Soon it was boiling. Then they brought up Nowintc and held him firmly. They said, 'Now we are going to put you in. If you don't cook, if you live, then you can have the girl.' Then they all laughed, for they thought he would certainly be boiled. But Nowintc thought, 'Maybe I won't cook; maybe I will cool the water like ice.'

So he said, 'All right, but put my legs in first. I'll boil upwards!' Then several strong men seized him and put him in the pot, standing, while all the people laughed. But as soon as his feet touched the water, 'pssst!' It sounded as if a cold object had been thrown in. Nowintc walked around in the pot and then jumped out. He was not hurt. All the other people were much frightened, and started to run, but Nowintc caught one young man. He was quite angry. 'Now it is your turn,' said he, and he threw him in the pot and held him in. In a few minutes he was entirely cooked. Then Nowintc walked back to the green girl.

Now all the people were greatly afraid of him. They talked to each other, saying, 'What tribe can he belong to?'

'And how can we kill him?'

'Let us make an iron fork with many sharp points. Then we will tell him, "If you can run into this fork, and not be hurt, then you can have the girl."' This they did, and told Nowintc. 'All right,' said he, 'I'll do it first, but one of you must do it after me.' They agreed. Now Nowintc thought, 'Maybe I will break the iron; maybe it won't hurt me.' So they made a great iron fork. Nowintc ran full into it, but the points all broke. They would not hurt him. 'Now fix it up the same way,' he said, and they did so. 'Now you run,' said Nowintc to a young man. He did so, and the iron points ran clear through him.

Now the people were greatly afraid of him, and wondered,. 'How can we get rid of him?' So they took him to a great forest of timber. 'Can you chop all this timber?' they said.

'Yes,' he answered. Then they gave him an axe and put him to work.

'When you chop it all,' said they, 'you can have the girl.' He worked hard all day, but cleared only a little ground. At nightfall they said, 'Well, Nowintc, go home now, and chop some more tomorrow.' So Nowintc went home and had supper with the green girl. Then he sharpened his axe and went to bed. But soon he got up, took his axe, and went to the forest. He felled each tree at one stroke, and by morning all the timber was down. Then he came back home. Next morning the people saw what had happened, and then they were even more afraid of him. 'We can't beat this fellow Nowintc,' they said. 'What tribe can he belong to?'

And the green girl said, 'No! You can't beat anything he does. If you try to, many of you may be killed.' So Nowintc lived with the green girl many days. Soon there was a girl born to them.

Now Nowintc wanted to go and see the yellow girl. He put on his veil and took the eagle feathers in his hands, and soon he was at her home, many miles away. She also had a father and mother. Nowintc slipped past them into the house where the yellow girl was. Then he took off the veil. The yellow girl laughed, and said, 'Where did you come from? Did you come to see your girl?'

'Yes,' he replied.

'Then you like me?'

'Yes.'

Then she said, 'But maybe my father and mother will not like you. Maybe they will tell all the people around here, and they will kill you. They will kill anybody here.'

In the morning the yellow girl got breakfast for the family. Then her father said to Nowintc, 'Well, Nowintc, do you want my girl? We will go out and see all the people, and fix it up.' So they went out together.

The people thought, 'How can we get rid of him?' Then they decided to heat a pot of water and put him in.

'If you are not hurt,' said they, 'then you can have the girl.' They thought it would certainly kill him, but Nowintc was not afraid.

He knew now that the hot water would not hurt him; so he said, 'If I am not hurt, one of you must jump in after me.'

'All right,' said they, and they laughed. Then they put him in, feet first, but he jumped out unharmed.

'Now you try that,' said he, as he threw another man in. Then he came back to the yellow girl.

'Weren't you afraid you would be cooked?' she asked. 'They are pretty bad people.' Then they spent the night together.

Now the people were very much afraid of him, but they disliked to give him the girl. So they led him to a tall pole, and said, 'Now, Nowintc, if you can climb to the top of this pole, you can have the girl.'

'Very well,' said Nowintc, and he climbed it. 'Now you do it,' said he. 'Who can beat me?' But all who tried it fell off. They could not beat Nowintc. But they thought they must somehow get rid of him.

'Let us make him walk a rope,' said they. So they stretched a long rope between two rocks. 'You must walk that rope,' they said. 'If you fall off, you cannot have the girl.' But Nowintc walked easily over the rope. He could not fall off.

Then he said to the others, 'Now you walk that.' Two other men then tried it, but they fell off and broke their backs.

'What can we do now?' they said. 'He is a very clever man.' Then they all went to the girl's father.

'Let him have the girl,' he said, and so Nowintc married the yellow girl.

Soon his father-in-law said, 'Well, Nowintc, go hunt deer and buffalo. You'd better ride the mule.'

But the yellow girl heard what her father said, and she went to Nowintc. 'That's a pretty bad mule,' she said; 'but just say to him, "Don't hurt me; I'll give you something good to eat. But kill that old man." Then let him feed on good grass while you hunt.'

So Nowintc rode the mule off. When they came to a good pasturage, he got off and said to the mule, 'Mule, look here! Don't kill me; I give you good feed. But kill that old man who starves and beats you.' Then he went out and killed a deer. He packed it on the mule's back and came home.

When he got home, all the people were standing around. They were surprised to see him, and said, 'What's the reason the mule didn't kill him?' Nowintc unpacked the meat and took it into the house, and the yellow girl cooked it.

Then the father said to one of the men, 'Put the mule in the corral and whip him.'

So one of the men took him in. He hit him on the head, and said, 'Why didn't you kill him?' but the mule only shook his head. Then the man beat him. This maddened the mule so that he bit the man in the neck and carried him to the river. Then he dropped him in and came back.

Now the yellow girl said to Nowintc, 'That's a bad mule. You'd better go out and feed him.' So Nowintc went and inquired about the mule. Another man came into the corral, asked the mule about the first man; and began to beat him. Then the mule grabbed him by the neck, and dropped him in the river.

Then the people said, 'We'd better kill that mule. He has killed two men.'

The yellow girl heard this, and said to Nowintc, 'They are going to kill the mule tomorrow. Let's run away on him!'

So at night Nowintc went to the mule and said, 'The people are going to kill you. We two will ride you away, and you must go fast.' Then Nowintc packed up some food, paints, and all the girl's things. They got on the mule and started off, and loped all night at a good pace.

When the yellow girl's father arose, the sun was up high. 'Why don't you get up and get breakfast?' he called. But the yellow girl was gone. Then he woke his wife, and told all the people. He went over to the corral, and found the mule gone also. He told all the people, 'My girl has run away with Nowintc. Let's kill them both!'

Now, the mule kept on going, and at last they came to a very wide river and swam across. They saw the people close behind them; so Nowintc said to the mule, 'We'll stop here and fight. We'll kill them all.' So they jumped off. Five of the people swam across after them, and found the trail and followed it. Then the mule rushed at them. He was very angry. He bit and kicked them until all were dead, and Nowintc captured all the horses. They were of all colours – bay, yellow, black, white, and roan. Now he had five horses and one mule.

The yellow girl said to him, 'These horses can ride a long ways.'

He asked, 'They won't balk, fight, bite, or kick?'

'No,' said the girl, 'they are all right.'

Then Nowintc said to the mule, 'Well, you are all right, too.' Then they set out again with the mule and horses. After many camps, twenty days, they came to Nowintc's house, and settled there. Soon they had children, two boys and a girl. Soon the boys were grown and able to ride horses.

The green girl's daughter was grown also. She asked her mother one day, 'Who is my father? I don't know him. How was I born?'

'Your father is far away at the other side of the swimming lake. His name is Nowintc,' the mother replied.

'Let us go to see him,' said the daughter; so they set out.

Now, Nowintc told his boys, 'Over there is a nice lake where we used to swim. It is a little hot and a little cold.'

'Let's go to see it!' said the boys; so they went. They undressed and went in to swim. Now, the green girl and her daughter came up to the lake. The boys saw them, and said, 'Let's go and speak to them!' so they dressed and went up to them.

The green girl saw that the boys were all yellow. One of the boys had his sister's ear ornament which belonged to the yellow girl. The green girl recognised it, and she said, 'Who are your father and mother?'

'Our mother is Yellow Girl, and our father's name is Nowintc,' answered one of the boys.

'Now I know you,' said the green girl. 'Girl, these are your brothers. These are Nowintc's boys. How many of you are there?'

'Three,' the boys answered. 'One girl at home.'

'I will go and see my father,' said the green girl's daughter. Then she and the boys went to Notwintc's house, but the green girl went back to her home. They came up to the house, and the yellow girl's daughter saw them coming.

'My brothers are coming,' she said, 'and one green girl with them.'

Her mother said, 'That must be my friend's girl.' When they came up, she said, 'Why didn't your mother come too?'

'She went back to her father and mother,' replied the girl, 'for they are old.' Then they welcomed her into the home. Soon Nowintc returned from the hunt and greeted his daughter.

The green girl's daughter stayed with Nowintc for a year. Then another Ute came to woo her. She asked Nowintc how he liked him, so Nowintc talked to him. 'Have you a father and mother?' he asked. 'Have you, many relations?'

'Yes,' answered the boy. 'Many over there.'

Then Nowintc questioned him further. 'You are a good fellow? Never get angry? Know everything? Got a father and mother, uncles, aunts, brothers, sisters, cousins, grandfathers, grandmothers, all relatives? Are you a good worker and good hunter – deer, buffalo, everything? You are an honest man?'

'Yes,' replied the boy.

Then Nowintc asked all his family what they thought of him. 'Yes, he's all right,' they all said.

Then he told the boy, 'All right. You are married now. Don't whip your wife, and don't hurt her. Hunt all the time and be honest.'

One day he said to Nowintc, 'We will go to see my mother-in-law.'

Nowintc said, 'Take along the mule to pack, but leave him outside the village, where there is good grass.' So they packed the mule and set out on horseback.

'Go along fast,' they said to the mule. For fifty days they travelled, and at last they came to the town.

Then young Nowintc said to the mule, 'Stay here and watch the horses, for maybe the men here would kill you. Listen to me!' Then he hung the saddles on a tree, and said to the mule, 'Watch these saddles.' Then they walked over to the house.

'This is my mother's house,' said the girl. Her mother saw her; and cried, 'Hallo, my girl! have you come home?'

And her grandfather said; 'What man is this?'

'Oh, he's my husband; he's a good man. Where's my grandmother? Hallo, grandmother This is my husband. He's a nice man.'

'What kind of a man have you for a husband?' said her grandfather.

'Oh, he's a Ute, Nowintc, just the same as my father.'

'Where has your father gone? Where's his home? Did you see a mule over there? Where is he?' asked her grandfather, who had heard of the mule from the yellow girl's people.

'No, I never saw any mule,' she answered.

Then the young man went to work. 'You know how to work corn?' asked the grandfather.

'Yes.' The old man watched how he worked. He worked well, making straight rows, and letting the water flow in between. 'My father does this way,' he said.

Now all the people were evil. They said, 'What kind of a fellow is this? What tribe? Let's kill him!'

'No,' said the old man,' he's a good worker.'

'This old man says "no,"' said the people. 'Let's take him to some other town!' So they took him to Yellow Girl's town. 'Let's go see Yellow Girl's father!' they said, and so they went to see him.

'What tribe do you belong to?' asked the old man. 'Are you a Nowintc? Where did you come from?'

'Oh, far back this way.'

'Do you mean north, west? Did you see Nowintc and Yellow Girl? Another Nowintc stole my girl, and we don't know where he went. She took along all her things, and a mule ran away with them. I think my girl talked to that mule. She told him something, and that's the reason he went. We were angry, and some people went after him. But he crossed the river and killed five men. Do you know where he lives?' the old man asked. 'Has he got many people over there?'

'Yes,' said the young man. 'He lives far off this way. You can't kill all his people.'

'Well, I'll go after him,' said the man. 'I will hunt my girl. All the tribe will go next month, and we will kill him and the mule. You'd better come along with us and show the way.'

'No,' said Nowintc. 'I'll stay and work.'

'I want another man to go with me,' said the yellow man. 'We will kill him with guns and arrows. We will fight all the Nowintc people over there.'

'All right,' said the young man, and he went back to the green girl's town.

The yellow man said, 'How shall we try to kill him?' but the other people said,

'No, this Nowintc is Green Girl's husband.'

And his grandfather said, 'No, I like him. He's a good worker. I'll go and see Green Girl's father.' They talked a long time.

'How do you like this man?' asked Green Man. 'What kind of a man is he?'

'Oh, we want to try to kill him, for we are angry with him. Old Nowintc stole my girl and mule. We went after him, and he killed five men at the crossing, so we are going to hunt him.'

'Well, this boy is all right,' said Green Man. 'He's a good worker, a good young fellow. I think you can't kill a good man. If you do kill a good man, then his friends will be angry and kill all your people. Then you lose everything. That's very foolish.'

But Yellow Man only said, 'All right. I'll go after my girl and my mule. We start in about a month.'

Young Nowintc heard all they said. After a few days he went out to see the mule and horses. He hid some good dry buffalo meat there and talked to the mule. 'That Yellow Man is angry. Next month he is going to kill you and Nowintc. Pretty soon I'll come here again, and then we'll go and tell Nowintc that another tribe is coming to fight. You had better wait here and watch the horses, for there is nice grass and feed here.' Then he went back. He took some of the dry buffalo meat with him, and gave it to the women. His wife gave some to the old couple. The old man tasted it, and said it was good.

'I brought it all the way from my father's,' said the girl. 'We call it buffalo meat.'

'Is that so?'

'Yes, all people eat it over there.' Very soon Yellow Man started with all his tribe.

Then young Nowintc said to his wife, 'We'll go and see your father, for he must fight pretty soon. We will tell your grandfather.'

But the girl said, 'No, we won't tell the old man. We'll run away.' So Nowintc went to the mule and put his saddle on.

'Well, mule,' said he, 'let's go home fast!' The old mule was now quite fat, but he jumped and kicked. Nowintc packed the mule and saddled the horses, and they went home fast.

Young Nowintc said to old Nowintc, 'Well, Nowintc, this Yellow Man is coming very soon. He will fight and kill everybody, the mule and all the people, for he has guns, arrows, tomahawks, and other weapons.'

But old Nowintc said, 'Oh, we don't care! We've got plenty of men. You'd better take another horse and ride around and tell all the Nowintc people. Get arrows, guns, and all weapons.'

So young Nowintc took a horse and rode all around. He saw all the Nowintc people, all the Ute chiefs, and told everybody the bad news. All the Utes gathered around. 'Yellow Man is angry,' he told them. 'Nowintc stole his girl and his mule. You must all fight. Fix your guns, arrows, and everything.'

'Let's fight!' they said, and they all came over. They all got arrows, service berry sticks, stone clubs, and all their weapons, and fixed them up.

They watched for Yellow Man's band every day, and at last they saw them coming. The next day they arrived, and they came close to the house where all the Nowintc people were ready. The war chief had a white horse, and he rode out in front and talked to Yellow Man. 'What are you going to do? Fight?'

'Yes,' said Yellow Man.

'All right,' said the war chief. 'Fight! We like it!' Then all the Nowintc people began to fight. The war chief hit the yellow people with his tomahawk. Young Nowintc rode a horse, while old Nowintc had the mule.

He said to him, 'Let's kill all those people! Ride into them and knock them down. Arrows and spears won't hurt you.' Then he rode the mule fast and whipped him hard. All the yellow people shot at them; but the mule knocked them down, and Nowintc hit them with his tomahawk. Then all the Nowintc men went home to dinner.

After dinner they fought again till sundown. The mule kept going, and arrows and weapons could not hurt him. Many of Yellow Man's people were dead, and they were forced back to stay for the night. Then the war chief said, 'Come on! Let's fight some more! Would you like some more fighting? All right! We'll fight some more in the morning!

They began to fight again in the morning. Almost all the yellow men were killed, and the Nowintc people surrounded them and closed in. They stopped shooting when Nowintc came close on the mule. He talked to Yellow Man. 'Well, do you want to fight some more?'

'No,' said Yellow Man, 'we want no more fighting. You are my girl's husband; you are my son-in-law. All right. I'm not angry.' Then he saw the mule. 'Nice mule,' he said. 'You're all right. We won't be angry any more. We will fight no more. I will go and see my girl, and then I'll go home.'

Nowintc said, 'Well, your people must not fight us any more. We must be friends with everybody.' Then he said, 'I went to see Green Girl's people, to see her father. I saw bad men there. They tried to kill me, but they don't know how to kill anyone. They can't hurt anybody, but they are very bad men. Maybe he would like to fight! We could whip him surely. I am angry at him, because he tried to cook and stick me. I made him stop, and he will never do that again. After that I went to see your people, and you tried to kill me in the same way. You tried to cook me! You tried to make the mule kill me; but he ran away, for he does not like you. You told the mule to kill people, and that's the reason he is bad. He wouldn't do it himself; this mule would not hurt anybody. If you stop doing everything that's bad, there will be no more trouble. Next time the mule may kill all your people.'

The Yellow Man said, 'Yes, I hear. I will go and see my girl. I will tell all my people to go home, and I will go after I see my girl.'

Then Yellow Man went to see his daughter. The mule watched him closely, and went behind him and laid his ears back. Yellow Man was frightened; but Nowintc told the mule, 'You must not hurt him.'

'Hallo, girl!' said Yellow Man.

'Hallo, father! These are your grandchildren, one girl and two boys.' They all shook hands and kissed each other. Then she cooked some buffalo beef, and gave her father some to eat.

'That is nice eating,' said he, 'but I must go home pretty soon.'

The next day the two boys went out hunting. They shot buffalo, deer, elk, and mountain-sheep, and brought the meat home. Then they dried and pounded it, and packed it in parfleches. They made blankets out of the buffalo hides and packed all on a horse. Yellow Man took it along. 'Well, you must come and see me some time,' he said.

'All right,' said they, and he went home.

He left the mule behind. 'All right,' he said, 'you can have this mule,' for he was afraid of it.

It was along ways to Yellow Man's home. He found only the women and children left, and they were all crying, for nearly all the men had been killed.

Soon afterward young Nowintc went hunting. He shot many animals, and dried and pounded the meat to make tcequqqwanti. Then he packed the meat and went with his wife to see the green people. He left the mule at home. It was a long journey. The green men asked him what the yellow men did. 'We talked to the yellow men,' they said. 'We said, "You can't kill good men. Maybe they will kill all your people." '

Nowintc told them, 'We saw the yellow men back there. They fought with the Nowintc people. They had arrows, bows, and tomahawks; but Nowintc beat the yellow men and killed over half of them. Then they surrounded them, and Nowintc said, "We will fight each other no more." That is all. Maybe Yellow Man will come over here to see you, and tell you all about it.'

Green Man said, 'All right. Go and work now. Your crops are all right.' Then the girl brought out the sacks of meat, and gave her grandfather some.

'This is buffalo meat,' she said. 'This is deer meat, this elk meat, this antelope meat.' He tasted all.

'That's all right,' he said. 'It is nice meat. I am not hungry any more.'

Then Yellow Man came over. The girl saw him coming, and said, 'It looks as if Yellow Man is coming.' He came into the house and saw Green Man.

'Hallo, my friend!' said he. 'All right, sit down, and tell me everything you have been doing.'

'All right. I'm tired. I've been a long ways about two moons ago. We are tired of war, tired of fighting. We had a big fight, and we are very tired. Nobody hurt me. All the others are dead or hurt, and I alone am not injured. One man fought us all. We thought we killed most of them, for we shot many times and saw many fall. After that I quit. A war chief told me to stop. "You must fight no more," he said. "We will not fight you any more; let's all make friends and have no more fighting; then anyone can visit anyone else anywhere!" "All right," I said, and so I came to tell you. I went to see my girl over there. I have three grandchildren, two boys and a girl. I got everything I wanted there, good meat buffalo, deer, elk, and antelope. I began to fight with many of my people, my friends. We thought we would beat them the next day, but many ran away and only a few were left. I gave Nowintc my mule. He has it now, and he has my girl too. He said, "Let's have no more fighting. Let's have everything quiet and everyone friends." "All right," and I came home alone.'

Soon Green Man went over to see Yellow Man's people. 'Well, how many came back?' he asked Yellow Man.

'Oh, most of them ran away from the fight. They were afraid. I thought they were all lost, for the women told me they were all killed, a thousand dead.'

Yellow Girl's boys went hunting one day. They packed the mule with the meat, and started with Yellow Girl to see her father. Nowintc stayed at home. 'You'd better take that mule,' he said to the boys. 'Leave him outside of the town, for there is good feed there. Maybe the yellow men won't like him.' They journeyed along slowly, and left the mule in some good grass outside the town. Then they saw Yellow Man.

'Hallo, father!'

'Hallo, girl!' They shook hands. 'Hallo, my grandchildren!' and he kissed them. 'Did you bring some buffalo-meat?'

'Yes.'

'That's what I like, all kinds of meat. It tastes nice; I like it. Isn't Nowintc coming?'

'No, he is staying home to work.'

'Why doesn't he come over? We will counsel what he said. You'd better come over.'

The yellow man told all the people to come over to a big talk, and they all came to the council house. Yellow Girl and the boys came in afterward and sat down in the middle. Then Yellow Man spoke. 'All my people! These are my grandchildren, Nowintc's children. He is everybody's friend.' Then all shook hands. 'We must all be friends now. We must not kill each other, and everything must be quiet. Hereafter anyone may visit anyone else in safety, and any tribe may marry with any other tribe.'

Coyote Juggles His Eyes and Becomes Blind

One day while out walking, Coyote came to a lake where there were many ducks and geese swimming around. He went close to the water and sat down. 'They look good to eat,' thought he; 'I wonder how I can catch them!' At last he decided to try walking on the bottom of the lake. He walked a long way out until he saw the birds' feet, and then he seized them and walked ashore. He did this until he had three or four big ones. Then he packed them home, and met his Indian friend. 'What do you call them?' he asked him.

The Indian called the ducks 'triqute' and the geese 'uwénunq.'

'What are they good for?' asked Coyote.

'They are good to eat,' replied the Indian; 'we use the small feathers for pillows to rest our heads, and the long feathers to feather our arrows.' So Coyote cooked the birds and ate them, and made arrows with the long feathers.

Then they went hunting fish. The Indian shot one and took it home. He showed Coyote how to use the bow and arrow, and Coyote went hunting alone. He stood on the bank of a creek, and a big fish came swimming along. Coyote shot at him, but the big fish broke the arrow. Coyote was so frightened that he ran home and told the Indian. 'Go again,' said the Indian, 'and kill the fish; he is good to eat, and you can dry and keep his flesh also.'

Then Coyote walked till he came to a big white-pine tree. He heard some laughing and talking, and saw some bears there, so he ran home and asked his Indian friend for some arrows. Then he returned and crawled up close to the bears, who were copulating. He heard the bear's wife say, 'Hold on! Coyote may come and see what you are doing.'

But the bear laughed and said, 'Oh, no, Coyote is a coward. He is afraid of everything. If he saw me a long ways off he would run.' Then Coyote came up close, shot him many times, and then chased him. The bear wondered, 'How did Coyote learn to shoot, and hurt me? I'll kill him some time.' He was very angry, but Coyote only laughed.

Another time Coyote was wandering around to see what he could find. He heard birds laughing and talking. So he crawled up close to the willows and brush by the lake, and saw many little birds in a tall tree. The little birds pulled their eyes out and threw them up in the willow branches. Then they shook the branches, and the eyes fell down in their places again. Then they laughed. Coyote asked them what they were doing with their eyes, and they said they were just having some fun. Then Coyote said, 'Let me try it!'

'No,' said they, 'you will lose your eyes; you can't do it.' But Coyote went and sat down by the lake. He felt crazy. He pulled his eyes out and threw them up in the willows. Then he shook the willows, but the eyes only fell on the ground. Now he was blind. He thought now he was certainly crazy. He heard water rushing far away, and followed it and sat down by the brook.

Soon two little girls came along. They did not see him; but he called to them, 'Hallo! Where do you come from? What tribe do you belong to?'

'Shoshone,' they replied. 'What tribe are you?'

'Just the same as you, Shoshone,' he said. 'I'll go along with you.'

'All right,' said they, so he covered his eyes and went along. Soon they came to a buffalo, and the girls told him to kill it.

'Yes,' said Coyote, 'but I left my arrows at home.'

'Never mind,' said the girls, 'we'll make one quickly;' so they made one out of bone.

'You'd better kill one,' they said, and so Coyote walked till he got the wind from the buffalo. Then he crawled up along the wind and shot several times. He hit and killed it, but he did not know it. He thought he had missed. Soon the girls came up. 'Why don't you skin it?' they asked.

'Well,' he replied, 'I was waiting for you.' Then he followed them up to the buffalo.

'Why don't you begin?' asked the girls.

'I haven't any knife,' he said. Then one of the girls handed him hers. He grasped blindly at it.

'What's the matter?' she said. 'Haven't you any eyes?' Then Coyote took the knife and tried to skin the buffalo, but he cut it all to pieces.

'What's the matter?' they said. 'You've cut the skin all to pieces.'

'Oh!' he said. 'I tried to skin it quickly. We'll throw it away and kill some more buffalo.'

Then the girls cooked the beef, and told him to come and eat. He walked past far below the fire. 'Where are you going?' they cried.

'Oh,' he said, 'I was just doing that for fun.' Then he came up and sat down in the meat.

'Why do you sit down in the meat?' they said. Then the girls made a wickiup, and Coyote went to sleep while they stayed up and packed the meat.

Then they thought, 'What's the reason he can't see? Maybe he has no eyes!' So they crept up to him, lifted the covering, and saw, that his eyes were gone. So they ran away and left him still sleeping. They found some old timber full of red ants, and bought it back to the camp. They put it under his head and then ran away. The ants ran all over his head and into the eye sockets and bit him.

Then he woke up and cried, 'Come here! The ants are biting me all over.' But there was no answer. Then he jumped up and smelled around till he found the girls' trail, and ran after them. The girls were now on a high hill, and saw him coming.

'What's the matter?' they cried.

'All right,' said he; 'I'll catch you.'

'All right;' they replied.

One of the girls had a purse with jingles on it. These made a great noise, and Coyote followed the sound. Now he was catching up to them. On the other side of the hill was a high cliff. The girls shook the purse, threw it over the cliff, and then ran to either side. Coyote ran right over the cliff and broke his leg. The girls came to the cliff and looked over. Coyote was far below on the rocks, eating the marrow out of the broken bone. The girls cried, 'Coyote, what are you doing? Eating your own leg grease? Shame!'

But Coyote said 'No! I killed a mountain sheep, and I am eating his bones. Better come down.'

'No,' said they, 'you are eating your own leg grease. Shame!'

CHAPTER 32

Western Mono

The Making of the World

In the beginning, Prairie Falcon, and Crow were sitting on a log which projected above the waters that covered the world. They asked Duck of what number he had dreamed, and he replied, 'Two.' Prairie Falcon assigned him the number three, and instructed him to dive into the water and bring up some sand from the bottom. Duck dived to get the sand, but, before he reached the bottom, the three days allotted him expired. He awoke from his dream, died as a result, and floated to the surface. Prairie Falcon, however, brought him back to life and asked him what the trouble was. Duck replied that he had come out of his dream and had consequently died and floated to the top.

Prairie Falcon now asked Coot of what number he had dreamed. Coot replied, 'Four.' Then Prairie Falcon assigned him two and ordered him to dive for sand. Before Coot had reached the bottom, however, the two days had elapsed and he came out of his dream. He, too, died in consequence, and his body floated to the surface of the waters. Prairie Falcon espied the corpse, recovered it, and resuscitated Coot. He inquired of Coot what had been his difficulty. Coot replied that he had passed out of his dream.

Grebe was the next individual whom Prairie Falcon interrogated as to the number he had dreamed of. Grebe replied that he had dreamed of five. Prairie Falcon arbitrarily assigned him four as the number of days which he should take in securing sand from beneath the waters. Prairie Falcon then ordered him to dive. Grebe was successful and secured sand in each hand, having gone clear to the bottom of the waters. As he was returning to the surface, he passed out of his dream state, died, and floated to the surface. Prairie Falcon resuscitated him and inquired if he had secured any sand. Grebe replied that he had and Prairie Falcon inquired what he had done with it. Grebe explained that it had all slipped from his grasp when he died. Prairie Falcon and Crow both laughed at him and said that they did not believe it. Then they examined his hands and found sand under the finger nails of both. They took that sand and threw it in every direction. That is what made the world.

A Visit to the World of the Dead

A man was in deep sorrow over the loss of his young wife. After much mourning, they buried her, and she went up into 'heaven'. Then he set out to recover her.

He was forced to pass through swarms of noxious insects and ferocious animals. First he encountered fleas, innumerable fleas, which nearly bit him to death. Then he encountered lice, exceedingly large lice, which nearly ate him. Next he encountered ants of many sorts, but after much suffering passed through them. Subsequently he encountered mosquitoes, gnats, yellow jackets, and hornets. After these he passed through swarms of horse flies and blow flies. Then he came to gopher snakes, then to water snakes, then to racer snakes, then to rattlesnakes, then to king snakes. Nevertheless, he passed through all of these. In succession he then met with foxes, raccoons, dogs, coyotes, pumas, wild cats, bears, and wolves.

When he came to Wolf's camp, Wolf told him to take some sand in his hand and to walk right across the river with it and not to stop. He instructed him to drop the sand as he waded along. Wolf also warned him not to smoke Coyote's pipe when it was offered to him at Coyote's habitation on the far side of the river. This was the advice that Wolf gave the man who was seeking his dead wife. Above all, Wolf cautioned him not to participate in any dance in the land of the departed.

'Do not talk to your wife, when you arrive there,' said Wolf. 'Just walk by and touch her on the shoulder with your elbow, and she will know that you want her to follow. Just keep on going the way you came.' Then added Wolf, 'When your wife walks behind you, she will talk to you and try to get you to look back; but do not do it. When you arrive at home, your wife will go to her grave. Then you send her mother to go and get her. You must not talk to her for ten days.'

The man followed Wolf's instructions and returned with his wife. Unhappily for him, however, he failed to observe the ten days' taboo against conversation, with the result that his wife returned to 'heaven'.

Walking Skeleton

The people were about to play hand games in the house. Walking Skeleton was travelling towards the house. He was climbing the mountain ridge below, just at dawn. He was singing. The people in the house were getting ready to play hand games and were just getting kindling for their fire, for the opposing groups played on opposite sides of the fire. At this juncture Walking Skeleton appeared. 'What are those people doing?' he asked as he thrust his head in the door and whistled. All of the people died, because they looked at Walking Skeleton when he whistled.

The people in the house had previously sent a girl outside of the house as a lookout. She put on a rabbit skin blanket when she went outside as guard. She had failed to see the approach of Walking Skeleton. Consequently, when she returned to the house she was astonished and grief-stricken to find the occupants dead, with the exception of a female child, who had been asleep and had not looked upon Walking Skeleton or heard his whistle. The child awoke about sunrise, and the girl opened the door for the little one to go out. When the two were together outside the girl began to sob and cried, 'What am I to do all alone in this world?' Finally she said to the child, 'We shall have to depart,' and she proceeded to collect what food she could. She could not tear herself away from her home at once, so she went about the house tidying things; she went around and around the house, back and forth. 'What shall we do now?' she queried as she took the little child by the hand. 'You gamblers certainly look fine now,' she said, ironically addressing the dead. After removing the things she wished to take; she set fire to the house and cremated the dead. Then she started with her belongings and the child, as the sun was mounting the sky.

The girl started on her wanderings, but she had not gone far before she thought of some buried pine nuts near the house. She returned for these and, after securing them, started again with the child and a large bundle. After she had gone half way up the ridge, the child became exhausted. The girl decided to stay there beside the trail. After depositing her bundle and leaving the child with it, she went out to dig some Indian potatoes. She gathered a basketful, made a fire and roasted them in the ashes. All this consumed considerable time, but finally the two sat down to partake of the potatoes. The girl kept looking about her apprehensively, fearing that Walking Skeleton might be about. Sure enough, he came along and sat down between the girl and the child.

'Eat some potatoes with us,' the girl invited.

'I surely will eat some,' responded Walking Skeleton. 'They certainly taste nice,' he said, after sampling them.

'Just help yourself,' said the girl, and she started away to dig more of them. She looked back when she got on the ridge and said, 'What am I going to do with myself now?' She looked about her and saw a rock pile which might serve as a refuge. She thought longingly of the people who dwelt safely far back in the mountains. Then she walked back to the edge of the ridge and had another look below at Walking Skeleton, for she thought she smelt something roasting. She saw that the little child had disappeared, and she perceived Walking Skeleton licking the child's blood from a rock. At the sight, tears poured down the girl's cheeks. When the monster had finished, he called to the girl,

'Your child is crying.'

She responded, 'I shall be there in a few minutes.'

Walking Skeleton called to her again, but she slipped behind a clump of bushes. She said, 'I will leave an echo here, so that when he calls, it will answer him. I think that I had better set out for a safer place.' She went to the edge of the ridge and peered over once more. Walking Skeleton was busy going through the bundle which she had been carrying. She stood there and watched him. 'Oh dear, what am I to do now?' she sighed. Then she started on her journey. She crossed two ridges. Then she said, 'This will not do. I will have to travel faster.' Thereupon she took a long pole, pressed one end of it against the ground and vaulted over a high mountain. About this time Walking Skeleton started to track her.

Beyond the mountain over which she had vaulted, she found a sage bush growing beside a big rock. She pulled the bush up by the roots and hid herself in the hole beside the rock, then she put the bush into place. About sundown Walking Skeleton reached the girl's hiding place. He dug around the bush a bit and then he said, 'I believe that I will wait until morning. I will sit up all night, so that she cannot escape.' He burned some logs, so as to have plenty of light. He lay there and kept turning and turning. 'I wish it were morning,' he said, after he had become weary of waiting. The girl heard him all night long and she was very much distressed over her precarious situation.

'I do not know what I shall do. I fear this will be the end of me,' she thought to herself. Daybreak, however, found Walking Skeleton sleeping soundly.

The girl heard his welcome snoring and said to herself, 'He is sound asleep. I do not think that he can catch me, if I leave now.' When she came out she stood right above him, stood there and looked at him, while he was sound asleep. She departed and crossed two ridges before Walking Skeleton awoke.

When he awoke he looked around for a minute or two, then he set to work to dig up the sage brush, seeking the girl for his breakfast. As he pulled the bush up by the root, he turned over and fell to pieces. His parts came together again and he exclaimed, 'Why did I sleep? My fresh meat has escaped.'

The monster now set out in pursuit of the fleeing girl and about sundown he overtook her again. She eluded him, however, and entered a cave. He went on by it, without realising that his quarry was so near. Once he had passed, the girl set out for the camp of her mother's brothers, Wolf and Coyote, who lived in the vicinity. Wolf, the older brother, had sent Coyote to the spring for a basket of water. There Coyote espied the girl. He ran back to the camp, telling Wolf, 'Why, elder brother, there is a very pretty girl at the spring.'

'All right,' said Wolf, 'I will go to see her.' He told Coyote to keep behind him, but Coyote ran ahead.

When Wolf arrived, Coyote said, 'I got here first. I want to marry this girl.' Wolf said, 'Stop that sort of talk,' and then addressing the girl, Wolf continued, 'My sister's daughter, how did you come here?'

The girl explained and then asked, 'What are you two going to do to help me? Walking Skeleton is close behind me.'

Wolf replied, 'I fear that we can do nothing for you. However, I have a big pelt in which you might hide. I will wrap you in it.' The two brother wrapped the girl and placed her on a platform in a tree. They had scarcely secreted her, when Walking Skeleton appeared.

'I want you to give me that girl, for I know that she is here,' declared Walking Skeleton. 'We know nothing about her,' protested Wolf and Coyote.

'I tracked her to your camp,' the monster continued.

'We like fresh meat ourselves,' retorted the brothers.

Walking Skeleton kept walking about, getting closer and closer to the girl's hiding place. 'I believe that I will stay here all night,' he said, so he had a meal with the two brothers. They brought out two pelts for him to sleep upon.

Wolf said aside to Coyote, 'Younger brother, we will not sleep tonight. I do not like the looks of this man.' Coyote made no response, but just rolled his eyes.

After Walking Skeleton had gone to sleep, the two brothers roasted trout for the girl. They wrapped them in tule and took them to her. 'You had better go along now, while he is sound asleep. We cannot do anything against him. When you eat this fish, drink water with it.' The girl took their advice and departed. When she had climbed to the top of the neighbouring ridge, she paused to look down in the canyon below.

When Walking Skeleton awoke, he said to Wolf and Coyote, 'You had better give me that girl. There is no use for you to try to conceal her from me.'

'What are you going to do with her, if we give her to you?' the brothers asked.

'Oh, I shall take her home and she will wait on me and get water for me.' replied the monster. Upon discovering that his quarry had again escaped him, Walking Skeleton once more took to tracking her.

Meanwhile, the girl had pushed back into the mountains and reached the camp of an aunt, who was named 'Joined-to-Willow,' because she was continually scraping willow bark for basket making. 'Aunt, what can you do for me? Walking Skeleton is after me. He is coming right now. Where are you going to hide me?' anxiously inquired the girl.

Her aunt's response was not reassuring. 'I fear that I can do nothing for you. Nevertheless, I will do the best I can. I will put you somewhere for the night.' So saying, she placed her niece in a burden basket and covered her with tule roots. She put the burden basket with its human load back among her other large baskets, so that it would not be conspicuous.

The girl had not been long ensconced in her hiding place when her pursuer arrived. The tracks led him unmistakably to the old woman's camp and he said to himself, 'It is useless for me to track further, for I know that the girl is right here. I am going to capture her this time.' He remained all night at the old woman's camp, but slept soundly.

Towards daybreak the old woman went to the girl and said, 'You had better leave, for he is sound asleep now.' The girl took her aunt's advice and departed.

At daybreak Walking Skeleton was again on her trail, exclaiming to himself, as he discovered her track, 'Ah! Here is her track.' However, the girl reached Skunk's house in advance of her pursuer.

'What are you folks going to do for me?' was her first question. Skunk possessed a quantity of pitch. He heated it so that it became exceedingly adhesive. Then he put it in holes dug the trail over which Walking Skeleton would travel. Walking Skeleton came hastening along the road, stepped into the pitfalls, and perished miserably, disappearing beneath the surface of the pitch.

The girl walked about Skunk's place for a while. She was very grateful for her deliverance. She said to Skunk, 'What a wonderful thing you did in catching Walking Skeleton.' After a time she decided to travel to Eagle's home. With her pursuer dead, she took a renewed interest in life and fell to admiring the beautiful things in Eagle's country. 'What beautiful flowers there are in this country,' she thought to herself, 'and how pretty the stars look at night. This is real life now.' Finally she reached Eagle's house. As she stood on the top of the great cliff, she surveyed the whole country. 'Well, this country looks like an ocean. This is the best part of the world that I have ever been in. I am smiling all over with joy.'

Eagle brought in a deer. He greeted his visitor. She returned the greeting. Then Eagle went in and made a fire. He invited the girl into his house as it was cold outside. 'There is room for you on one side there,' he said. 'Keep yourself warm.' After seeing her comfortably settled he set to work to skin the deer he had brought. After he had finished he came in and put the pot on the fire to make stew. When it was done he said to the girl, 'Come now, we will have our lunch. You may have the pot of stew.' He gave her the pot, only taking out a small piece of meat for himself.

'All right. This is quite a treat for me,' said the girl.

Then Eagle directed her, 'You must sleep in the same corner you are sitting in. Sleep right there. Tomorrow night you may move your bed a little closer to my bed.'

'All right,' said the girl. 'I will share this house with you.'

Then Eagle said, 'We will cohabit in ten days, but not before.'

Nevertheless, in two days the girl bore two children, and in a few days a big band of children had been born. 'Now we are getting too many. We had better pair them off,' Eagle said. 'My wife, we will pair them off and name them. They will be different tribes of people' He proceeded to pair them off. 'This pair will be Usomu (Miwok),' he said. 'This pair we will call Chukchansi. This pair we will call Mono.' Then he sent all the pairs out. Thus he paired the tribes and sent them out. 'Now you all establish homes and settle down. This will make the world. You people increase, for this world looks too bare. Fill it.'

All went to their places. They all went away happy. Eagle looked over the cliff himself to see them start. 'How beautiful it is to see people walking,' he said. 'The world certainly looks nice.' Then addressing the girl, he said, 'Now we are going to kill deer, as I did when we first met. We are only two now, paired off.'

The Adventures of Haininu and Baumegwesu

Coyote made a fire, a large fire. He sat down by it and cried. Then he sang, 'Yo i hini, yo i hini wau!' Said Coyote to himself, 'My tears drop down all around my flanks. I wish my sister's sons, Haininu and Baumegwesu, would come. If they would come, I would go with them.' The two nephews appeared close by the fire.

'What are you going to do, uncle?' asked Haininu.

Coyote replied, 'What do you expect me to do? I am going with you. I am going along when you get that yellow jackets' nest. I will clean it very thoroughly.' So they started.

They encountered Roadrunner, who was also Haininu's mother's brother. What are you going to do?' queried Haininu.

'I am going along too,' replied Roadrunner.

Next they came to House Finch's place and Haininu said to House Finch, who was also his mother's brother, 'What are you going to do?'

House Finch responded, 'I am going along too.'

Then they arrived at the camp of Brewer's Blackbird. 'What are you going to do, mother's brother?' asked Haininu.

He replied, 'I am going along too.'

A creek was reached and there Haininu shot a large salmon with his bow and arrow. When he killed it, the water rose and nearly overwhelmed him. It pursued him. He jumped from cliff to cliff far back in the mountains, but the water still followed him. Finally he got out of reach of it, but he was so exhausted that he fainted. When he revived he asked himself, 'Who is doing this to me? I am going to see you again,' he said, referring to the salmon and the water of the creek which had pursued him. He was all covered with mud when the water receded. He looked over the edge of the cliff on which he was resting, put over his bow and arrow so they leaned against it and then slid down to the bottom of the cliff on them. He returned to the place where he had shot the large salmon. Then out of revenge he shot all of the salmon he could see, a task which was made easy because the water was low. 'That is what I can do to you now,' he said. He walked around amongst the slaughtered salmon in the now waterless creek bed. All of the water had disappeared when he killed the salmon. 'This is what I can do to you,' he said.

He took his departure and caught up with his brother Baumegwesu, who had gone on with his uncles. As they proceeded Haininu espied two bears swinging. He said to them, 'Friends, you are doing something fine there. Let me swing.'

The bears replied, 'Yes, it is nice. You may swing.'

The bears swung him on the tree and then let go. He was projected upward, but alighted feet first, though buried up to his neck in sand. The bears laughed and went into their house, leaving their cubs outside. Haininu killed and skinned the cubs and took their flesh in the house. 'My father's sisters,' he said, 'here is some deer meat. Eat it.'

The bears remarked, 'It smells like our children, and it tastes like them.' Then they vomited. The bears pursued Haininu, who called to Baumegwesu, across the creek to put his leg out so that the bears might cross on it. Baumegwesu did so, but when one bear was halfway over, he withdrew his leg and she fell into the water and was drowned. One bear was left and that is why there are still bears in this country today.

The two brothers went on until they neared the home of their father's sisters, the Winds. There Baumegwesu said to Haininu, 'You go over there and see our aunts and get a basket from them.' This was at a big cave, in the mountains, called Piyau. The Winds lived in the cave. When Haininu entered Piyau cave, the habitation of his aunts, he seized each of the old women by the ears. They protested, 'Ouch! Nephew, do not do that. You are always treating us this way.'

'Give me a basket, aunts,' he demanded. 'I want to put some of my food into it. We are going down to the plains.' As soon as they turned their backs, Haininu mischievously made holes in all of their baskets by shooting arrows into them. When the Winds perceived what he had done, they became whirlwinds and pursued him. They chased him, overtook him, and beat him with large tree limbs.

He kept shouting his name as he jumped this way and that to escape their blows. They finally gave up in despair, as he was too agile for them, and went home. Haininu followed them back and shot them and all but two of their children, who escaped. They secreted themselves in crevices in the cliff. Haininu tried to poke them out, but could not. We would not have wind today if these two little ones had not escaped.

Baumegwesu sat singing his own name, while Haininu was having the tussle with the Winds. 'I did not send you to murder our aunts,' scolded Baumegwesu, 'but you are always getting into mischief. We will travel now.' They had not gone far before Baumegwesu said, 'My younger brother, you go to our father's sisters living over there and try to get a basket from them.' These aunts were Rattlesnakes.

To Haininu's request they responded, 'Yes, my nephew, we have baskets for you here. Let us enter and seek a good one.' They selected their best basket and handed it to Haininu. 'This is the best we can do, nephew,' they said. Haininu departed and the aunts sat down to resume work on the baskets they were making. 'What is the matter with this basket?' asked one, 'it is full of holes.'

'Mine too,' said the other, for Haininu had been up to mischief when their backs were turned.

'We will cut across here and get ahead of our nephew before he gets far up the road. Run quickly.' They hastened and hid themselves at a fork of the trail ahead of Haininu. As he passed each one bit him on the leg, one on the right, one on the left. Haininu sat down on a great rock, where one can still see his blood. He fainted. His legs swelled and rotted. Baumegwesu came to see what the trouble was. He whipped Haininu's legs with an arrow. The swelling subsided and Haininu awoke. 'What are you doing to me?' he asked. 'I have been sleeping right here.'

'You certainly have not been sleeping here. I told you not to do this thing. You are always bothering our poor aunts,' thus Baumegwesu reprimanded him. Haininu ignored the reproof and said, 'You go ahead, brother, and I will follow shortly.' He ran back to his aunts' house and shot both of them. One child escaped.

'Well, I do not believe that you amount to anything, so I will let you go,' said Haininu to the escaping child. Haininu hastened to overtake his brother. When he caught up with him, Baumegwesu asked, 'What have you been doing now?'

'I went back and killed those old women,' said Haininu. 'They cannot get the best of me.'

They camped near Napasiat, where they found a yellow jackets' nest under a stone. Haininu said, 'We will leave this one for the Indians in this part of the country. We do not want to dig this one out. We will go down to the plains and get a large one.'

They made a bait for the yellow jackets. It consisted of a grasshopper's leg with a white feather tied to it. The feather was to serve as a guide when the grasshopper leg was being carried away by a yellow jacket to its nest. It was not long before a yellow jacket started to carry it away. Then Haininu saw a yellow jacket with a piece of deer meat, also a giant yellow jacket carrying a deer's antlers. Haininu left his companions and followed the giant yellow jacket that was carrying the deer's antlers. He followed it to its nest. Then he returned to his companions, singing his name as he went along, 'Haininu, Haininu.'

Coyote heard him singing as he approached and he sang too. 'Oh, I am so happy,' said Coyote, as he thought about the coming feast.

Haininu tarried with Vulture. 'Give me one of your feathers,' requested Haininu.

'All right,' said Vulture, 'I will give you one.' So saying, he pulled out the largest and handed it to Haininu.

'Yes. This is what I want,' said Haininu.

'You may have anything you want,' said Vulture. 'You know your mother's brother always gives you whatever you wish.'

Haininu next visited Great Horned Owl and asked him, 'What are you going to do?'

'I am going down to eat my fill of yellow jacket grubs,' said Great Horned Owl.

'Well, come on then,' urged Haininu. As they proceeded they encountered Raccoon.

'Well, mother's brother, what are you going to do?' queried Haininu.

'I am going down to eat my fill of yellow jacket grubs,' replied Raccoon.

'Well, come on then,' invited Haininu.

Baumegwesu sang when they arrived at the yellow jackets' nest. He instructed Haininu and the uncles to go and gather pine needles for the roasting. After they had secured the pine needles, Baumegwesu changed his mind and said, 'This is not the nest we are seeking. We ought to have a larger nest. We will have to seek further. This is a different one.'

Again they used a grasshopper leg for bait and a yellow jacket took it. Haininu followed him way over to the Coast Range, located the nest, and then returned to report to his older brother.

'No. That is not the nest, either,' said Baumegwesu.

They fixed another bait. It was carried towards Mariposa by a yellow jacket. Coyote, meanwhile, had developed such an appetite that he had eaten all the pine needles that had been collected. He complained, 'I am so very hungry. When will that yellow jackets' nest be in sight?' Then Haininu followed the yellow jacket toward Mariposa. When he returned to his companions, he found the deer's antlers again in the same hole where he had first found them.

Baumegwesu now declared that after all this was the nest they were seeking. 'That is the one,' he said. 'Bring the antlers here. That is certainly the nest.'

Haininu went out and gathered pine needles. 'Are these right, my elder brother?' he asked Baumegwesu.

'No. You have gathered the wrong kind,' replied Baumegwesu.

So Haininu started again in the morning. Then he came in with a big load of pine needles. 'Are these all right?' he asked.

Baumegwesu said, 'Yes. That is the kind I told you to get in the first place.'

Haininu protested, 'You make so much work for me, elder brother. Why did you bring that old uncle Coyote? He ate all of our pine needles to begin with.'

Baumegwesu warned him, 'You had better say nothing about him. We have our nest and we do not care.' Then Baumegwesu continued, 'There are not enough pine needles. You will have to get some more.'

'Oh dear,' sighed Haininu, 'what work!' He went further this time, crossing the mountains and securing needles from the pinon trees.

When he returned with his burden, Baumegwesu said, 'This quantity is going to be sufficient to cook the nest. This is the best thing you could get.'

Then Baumegwesu discovered that they had no fire drill. 'We have forgotten our fire drill and hearth,' he said to Haininu. 'Go back to Napasiat and get them.' As the yellow jackets' nest they were about to cook was at Yoninau, between Fresno and Coalinga, this order meant another long trip back into the mountains for Haininu. However, he set out on the errand and in due time returned with the implements . 'You have brought the wrong ones,' said Baumegwesu, when Haininu handed him the sticks. He sent Haininu back again. Baumegwesu said, 'Oh yes, here it is,' referring to the first drill which Haininu had brought. 'What am I thinking of. This is it, my younger brother. This is what I told you to get.'

They now filled the yellow jackets' hole with pine needles. Baumegwesu secured a spark with the fire drill and blew it into flame. When the nest was cooked they took it out, they took it out, they took it all out. They kept digging and the nest seemed to get bigger and bigger, wider and wider. Coyote cried, 'I want the bottom one, the last.'

Then his companions said, 'Feed him separately. Do not let him eat with us.'

This pleased Coyote, for he said, 'If I eat separately, I shall have that much more.' Coyote got the best. They finished the feast and prepared to travel the following morning.

'We will divide what is left of the yellow jackets' nest,' said Baumegwesu. 'You had better all go home now.' The division was made and each started for home with a little bundle of yellow jacket grubs.

Different tribes of Indians met Haininu and Baumegwesu when they were returning. The two brothers made a house at Yuninau, a high hill near Friant. They did not like it, however, and Haininu left, but Baumegwesu remained behind singing. Baumegwesu after a bit noticed the absence of Haininu and said to himself, 'Where has my younger brother gone?' Then Baumegwesu from his station on the hill Yuninau could discern Haininu on the plains below. Different tribes were chasing him, but his vulture feather, which he wore on his head, was still in sight. 'My brother is yet alive,' said Baumegwesu. Haininu and his pursuers, who were shooting at him, drew near. Baumegwesu spread out his bow and arrows to dry and, when the people got close, he shot at them. While Baumegwesu was shooting these people, Haininu went off a short distance and lay down, quite exhausted. His pursuers were very weary, too, as Baumegwesu shot them.

When the slaughter was over, Baumegwesu went to Haininu and kicked him. Then he beat him with an arrow and asked, 'What is the matter with you?'

'Do not disturb me,' protested Haininu. 'I am sound asleep.'

Baumegwesu laughed ironically, 'Yes, you are!' Then he ordered Haininu to arise and start the fire. When the fire was kindled, Baumegwesu butchered the different tribes of people to eat. He made charqui of some; others he roasted. He put some on the coals, but they disappeared. 'I do not think the meat has been consumed by the fire,' said Baumegwesu in wonder. 'Next time I shall watch it.' Then he put a whole head on the fire to roast and held it by the horns, for these people had horns. He stirred the fire, still holding the head by the horns, but it slipped away from him and turned into Elk. It started to pursue Haininu, but it travelled slowly. Haininu retired into the mountains with Elk after him. He arrived at a village. 'What are you going to do for me?' he asked the people. 'Something is after me.'

They replied, 'We can do nothing for you.' He passed on and approached another village. 'What are you going to do for me? Something is after me.'

'We can do nothing for you,' was the reply.

At last he arrived at Skunk's habitation. 'What are you going to do for me? Something is after me,' pleaded Haininu.

Skunk replied, 'We have some soapstone here. We might make some red hot stones. They started a fire as quickly as they could and heated some stones. After a time Elk appeared. 'Where is that man I am following?' he asked.

'We have already butchered him,' responded Skunk. 'Open your mouth wide and we will give you what is left.' Elk obeyed, and Skunk threw the red hot stones in the gaping mouth. Elk boiled and burst. 'That is the way we fix them,' boasted Skunk.

The Coyote Called 'Another One'

Yellowjacket had three sons, all coyotes. The three went down to spear salmon at Italian Bar on the San Joaquin river. Another coyote came by; he was a male also. He went to Yellowjacket's three sons and asked them their names. They replied that their name was Coyote. Thereupon the stranger coyote said, 'That is not my name. Your names are different from mine. Go to Jackrabbit and ask him my name. He knows it.'

The stranger coyote, accompanied by one of the three coyote brothers, proceeded to Jackrabbit's habitation. As they went along, the stranger coyote fell behind, so that his companion approached Jackrabbit first. Jackrabbit greeted him, saying, 'Hello, Coyote.' Then when the stranger coyote came in sight, Jackrabbit exclaimed, 'Oh! Here is another one.' Then the stranger coyote said to the other coyote, 'I told you that Coyote was not my name. My name is Another One.'

The two returned to where the others were still spearing salmon. All the while the stranger coyote was wishing that he might be a woman, for he wanted to cohabit with one of the brothers. He hit upon an idea and decided to go home. 'I am going home,' he said to the three brothers. Upon arriving at home, he hung himself by his hind legs. That changed him into a woman.

Next morning he repaired again to the place where the three brothers were spearing salmon. He sat nearby for a long while, then he arose and proceeded towards the three. One of them said, 'Another One is coming.'

Another brother said, 'No. It is a woman coming.'

The third disagreed and said, 'It is Another One.' They joked with one another as to who should marry the woman, if it really were one.

Finally the youngest said, 'I am going to marry her and I am going to take her home. Mother will help care for her.'

The other two brothers said, 'We will stay here. You take her home immediately.'

'Let us go home,' the youngest brother said to the stranger coyote who now appeared as a woman. On the way home they tried to cohabit. The youngest brother then discovered that his would-be bride was a male. He did not let the impostor know that he was aware of this fact, but he made an excuse to return to his brothers, saying that he had forgotten something. While returning to the fishing place, he met a number of cowboys who were seeking Another One, because he had stolen something from them. With them he returned to his two brothers. Then it was that it became known that they were seeking 'Another One,' although the cowboys did not know him by that name. Then the youngest brother returned with the cowboys, to show them where he had left Another One. They found him fast asleep. They put a rope about his neck, skinned him alive and turned him loose. He came to the three brothers, who laughed at him. They nearly laughed themselves to death. Another One cried at every twig that touched him, for being nothing but raw flesh, he was bleeding all over.

CHAPTER 33

Winnebago

The Man Who Visited the Thunderbirds

In the beginning, Earth-Maker created the world and human beings; but these were so weak that they were powerless to repel the attacks of the evil spirits and the man-eaters or giants. These were invariably victorious over the people until Earth-Maker sent Hare to deliver the latter from their enemies. After many hardships Hare succeeded in ridding the world of all the evil spirits that had molested it for so long a time, and, in conjunction with the Trickster established the Medicine Lodge.

The story I shall tell you now is supposed to have taken place in the time intervening between the sending out of the Trickster and Hare.

The giants had attacked a certain village, burnt all the lodges, and killed and eaten all the inhabitants with the exception of ten small boys and one little girl, whom they wished to save until they had grown older. The children thus left alone, after they had dried their tears, spent all their time in fasting and hunting. As they grew older, all they knew about themselves was that they were brothers and sister. They knew nothing about their parents, nor about the place they had come from. They had a long lodge with five fireplaces and three entrances – one in the east, one in the west, and one in the south.

The beds were so arranged around the fireplaces that the eldest brother slept directly opposite his sister.

This sister was treated with all imaginable love and consideration by all her brothers. They would not allow her to do any work. They themselves got the fuel, built the fire, cooked the food, washed, dressed, and combed her hair. As soon as these tasks were over, they would go out hunting and fasting. One night when they were all in bed, it seemed to the eldest brother as though he heard someone talking to his sister. He kept awake all night, but was so shocked and thunderstruck that he could not utter a word. He listened again; and now there was no doubt but that someone was talking to his sister, although he could not see him. He watched carefully to see if he could detect the person or discover him when he left the lodge. At break of day, however, in spite of his struggle to keep awake, he fell sound asleep; and when he woke up, the person had gone, and his sister was sleeping peacefully. He thought this rather peculiar, but said nothing to any of his brothers or to his sister. He went hunting, as usual, in the morning, and on his return went to sleep. Again the same thing happened, and again just at daybreak he fell asleep. There seemed to him no doubt now that the person speaking to his sister had forced him to fall asleep just as he was leaving the lodge. The third and fourth nights the same thing was repeated; but at daybreak of the fifth day, to his own surprise, he remained wide awake. He sat up and looked around to see if his brothers were all in their proper places. They were sleeping soundly and peacefully. Very much perplexed, he got up, and, waking his brothers, he prepared everything as usual, and then went hunting.

It was generally their custom, when starting in the morning, to go together along a certain path for a time, and then separate. This morning, however, just before they were to separate, the eldest called out to his brothers, 'Let us stop here a little and smoke before we separate. We ought to do this oftener, so that we can talk things over.' So they sat down, smoked, and chatted; then suddenly he rose and said, 'Brothers, I have had a reason for asking you to stop and chat today. I am afraid something terrible has happened. During the last four nights a man has been talking to our sister. I myself heard him. For the first three nights I thought one of you was doing something disgraceful; but I was so choked with shame, that I could not say anything to you about it. On the fifth morning, however, I heard him go out, and, sitting up, I looked at all of your sleeping places, and took particular care to see if any of them were disordered or if any of you were disturbed in your sleep; but you were all sleeping quietly.'

After he had finished speaking, the brothers discussed the incident, and finally came to the conclusion that the person who had appeared to their sister must have been some good spirit. They knew that such had happened before to other people; and in a way they felt glad that their sister had been selected, for they felt sure that it was no evil thing. They said nothing to her, preferring not to embarrass her; nor did they question her about what the eldest brother had heard. Thus things ran along for a few months without the brothers gaining any information. Finally the sister came to them one day, and told them that she was pregnant. They did not show the least surprise, but merely thanked her for the welcome information, and assured her that they were glad to know that they would soon have a new companion. They told her to take good care of herself and to do no work of any kind.

Months ran along in this way until the time came for her delivery. As soon as she told her brothers that she was about to be delivered of a child, they built her a little camp near their own, for in those times it was not customary for Indians to be present at the confinement of their relatives. They supplied the lodge with a nice fireplace, and provided for her as best they could. When all was in readiness, she entered the new lodge where some of her younger brothers were still working. Not very long after her entrance a small iron cradle decorated in the most beautiful fashion was suddenly thrust in through the door. The brothers ran out immediately to thank the donor, but no one was to be seen. (As a matter of fact, it was the father of the child about to be born who had made the gift, but this the brothers did not know.) After a short time the brothers left the lodge, and the sister remained alone to be delivered of a boy. No sooner had the child been born than the ten brothers came in, congratulated her, and immediately proceeded to take care of their young nephew. So well did they do this, that soon nothing was left for her to do but to nurse him. The youngest brother detailed himself especially for the work of taking care of his little nephew, quitting hunting entirely, and staying home with him. Indeed, he seemed to love the little fellow more than all the others.

Thus things went along until the baby could eat, though not talk One night the eldest brother was awakened, and, sitting up in his bed, again heard some one talking to his sister. No one could be seen, however; and as on the former occasion, so now, despite his efforts, he fell asleep at daybreak. The second night the same was repeated; but on the morning of the fifth day he remained awake, and he saw the person get up and walk out of the lodge, followed by his sister, who took her sewing-material with her.

When the brothers got up in the morning, they discussed the incident, but showed no surprise; because it did not seem strange to them that their sister should have followed her husband to his home, wherever that was. In the belief that such was the case, they went out hunting as usual. However, when they returned in the evening, and found out that their sister had not returned, they became worried, and the eldest one said, 'I think we had better try to find out where she has gone.' In the morning he arose and went to seek her, the other brothers having gone hunting, as usual. When they returned in the evening, the eldest had not returned, and they resolved to send out the next one to look for him. As the second did not return, they became very anxious, fearing that something might have happened.

So they said to one another, 'Let two of us go in search of our sister.' So the next morning the two next in age set out, not to return. Again two were sent out, and they did not return. Only four brothers were left now, and they finally decided to leave the youngest one home to take care of their little nephew, while they would start in search of the missing ones. They did not return.

Now only the youngest brother was left; and, much as he desired to start in search of his brothers, the thought of his little nephew left alone unnerved him. 'No,' he said to himself, 'it won't do for me to leave my nephew all alone. Surely something has happened to my brothers. Yes, I am going to see what has happened to them; and if I have to die, well, all right! I don't want to live alone.'

Ever since his sister had left, the youngest brother had been feeding his nephew on deer brains. He would boil them and make a gruel out of them (this is supposed to be the most excellent food for an infant who has no mother to nurse him). The infant was still strapped to his cradle board. So, when finally the youngest brother prepared to go in search of his lost brothers, he placed the cradle board against the wall of the lodge, and prepared some deer tail, which he boiled until it became soft. Then he freed the baby's arms so that they could move freely, and suspended the deer skin from the top of the lodge in such a way that the infant could reach it whenever he wished. Then he started out.

He had proceeded only a little way when he heard his nephew crying, and, losing heart, he returned. 'Don't cry, little nephew!' he said, 'for if Earth-Maker will let me, I will return soon.' Then he started again, and went a little farther; but he heard his nephew cry, and returned. The third time he started, he proceeded still farther, but again returned. The fourth time he started, he ran, for he did not want to be tempted to turn by hearing the cries of his nephew.

He took the trail of his brothers, and followed it until he came to two camps – a small one and a large one. He entered the first one, and found a very old woman sitting there. As soon as she saw him, she addressed him thus: 'My poor grandchild, sit down here! I am very sorry for you.' And then she went on to tell him what had happened to his sister and brothers. She told him that the person who had been talking to his sister the last time was a bad spirit; but that the sister had mistaken him for the father of her child, and had accompanied him to this camp. However, he was not the father, as she afterwards found out. All his brothers had been killed by this bad spirit; and she did not believe that he, the youngest, would escape their fate. The old woman then proceeded to tell him that his sister was by this time so completely under the influence of this bad spirit, that she was as bad as he, and preferred to help her husband rather than her brother.

'Now, listen, my grandchild! The first thing that the bad spirit will ask you to do tonight will be to prepare a sweat bath for him; and in order to do that, he will tell you to fetch a certain stone. That stone belongs to him, and it is placed there for a certain purpose. Just as soon as you touch it, it will begin to roll down the hill, and you will roll with it. That is how some of your brothers met their death. Now, you just take a pole, walk up the opposite side of the hill, and touch it with the pole, and it will then roll down the hill. As soon as it has stopped rolling, you can pick it up and take it home. When you have brought this home, your brother-in-law will tell you to get the bark of a certain very large tree. That tree belongs to him, and he keeps it there for a certain purpose. Just as soon as you touch the bark of the tree, the bark will fall on you and kill you. Some of your brothers met their death in that way. Now you take a stick and go as near as you can to the tree, and throw the stick at it. It will hit the bark, which will fall off. Then just take as much of it as you want and bring it to him. When you have brought this, he will send you out again and tell you to fetch the lodge pole for the sweat house. When you get to the place where he has sent you, you will find four large rattlesnakes lying curled up. These are what he meant you to get. Some of your brothers met their death there. They were killed by the snakes. So now, my grandson, take some tobacco along with you and give it to them, and ask them not to hurt you. Those snakes do not belong to him; but he is more powerful than they, and he keeps them there as his slaves. He just gives them enough to eat and to drink. However, they have never had anything to smoke, and they will be glad to accept your gift and not molest you. I shall put in my influence to help you with them, and then you will be able to take them with you. When you come to your brother-in-law's place, put their heads in the ground and twist their tails and so you will have the finest of lodge structures. After this has been done, he will tell you to pick up the stone with your naked hand and carry it into the sweat house. Now, you know the stone belongs to him, and his purpose is to have it stick to your hand and burn you up. That is how some of your brothers met their fate. Now, my grandson, when it comes to that point, try to find some excuse to leave him, and come over to see me before you pick up the stone.'

Shortly after the old woman had finished, the sister entered, and, seeing her brother, immediately addressed him. 'Brother, I have brought you something to eat.' Then she handed him a wooden bowl containing a large amount of liver as dry as a bone. He took the bowl, and, as soon as he had noticed the contents, threw the bowl and liver straight into the face of his sister. 'I am not accustomed to eating this of food,' he said. 'My brothers, who brought me up, never gave me any food like this.' His sister then left the lodge, and, it being suppertime, the old woman cooked him a supper of vegetables. After he had finished his supper, his sister came in again. 'Tenth Son, your brother-in-law wants you to prepare his sweat bath. He is accustomed to use a certain stone that you will find yonder on the hill, and which he wishes you to get.' Then she left the lodge. Her brother went to the hill, and, following the advice of his grandmother, ascended it on the side opposite the stone, and touched it with his stick, when it rolled rapidly down the hill.

He then carried it to his brother-in-law's lodge, but left it outside. Then he went in to inform the latter that he had brought the stone. His brother-in-law merely nodded, and told him to fetch the bark for the lodge structure. This he set out to do; and when he came near the tree, he carefully took a position of safety, and touched the bark with his stick. It fell with a terrific crash, and he took as much as he needed and carried it to his brother-in-law. The latter merely nodded when it was brought, and sent him to get the lodge poles. When he came to the place where the snakes were confined, he took some tobacco and threw it to them. They accepted it, and allowed him to seize them and carry them to his brother-in-law. Arrived there, he stuck their heads in the ground, and twisted their tails, thus forming the poles of the sweat bath lodge. Then he put the bark over these poles, and the structure was complete. As soon as everything was in readiness, his brother-in-law told him to place the stone in the lodge. Instead of doing this, however, he got up some excuse and went to see the old woman. She prepared something for him, rubbed his hands and arms with it thoroughly, and told him to return to the sweat bath lodge immediately and do as his brother-in-law had asked. This he did, and, much to the disgust of the latter, the stone did not burn him in the least. Indeed, he got so provoked that he said to him ironically, 'You think you are a clever fellow, don't you? I don't want to take a bath at all.' And with this he went to sleep, and Tenth Son returned to his grandmother, with whom he stayed over night.

That night the old woman gave him further advice. 'Grandson, you have done nobly, and I am very proud of you; but the hardest still remains to be done. Tomorrow your brother-in-law will ask you to go out hunting with him, and he will take you out a considerable distance until he shall have killed a large buck deer, which he will ask you to pack with your bowstring so that the antlers of the deer are near your back. His intention is to have you run the antlers into your skull. If he does not succeed in that, he will step on the tail end of your moccasin, to make you stumble and have the antlers break your back. Some of your brothers met their fate in that way.' Then both fell asleep.

Early the next morning his sister came and said, 'Tenth Son, your brother-in-law wants you to go hunting with him.' So he went along with him; and after they had continued on their course for some time, the brother-in-law killed a big buck deer and told the boy to pack it. The boy knew what was going to happen, but nevertheless he said, 'I have not got any pack-string. How can I pack it?'

'Why, take your bowstring and do it. What is the matter with you, anyhow? Come, I will pack it for you,' he was answered angrily. So he untied the boy's bowstring and packed the deer for him. He doubled the deer up so that his antlers were quite near the boy's back. But the boy had been careful enough to secrete a whetstone under the hair of his forehead, as his grandmother had instructed him, so that the bowstring would touch this stone instead of his forehead. When all was in readiness, they started home. The brother-in-law waited to see what would happen; but, as the bowstring did not seem to cut the head of the young man, he proceeded to step on the tail of his moccasins. To his surprise, the bowstring broke in two, causing the boy to stumble, but not injuring him, for the bowstring went one way, and the pack the other.

'What did you do that for?' the boy asked.

'Oh, just for fun,' his brother-in-law answered. 'I wanted to see what you would do.' Then, much provoked, the bad spirit packed the deer with his own pack strap and walked home. The young boy returned to his grandmother.

The grandmother prepared the supper, and said to him, 'Grandson, you have done wonderfully well. You have fared far, better than any of your brothers; but tomorrow will be a very hard day, and I don't know how I am going to help you. Your brother-in-law will ask you to go out hunting again, and will send you to head off a deer. Then suddenly it will commence to snow severely; and before you are aware of it, you will be alone in the timber with no footprints to guide you. I shall not be able to help you then; but if you can think of anything that you obtained from the good spirits while fasting, or of any other way whereby you can protect yourself, do so tonight. That is all, my grandson.'

In the morning, as usual, the sister came, and said, 'Tenth Son, your brother-in-law wants you to go out hunting with him.'

So, he accompanied him, and they went along until late in the afternoon. Suddenly a bear jumped out of the brush, and, on seeing the hunters, ran away. The brother-in-law called the young boy, and said, 'Now, you stay here while I take after him; and don't get frightened, because you can see my tracks right along.'

As soon as he got out of sight, it began to snow and got very cold. The boy was not prepared for this, and had no extra garment. He kept in the track of his brother-in-law as long as it was visible, but the fast-falling snow soon obliterated the last trace. He was lost. He stood there without moving for some time, and then began to cry. He cried not so much for himself as for his little nephew, whom he pictured to himself left alone to starve. Suddenly be heard a voice near him. He wiped his tears away, and there in front of him stood a tall man.

'Tenth Son, don't you know me?'

'No,' answered the boy, 'I never saw you before.'

'Why, uncle,' the person said, 'I am the one whom you left in the cradle board when you ran away from me. Your brother-in-law is right over the hill yonder, skinning the bear. You go right over there now, and you will see that he has a nice fire built for himself. He is cooking some meat. When you get there, just take the meat that he has cooked out of the fire, and eat it yourself. He'll tell you to put it away; but don't pay any attention to him, and go right on eating. Afterwards he'll tell you to take the bear and pack it; and then you just tell him you won't do it; let him do it himself. He will then threaten to kill you, but you just keep on refusing. Then he will get very angry and get ready to strike you. Just when he raises his club, call out, "Waka djatcora! Nephew, I'm about to be killed," and I shall be there to help you.'

So the young man did as he had been told, and found his brother-in-law busy skinning and cooking the bear. He went straight to the fire and took the cooked meat out. 'What are you doing there?' said the brother-in-law. 'Put that back, and don't touch it again.' The young man paid no attention to him. The brother-in-law said nothing for a while. Then he said, 'Tenth Son, pack the bear for me.'

'I will not,' answered the latter; 'do it yourself.'

'If you don't do it,' retorted the former, 'I shall kill you.' But the young fellow persisted in his refusal, and this so enraged his brother-in-law that he lifted his club to strike him.

Just as he was about to strike him, the boy cried out, 'Waka djatcora! Nephew, I'm about to be killed.' Immediately there stood in front of him his nephew. The nephew then addressed the evil spirit.

'What are you trying to do to the boy?' he asked.

'Oh, nothing,' the brother-in-law answered; 'I was just fooling with him.'

'Well, I'll fool with you too,' the nephew said. And with that, he lifted his club and struck him on the head. It was like a thunder crash, and the evil spirit was smashed to pieces. There was nothing left of him. Then the nephew addressed his uncle. 'I'll take the bear home for your grandmother.' He thereupon packed the bear. 'Uncle,' he continued, 'my mother has wronged you much, and although she was influenced and compelled to do much of what she did by the evil spirit, nevertheless you have a right to do with her what you will. I leave that to you entirely. If you think that you have suffered so much pain and hardship that you ought to have your revenge, you may kill her.'

'Well,' answered the uncle, 'I have indeed grieved very much, not so much for my brothers and myself as for you; and, although I know she was influenced by the evil spirits, she must not live.'

So they went home to the old woman, and then the uncle went to his sister's camp, killed her, and set the camp afire. They cut up the bear into chunks, and gave it to the old woman. Then the uncle said, 'Grandmother, I am going to leave you,' and the grandmother said, 'All right, grandson, I am going to leave you also. This is not my home. I just came up here to help you. My home is way down underneath the earth. The meat you gave me will last me almost as long as the world lasts, and all that I ask of you is to remember me occasionally by sacrificing some tobacco. I am the head spirit of the mice.'

After she had departed, the nephew said, 'Well, uncle, now I'll have to leave you too. I am going to my father. I only came here because my father asked me to.'

But the uncle said, 'Nephew, if you go away, I'll go along with you. You are not going to leave me here alone, are you?'

But the nephew replied, 'Uncle, Earth-Maker does not permit us to take human beings to our homes; and I am sure my father would not like it. If you don't come along, I'll give you all kinds of supernatural powers. We can give greater supernatural powers for the warpath than any other spirits Earth-Maker has created. I'll also endow you with long life, and allow you to give to your children as long a life as you wish. I will also see that you have abundant game. You will only have to sit at your door to get all the game you desire. And as much wealth as you desire I will bestow on you. As Earth-Maker does not permit us to take human beings like yourself to our homes, you can only see us when we come on earth or when we appear to you in visions, when you are fasting.'

But the uncle continued, 'No, nephew, I am going along with you. I can't live without you.'

As the nephew saw it was of no avail, he said, 'Step in my trail four times as you are about to start.' And the uncle stepped in his trail four times as he was about to start, and up they went.

They came to the western horizon. When they came pretty near the home of the nephew, the uncle saw that the country was very similar to our own. They continued until they came to an oak timber; there they stopped. The nephew thereupon took his uncle between his palms and rubbed him; and he became smaller and smaller, until he was about the size of a thunderbird egg. Then he placed him in a nest in the fork of one of the oak-trees, and said to him, 'Uncle, stay here and be contented. Don't be uneasy. I shall come back to you in four days to see how you are getting along.' He then went home to his father.

His father asked him, 'Well, son, what have you been doing?' He knew very well what his son had been doing, but he merely asked the question to see what answer he would get.

The son answered, 'Father, I have brought my uncle along with me.'

'Well, where is he?'

'Over yonder in the tree. I'm going back to see him in four days.'

'Well, son, it is not our custom to do what you have done; but as you have got him over here, I guess we will let it go.'

After four days the nephew went to see his uncle, and he found him with his bill just sticking out of the egg, like a little chicken. 'Uncle, you are doing fine; just be contented, and I will be back to see you in four days.' When he came again, he found his uncle just hatched. 'Uncle, you are doing fine; just be contented, and I will be back in four days.' When he came again, he found his uncle standing on the edge of the nest. 'Uncle, you are doing fine; just be contented, and when I return in four days, you can go to my father's house with me.' When he came again, the uncle was standing on the top of the tree, just over the nest – a full-grown beautiful thunderbird. 'Ah, uncle, you look fine! Your feathers are far more beautiful, and you look far stronger than any of the rest of us.' Thereupon the uncle jumped from the tree, and found his bow and arrows lying on the ground ready for him. He picked them up, and, together with his nephew, went to the home of Big Hawk, the chief of the Thunderbirds.

Here he stayed for a few days. One day he said to his nephew, 'Let us go out, take a look at the country, and shoot some pigeons.' So he and his nephew went around shooting pigeons with bow and arrow, and they would stop to build a fire and cook their pigeons in the open.

(The main food of the thunderbirds at that time were snakes and all kinds of subterranean and aquatic animals.)

One day toward evening, the uncle, who was doing all the shooting, as his nephew only used a club; aimed at a pigeon; but the arrow missed aim, and struck a spring, where there was some white chalk. He went to get his arrow, and painted himself with the chalk that had adhered to the point of the arrow. When he joined his nephew later, the latter saw the chalk on his face, and said excitedly, 'Where did you get that, uncle?'

'What do you mean?' asked the uncle.

'Why, what you have on your face. Those are the faeces of the beaver, and big ones, too. You just give that to my father, and tell him that he may use half of it for himself, and give the other half to his people.'

The uncle said 'You are speaking foolishly, nephew; I have not seen any beaver.'

The nephew, however, replied, 'Uncle, that is a beaver, and that is all there is to it:'

'Well,' answered the uncle, 'you can tell your father whatever you want to, but I'm not going to give him something I have not seen.' With that they started home, the nephew hurrying in order to inform his father of the great game they had discovered.

When they got home, the nephew told his father that his uncle had found a very large beaver, and had given half of it to him and half to his people, to be used at a feast. The old man was delighted at this, and in the morning he took as many people as wanted to come along, roused the beaver out of his hole, killed him, and gave a great feast. From that time on the uncle and his nephew went out to hunt beaver regularly, and each time they found more. They also discovered other animals – leeches and different species of worms.

After the uncle had lived among the thunder beings for a number of years, hunting with his bow and arrow, the chief thunder beings decided to hold a secret meeting and discuss the advisability of keeping him among them. Big Black Hawk was also there. At that meeting it was decided that it would be impossible to keep the uncle with them forever. While he was unquestionably benefiting them very much, nevertheless it did not seem proper that an earth-born individual should live with thunder beings. They did not decide upon any definite date, but they determined that he should not stay among them very much longer. When some of the younger Thunderbirds heard of this decision, they resolved to get rid of him as soon as possible.

Now, there was a very large water spirit who inhabited a lake near by, whose banks were so steep and precipitous that the thunder beings could never harm him with their thunder and lightning. They would often go around to look at him, but they could never injure him.

The scheme of the young Thunderbirds was to entice the uncle to the lake, and, while pretending to have him look at the water-spirit, push him in. So they told the nephew to come along with them, bringing his uncle. 'Tell him,' they said, 'to take his bow and arrow along, for we are going to look at the water spirit, and perhaps your uncle, who does such wonderful things, can devise some means of capturing the spirit.'

So they all went to the lake, and while the uncle was looking at the water spirit, they pushed him in. The bank was extremely steep, and he was immediately killed. Then they went home, leaving the nephew to weep for his lost uncle.

The nephew commenced mourning for him and walked around the lake for four years. One day while thus walking, he noticed a wing feather drifting toward the bank. He took it home with him, rubbed it between his palms, and transformed it into a thunderbird egg. Then he put it is the fork of an oak tree, and he said, 'Uncle, I shall be back in four days.' When he returned after four days, the bill was just sticking out of the egg. 'That's all right, uncle, I shall be back in four days.' When he came back, the egg was fully hatched. 'It's all right, uncle, I shall be back in four days.' At the end of the four days, the uncle was standing at the edge of the nest. 'It's all right, uncle, I shall be back in four days.'

In the mean time the nephew had spoken to his father, Big Black Hawk, and he had said, 'My son, we can't have that uncle of yours around here; you will have to take him back to the place where he came from. You may tell him that he may have anything he wants.'

Then the nephew went to his uncle and found him perched on the top of the tree just over the nest, but he did not look as beautiful nor as strong as he did the first time. He looked like an ordinary thunderbird. He came down to greet his nephew, and they talked for a long time. The nephew told his uncle how he had mourned his death, but, in spite of all, his father would not allow him to stay with them. 'Earth-Maker would not like it, my father says, for he would not want human beings to live together with the thunder beings. Uncle, I have grieved long over what the thunder beings did to you, and I am now going to take my revenge by telling you something. My father says that he will give you any one of the war clubs that we possess. When you enter the lodge, you will see a large number of them hanging along the walls of the lodge. Some look much better than others; but there will be one right next to the door, that looks the shabbiest of them all. Take that one, and then you will make them weep just as they made me weep.' Then they went home, and Big Black Hawk told the uncle that he must return to earth, but that he would give him any of the clubs that he saw suspended in the lodge.

The uncle got up, walked around the lodge, examining the clubs one after another. When he got near the door, he turned around and said, 'I thank you all for giving me this club, the worst of them all, for I don't want to take the best one that you have. I shall be perfectly satisfied with this shabby one.' He took it, and, just as his nephew had said, all the thunder beings hung their heads and wept.

In the centre of the lodge there was a little bowl filled with some liquid. Big Black Hawk got up and presented it to the uncle, and told him to drink. As he drank he seemed to hear the voices of millions of people begging for their lives. What he drank was really the brains of all the people that he was going to kill on the warpath. 'What happened while you were drinking,' Big Black Hawk said to him, 'is a vision of what that club that you took is going to do for you.'

Then the nephew took his uncle, and, rubbing him between his palms, transformed him into human shape again, and accompanied him back to earth. He said to him, 'Uncle, you may see me whenever you want to,' and he bade him goodbye and left him.

The uncle joined a tribe of Indians, and immediately began to go on the warpath; and by virtue of his wonderful club he was able to kill as many persons as he wanted to.

After he had gone on doing this for several years, the thunder beings held another council, and Big Black Hawk said, 'This will never do. If that man keeps on, he will soon destroy all the people on the earth. That club must be taken away from him.' So he sent his son down to tell his uncle that his club would have to be changed. The nephew came to the earth, and told his uncle that he would have to take his club away from him, but that he would substitute one in its place that would do him excellent service. The uncle was very much displeased to hear this. Then the nephew called a meeting of all the different spirits of the earth. He had his uncle make a club exactly like the one that was to be taken away. He also told him to make a whistle. If ever he was on the warpath, and would blow that whistle, it would be the same as the voice of a thunderbird, and they would send him their powers. The club, too, would possess great powers, although it would not possess the magical power of the first club.

Then the spirits who were assembled in council said, 'We will endow him with our special powers.' The snake gave him the power of concealing himself. The carnivorous birds gave the power of telling where the enemy was, and of seeing them in the night-time. 'In return for this, we shall eat the flesh of the people you kill,' they said. The spirits underneath the earth said, 'We shall give you a medicine. If you paint yourself with it, you will have more strength than your enemies. You will be able to outrun them; and if they follow you and get your scent, this will overpower them, and they will not be able to go any farther.' Then the nephew returned to his home. The war club and the powers bestowed on the uncle were handed down from one generation to another; always remaining in a certain clan.

Thus things went on until the Indians came in contact with the whites. They saw the steel points of the whites, and thought the club would look better if it contained these points. This they decided to do after a great meeting and feast had been held.

Origin of the Thunderbird Clan and of Their Spirit Abode

In the beginning Earth-Maker was sitting in space, when he came to consciousness; and nothing else was there, anywhere. He began to think of what he should do; and finally he began to cry, and tears began to flow from his eyes and fall down below him. After a while, he looked below him, and saw something bright. The bright objects were his tears, that had flowed below and formed the present waters. When the tears flowed below, they became the seas as they are now. Earth-Maker began to think again. He thought, 'It is thus: if I wish anything, it will become as I wish, just as my tears have become seas.' Thus he thought. So he wished for light, and it became light. Then he thought, 'It is as I supposed, the things that I wished for, came into existence, as I desired.' Then he again thought, and wished for the earth; and this earth came into existence. Earth-Maker looked on the earth, and he liked it; but it was not quiet; it moved about, as do the waves of the seas. Then he made the trees, and he saw that they were good, but they did not make the earth quiet. Then he made the grass to grow, but the earth was not quiet yet. Then he made the rocks and stones, but still the earth was not quiet. However, it was nearly quiet. Then he made the four directions (cardinal points) and the four winds. On the four corners of the earth he placed them as great and powerful people, to act as island-weights. Yet the earth was not quiet. Then he made four large beings and threw them down, toward the earth, and they pierced through the earth with their heads eastwards. They were snakes. Then the earth became very still and quiet. Then he looked upon the earth, and he saw that it was good. Then he thought again of how things came into existence just as he desired. Then he first began to talk. He said, 'As things become just as I wish them, I shall make one in my own likeness.' So he took a piece of clay (earth) and made it like himself. Then he talked to what he had created, but it did not answer. He looked upon it, and saw that it had no mind or thought; so he made a mind for it. Again he talked to it, but it did not answer; so he looked upon it again, and he saw that it had no tongue. Then he made it a tongue. Then he talked to it again, but it did not answer; and he looked upon it, and he saw that it had no soul; so he made it a soul. He talked to it again, and this time it very nearly said something. But it did not make itself intelligible, so Earth-Maker breathed into its mouth and talked to it, and it answered.

As the newly-created being was in his own likeness, Earth-Maker felt quite proud of him, so he made three more just like him. He made them powerful, so that they might watch over the earth. These first four he made chiefs of the Thunderbirds; and he thought, 'Some will I make to live upon the earth that I have made.' So he made four more beings in his own likeness. Just like the others he made them. They were brothers, Kunuga, Henaga, Hakaga, and Nayiga. He talked to them, and said, 'Look down upon the earth.' So saying, he opened the heavens front of where they sat, and there they saw the earth spread out below them. He told them that they were to go down there to live. 'And this shall I send with you,' he added, and he gave them a plant. 'I myself will not have any power to take this from you, as I have given it to you; but when, of your own free will, you make me an offering of some of it, I shall gladly accept it and give you what you ask. This shall you hold foremost in your lives.' It was a tobacco-plant that he had given them. He said also, 'All the spirits that I create will not be able to take this from you unless you desire to give it by calling upon them during fasts and offering it to them. Thus only can the spirits get any of it. And this also I send with you, that you may use it in life. When you offer anything, it shall be your mediator. It shall take care of you through life. It shall stand in the centre of your dwellings, and it shall be your grandfather.' Thus he spoke to them. What he meant was the fire. And then he gave them the earth to live on. So the four thunder spirits brought the four brothers down to the earth.

The oldest one, Kunu, said while on their way down, 'Brother, when we get to the earth and the first child is born to me, I shall call him King (chief) of the Thunders, if it be a boy.' On they came down towards the earth. When they got near the earth, it began to get very dark. Then the second brother said, 'Brother, when we get to the earth and a child is born to me, if it is a girl, it shall be called Dark.' They came to a place called Within-Lake at Red Banks, a lake near Green Bay. On an oak tree south of the lake is the place where they alighted. The branch they alighted on bent down from their weight.

Then said the third brother to his brothers, 'The first daughter born to me shall be called She-Who-Weighs-the-Tree-Down-Woman.' Then they alighted on earth, but the thunder spirits did not touch the earth.

Then said the fourth and last brother to his brothers, 'Brothers, the first son that is born to me shall be called He-Who-Alights-on-the-Earth.' The first thing they did on earth was to start their fire.

Then Earth-Maker looked down upon them, and saw that he had not prepared any food for them, so he made the animals, that they might have something to eat. The oldest brother said, 'What are we going to eat?' Then the youngest two took the bow and arrows that Earth-Maker had given them, and started towards the east. Not long after, the third brother came into view with a young deer on his back; and the youngest brother also came with a young deer about two years old on his back. The deer that were killed were brothers, and those that killed them were also brothers. They were very much delighted that they had obtained food.

Then said they, 'Let us give our grandfather first taste.' Saying thus, they cut off the ends of the tongues, and the heart, and threw them into the fire with some fat. The first people to call on them were the War-People. They came from the west. Then came four others. They were the Thunders. Thus they were called, the youngest brothers. Then came those of the earth. Then came those of the Deer Clan. Then came those of the Snake Clan. Then came those of the Elk Clan. Then came those of the Bear Clan. Then came those of the Fish Clan. Then came those of the Water-Spirit Clan, and all the other clans that exist. Then there appeared on the lake a very white bird, Swan they called it; and after that, all the other water-birds that exist came. And they named them in the order of their coming, until the lake was quite full. Then the people began to dress the deer meat. Suddenly something came and alighted on the deer meat.

'What is that?' they said.

Then said Kunuga, the oldest brother; 'It is a wasp; and the first dog that I possess, if it is black, Wasp I shall call it.' Thus he spoke. 'And as the wasp scented and knew of the deer-dressing; so shall the dog be towards other animals; and wherever the dog is, and animals are in the windward, he shall scent them.' They made a feast with the deer for Earth-Maker, and threw tobacco into the fire and offered it to him. And to the other clans they showed how fire was to be made, and gave them some.

'For,' they said, 'each of you must now make fire for yourselves; as we shall not always lend you some.' There the people made their home. It was just the time of the year when the grass comes as far as the knee (summer).

One day they reported that something very strange was near the camp; but they said to themselves, 'We will leave it alone.' In a little while it moved nearer. Thus it moved toward the camp, and soon it began to eat deer bones. They allowed it to become one of the clans, and took it into their house. It was the dog or wolf. They killed one of them, and made a feast to Earth-Maker, telling him all about what they had done. In the beginning the Thunder clansmen were as powerful as the thunder spirits themselves. It was the Thunder People who made the ravines and the valleys. While wandering around the world, the Thunder People struck the earth with their clubs and made dents in the hills. That is the reason that the upper clans are chiefs of all the others, and that the least of all are the Dog People. So it was.

One day the oldest of the brothers lay down and did not rise again, and he did not breathe, and he became cold. 'What is the matter with our oldest brother?' the three others said. Four days they waited for him, but still he did not arise. So the second brother was asked by his youngest brother what the trouble was. But he did not know anything about it, and told him to ask his third brother; but he did not know, either. Then the two older brothers asked the youngest one; but he did not now, either. Then they began to mourn for him, not knowing what do or think. They fasted and blackened their faces, as we do now when we are mourning. They made a platform and laid him on it. When the snow fell knee-deep, the three brothers filled their pipe and went towards the place of the coming of the daylight, the east. There they came to the first being that Earth-Maker had placed in the east, the Island-Weight, as he was called. They came to him weeping, and went into his tent, turning the stem of their pipe in his mouth.

They said, 'Grandfather, our brother Kunu has fallen, and is not able to rise again. Earth-Maker made you great, and endowed you with all knowledge, and thus you know all things.'

He answered, and said, 'My dear grandsons, I am sorry, but I do not know anything about it; but as you have started to find out, I would refer you to the one ahead of me (the north). Perhaps he can tell you.' So, weeping, they started for the next one. When they got there, and told him their troubles, he told them he could not help them.

'But,' he said, 'perhaps the one ahead of me knows.' So they started for the third one (the west), but from him likewise they could learn nothing. He also referred them to the one ahead (the south). When they reached the fourth and last one, they entered the lodge, and, behold! there sat the three to whom they had gone before. Here they asked the last one for help; and not only he, but the other three also, answered them, 'Grandsons, thus Earth-Maker has willed it. Your brother will not rise again. He will be with you no more in this world. And as long as this world lasts, so it will be with human beings. Whenever one reaches the age of death, one shall die, and those that wish to live long will have to attain that age by good actions. Thus they will live long. Into your bodies Earth-Maker has placed part of himself. That will return to him if you do the proper things. This world will come to an end some time. Your brother shall keep a village in the west for all the souls of your clan, and there he shall be in full charge of all of you. And when this world is ended, your brother shall take all the souls back to Earth-Maker; at least, all those who have acted properly. Thus it was. Now you may go home and bury your brother in the proper manner.' The Thunder People thanked the four spirits and left their tent. When they got home, they took their brother's body; dressed him in his best clothes, and painted his face. Then they told him where he was to go, and buried him with his head toward the west, and with his war club. They placed the branch of a tree at his grave, and painted a little stick red and tied it to the tree, so that nothing should cross his path on his journey to the spirit-abode. If any thing or animal should cross his path on that journey, he must strike it with his club and throw it behind him, so that those relatives he has left behind on earth might derive blessings in war and attain long life. He would have his pipe and food along with him on his journey, and thus the things that he throws behind him will be a blessing for those still remaining on earth. Also the life he leaves behind him (i.e. the years that, had he lived to a normal age, are still due him) and the victories that he might have gained – all these he is to give to his relatives. The riches he might have had – or, in fact, anything that he could possibly have had – he is asked to give to these relatives. Then they will not feel so unhappy and lonesome. Such is the story up to the time that the spirit starts on his journey to the spirit land.

The Winnebagoes always encouraged one another to die on the warpath, because, if one dies in battle; the person would really not lose consciousness, but simply live right on in the spirit, and death would seem to him as if he had stumbled over some object. So they would say. If you wish to have a happy life as a spirit, do not die in your house. If you die in your house, your soul will wander all over the earth in want, and when people eat at the four-nights' wake, you will not get anything. If they drink water, you will remain thirsty. It is said that people not dying on the warpath will, as spirits, have to content themselves by pointing to food and drink, and licking their fingers. Those that die in battle have a village four days' distant from the general village of the souls. They are in need of nothing, as they plant and raise their own food, and have so many clothes that they look as if they were covered with furs. They play ball and have lots of fun, ride horseback, and dance. If any of them should desire to return to the earth and become alive again, they can do so. The wounds, however, from which they died, remain with them in the spirit world. Those who lost their scalps are without scalps. Some are without heads, and some without scalp locks. They can see their relatives here on earth whenever they wish to. So the people encouraged one another to die bravely and on the warpath.

CHAPTER 34

Yavapai

Origin Story

The people of the first generation (or 'creation') came from under the ground. They were originally at the bottom of a great hole in the Redrock country. In the hole grew a 'dog-tail' tree (kasarrwehe, a white pine-like tree which grows high in the mountains) and over it grew grapevines. The underground people climbed up this tree to the surface of the world. Their leader was Hanyiko.

Hanyiko sickened and lay on the earthen floor of his hut. His daughter, a shaman, disliked him because he was not good to her. She had made him sick. He lay ill for a long time. A male shaman sang over him, trying vainly to cure him. He got steadily worse, his flesh wasting away.

The sick man said to the people: 'I want you to make an sekaamcha.' The people made a roofless house for him, not knowing what an sekaamcha was. They asked the sick man if that was what he meant. He replied: 'No, not that one.' Then the people said they would make something different for him.

They cut wood, set up four corner posts, and made a shade. They asked him if that was what he wanted. He said: 'No, that is not right. I did not mean that one.'

The people wondered what kind of house he wanted. No one understood. Then two or three men went over to a creek where cottonwoods grew. They cut one for a post, leaving some branches and leaves on it, and brought it to the sick man. They dug a hole, set it upright, and tamped the earth around it. 'Is this what you want?' they asked the sick man.

'Yes,' he said, 'that is all right.' The shade cast by the leaves shifted as the sun moved, hence the name sekaamcha (se, shadow; kaamcha, around).

The sick man said, 'Put me in the shade of this tree.' The people did so, lifting him by the skins on which he lay; four men moved him.

The sick man said to the people: 'When I die, burn my body. Burn it well; keep turning it, so it burns thoroughly. Burn it till it is all gone. Note where my heart burns on the ground. Get fresh earth and pile it on the spot where my heart burns.' Those were his only instructions about his funeral.

'After you people go away and are scattered around, remember the star salaia. That will be my left hand. You people count the months. When that star comes up just before sunrise, you begin counting month one. When two stars, inekwal, appear just before sunrise in the east, that will be my eagle feather head ornament. You begin counting month two by that. The next time, when you people see the five stars in the east just before sunrise, that will be called sal, my right hand. You begin counting month three by that. That will be a very cold time. Next time my whole body will come out. That will be the red star enee, the marker of month four. Month five you will begin counting by the new moon. Month six will be springtime. In the month six all the trees will bud, cottonwood and others; also grass will appear. You people will feel happy at that time when you see the new leaves. Month seven will be warmer, flowers will bloom, seeds will commence to ripen. Month eight will be hot and some fruit will be ripening from that time on through the summer. That month lemon berries will get big. In month nine they will be ripe. In month nine saguaro will also flower, and by the end of the month the flowers will be gone and the fruit appearing. In month ten saguaro will be ripe; then you people eat it. Month ten will be very hot. In month eleven lava (opuntia) will be ripe, turning dark red. You people eat it. In month twelve harvest will be nearly over. Next will commence month one.'

He called the names of all living things so people would know them.

'Watch the earth you put over my heart, but do not touch it. Go now and then and see that nothing disturbs it. Take good care of it. You people take good care and see if in warm weather a green sprout appears. Take care of it daily as it grows. You will call that maize. When it matures it will have fruit, which you will break off, so as to eat the seed. Boil it and eat it, or grind it on a metate and then boil and eat it. Save some of the seed to plant in the ground. It will reproduce many fold.'

After he said all of this, he died. They prepared his body for the pyre. Coyote, a bad man, was there and the people feared he would steal the corpse. So an old man shot a fire drill with a bow far away to a mountain in the east, named wio. Coyote ran toward the fire which started where the drill struck. The people told him to go and investigate the smoke. 'You are the great runner,' they said. He went, running fast, but constantly looking back.

The people hastily built the pyre, putting the corpse inside (between two layers of wood). They set fire to the pyre. The people stood all around it, using long sticks to turn the corpse so it would burn quickly.

Coyote was still running toward the east.

Before the man sickened, people had said that when a person died he would come back to life in four days. Coyote heard people talking about this and he said: 'Well, the dead man will not come back in four days. He will be gone forever. It is better that way.'

The people said: 'All right.'

Coyote had a son and a daughter. The daughter was a beautiful girl. She sickened and died. Coyote came to the people and said, 'You people said the dead should come to life in four days.'

'Yes,' they replied, 'we said that, but you objected, so we have what you said already. Your daughter is gone forever. She will not come back.' She did not come back to life.

Coyote had said that people should not come back, so the man Hanyiko, did not come back.

When the man's body was burning, Coyote, on his way east, looked back and saw the fire. Again he looked back and saw the fire. Then he turned and came back. He said to himself: 'Maybe they are burning the dead man's body.'

The corpse was burned except for the torso. The legs, arms, and head had been burned off. The people were turning the torso with their sticks. They saw Coyote coming from afar. They said: 'Coyote's coming. Be careful. Burn it well.' They began circling the fire, keeping close together so Coyote could not get through.

Coyote came to the people. 'Where shall I stand?' he asked, as he ran around the ring of people. Nowhere could he find a hole.

Badger, a short man, was in the circle. Coyote jumped over him, ran up to the fire, seized the chest of the corpse, jumped back over Badger's head, and made off with it. People hit him with their sticks and chased him, but he outdistanced them. Far away he went and ate the heart.

The people put earth where the heart had lain. They watched it and cared for it. After a time a green sprout of maize appeared. They daily cared for it. It grew every day, finally becoming large with many big ears. People picked the maize and ate it. Some planted more.

After that, the month one star appeared. The people remembered what the dead man had said and counted the months. The month two stars appeared, and the people named the month two. The third month stars appeared and they counted month three. Then when the big red star came they counted month four. It was the man's body. They named it enee, instead of calling it Hanyiko.

The people said when it was storming and snow blanketed the mountains at a distance that that was cornmeal, which they would go over to get and eat. Coyote said: 'What are you people talking about? You say that is cornmeal when the mountain turns white. Why that is snow. Nobody eats that.' Coyote had beaten those people again. First he caused death; now he prevented snow being cornmeal.

'All right,' the people said.

When it rained many days, the dry wood was not wet and people easily made fire. Coyote said: 'Why, with all that rain on the wood it will get wet.' This was the third time Coyote had made trouble for the people. However, they did as Coyote bade and went wherever he wished them to go. People sickened and died, but did not come back to life.

The people heard something making a noise underground. 'Perhaps it is water coming from underground,' they said. They looked into the great hole from which they had come forth. They saw the water rising in it. The water was coming because Coyote had stolen Hanyiko's heart. The people were now talking about Coyote, saying that he was the one who had caused this calamity. 'Now the water is rising and we shall all drown,' they said.

The people, who were living in the Redrock country on the east side of the Verde valley, talked about getting a big log and hollowing it. They gathered all kinds of seeds to put in the log. They told one young woman (Komwidapokuwia): 'You enter the log and sit inside of it. The water is coming and we shall drown, but you will be saved. When you feel the log lifted by the water just sit still. The log will ground on a mountain side, but just sit still. After a long time open the hole a little. If the land is dry, you may get out.' Then they put her in the log with the seeds and fruit and sealed it. The water rose and drowned all living things.

The woman felt the water lifting her log and bumping against the mountain sides. For a long time it was in motion. Then it lay still. She did not open it immediately. She waited a long time. Then she made a little peep hole. She could see land. (No one knows where the log stranded; some say in the Redrock country). The land was damp. She went out. She continued to eat the seed and fruit which had sustained her during the voyage. When the land dried and things grew again, she collected more seeds and fruits.

From Komwidapokuwia came the second generation or creation. She spoke the Yavepe (Jerome-Verde Valley) sub-dialect.

She travelled around, but was lonesome. She picked up and ate the fruit which had developed since the flood. She saw a place where water was dripping. She lay under the dripping spring. Water dripped into her vagina. Next morning she did the same, every morning the same, opening her legs toward the sun. After a time she bore a daughter. The girl grew up very quickly. No one knows her name.

Her mother took her to the dripping spring, but the water would not drip because it saw she was its daughter. So the mother lay on top of the girl; when the water dripped, not seeing the girl, the mother slid off and water entered her vagina. The sun did not come up properly as the girl lay there, because he saw she was his daughter. So the mother lay on top of the girl and as the sun came up properly, the mother slid off and the daughter was impregnated.

After some days the girl bore a son, who was named Skatakaamcha (kaamcha, travelling) by his grandmother as she put him in the cradle she had made.

The boy grew rapidly, but was still small when his mother, collecting seeds in the Redrock country, was seized by an eagle. The eagle took her to his eyrie and fed her to two eaglets. The boy did not know of his mother's fate. His grandmother reared him, but did not tell him what had happened to his mother. She called him grandson always. She made him a little bow and arrow. He walked around near camp killing lizards and little birds, which he took to his grandmother.

When he was still a very small boy, his grandmother told him to run to the east a little way each morning before sunrise. His footprints are still to be seen to the eastward in the Redrock country.

One day he saw a hen quail. He flipped a stone at her and broke her leg. She ran into the bushes, but the boy caught her.

The quail pleaded with him: 'Please don't kill me, but fix my leg, grandson. I'm going to tell you something.'

'All right,' said the boy, 'I'll fix your leg.' He rubbed some grease from his temple and put it on the quail's leg, making her well immediately. 'Here we are, I have made you well,' the boy said.

The quail asked: 'Did your grandmother tell you anything? Why does she call you grandson? Did she tell you of your mother?'

He replied: 'Yes, she calls me only grandson.'

The quail said: 'I am going to tell you something right now. Your mother was gathering seeds when an eagle caught her and fed her to the eaglets.'

The boy felt badly when he heard this. He returned to his grandmother. He did not talk to her. He just lay down on his bed. He did not talk to his grandmother. Next morning he said nothing. He did not talk to her for four days. He ate nothing for four days. She urged him to eat without avail. She asked him what was the matter. He would not answer her.

He talked to her on the morning of the fifth day. He said: 'Grandmother, you did not tell me anything about what happened to my mother. Over there I heard the story of my mother. The eagle caught her when I was a baby. That is the story I heard over there. Why did not you tell me that story?'

Komwidapokuwia wept. 'I did not feel like telling you that happened. Yes, when you were a baby, the eagle that lived over by the cliff caught your mother. I did not want you to feel badly. That is why I did not tell you. I have taken care of you since you were a baby. Now you are grown. Do not think any more about it. Come, eat with me now.'

For four days he ate breakfast with his grandmother. After breakfast he walked around outside, thinking. He walked toward the Verde river. He crossed it and arrived at the mountain upon which Jerome is now situated.

In those days animals talked like human beings. A small bird named bitsipisa was living there. The boy went to his home and talked with him. The other animals also came and talked with him. The boy talked with the animal people.

Near the Redrock country a big bakapa (wild bull?) was lying. He was mean to everyone. The boy talked about this to the animal people. He wanted to kill that bull. The people assented. He asked which was the easiest way to kill it. Someone said: 'Begin digging in the ground here and tunnel until you are under the animal.' They told Badger to dig the hole.

Badger dug the tunnel with the boy and the people following him. When under the animal, an opening was made, so the boy could look up at it. He saw that its heart was right above the opening. The boy heated his stone knife in a fire which he built in the tunnel. He thrust the red-hot knife into the bull's heart. It jumped up, hooked its horn in the ground, then fell dead.

All of the people rushed out of the tunnel with the boy. They cut the hide and meat from the dead animal. The boy got the stomach and the blood of the animal. He made a garment of the stomach, filled it with blood, and wore it around his body. He looked like a big bellied man.

The eagle at Redrock saw him from his lofty eyrie. The boy left the people and walked towards the eagle's place. When close to some bushes the eagle swooped down to kill him, his wings making a rushing noise. The boy lay belly down. The eagle tried to seize him, but only scratched him. The boy stood again. The eagle wheeled and came at him again, but again failed to grasp him. Again the boy stood and the eagle swung around for another attempt. This time the boy lay belly up. The eagle's talons sank into his garment of bull's stomach, and the bird carried him to his eyrie on a high rock and laid him down. The boy had his eyes slightly open.

The eagle went off a little way and the eaglets approached to devour the boy. The boy told them not to and they desisted. After a time the old eagle returned and asked: 'Why don't you eat this one?'

They replied: 'He made a noise.'

The old eagle said: 'Perhaps he is rotten and spoiled, though I killed him this morning.' The eagle seized him by the belly again, so that the blood gushed forth, and said to the two eaglets: 'This is the way I killed him.' Then the eagle flew away.

The boy stood now and spoke to the eaglets. 'You children tell your mother that I am eaten already. I am going to hide over here.'

'Yes,' they said. So he hid. In a little while the mother eagle came. The eaglets did not tell her that the boy was hiding. The boy got up slowly. At his belt was a stone bladed axe, with which he struck the eagle on the head, so that she fell dead at the bottom of the cliff.

Again the boy talked to the eaglets. He asked the little one: 'How many big eagles live here?'

'Only two,' was the reply, 'my mother and father.'

'Let your father come, but say nothing to him,' requested the boy.

'Yes,' said the eaglet. So the boy hid near the male eagle's perch. He heard the bird coming.

The male eagle said to the eaglets: 'I thought you fell down the canyon, for I heard a big noise.'

The little one said: 'No, I did not hear anything over here. I did not hear anything.' The male eagle sat on the perch and looked in all directions. The boy struck him with his axe and he fell to the bottom of the canyon.

The boy returned and asked the eaglets if there were only two big ones. They said: 'Yes.' He then killed the eaglets and threw them down into the canyon. He looked down from the eyrie and tried to descend. He could not, because he was on such a high rock. He sang a song, which his grandmother had taught him. He rolled some black (really dark red) medicine in his hands and put it on his right foot. Then he raised and lowered his foot several times resting on the heel. Then he pressed the rock with his hands. The rock went down about halfway. He was able to press the rocks down only halfway.

He looked down and saw Kampanyika (Bat) gathering seeds. She was an old woman. He called to her, his relative: 'Grandmother, come up here and take me down.'

She answered: 'Grandson, what are you doing in that evil man's place?'

'Well, come up, and take me down, and I'll show you something,' he said.

Bat came up to him. She had a burden basket on her back. 'Well, my grandson, if you will sit in this basket and not open your eyes, I'll take you down.'

So he got in the basket and closed his eyes. She took him down. He wondered why he must keep his eyes closed. He thought she must be near the bottom, so he opened his eyes a little. Then she fell down very badly and was hurt. He was not hurt, because of the medicine on his feet. He picked up Bat-woman and healed her by rubbing grease from his skin on her. The old woman was glad. He told her: 'Come, grandmother, I'll show you something,' and he showed her the eagles' bodies lying there. She picked up the eagle feathers and other things as she danced around. She put them in her basket.

He told Bat-woman he was going home to his grandmother,

Komwidapokuwia. Then he departed. He arrived home at sunset. She was crying for him, for she thought the eagles had eaten him. She was lying on the floor. She had burned all his belongings. He said to her: 'Grandmother, why are you lying there crying? Look here,' and he threw her the eagle feathers. 'Is this what killed my mother?'

She said: 'Yes.'

'I killed them all,' he said. She was glad and she picked up the feathers and danced around with them.

He stayed with his grandmother and planted maize by the river Verde, near the water's edge.

After a time the boy got a wife. One day his wife went to the river through the maize field to get water from a scooped-out water hole. A Fossil Creek man named Matahaya (Wind) met her there. He stole her and took her south fifty or sixty miles.

The boy thought about his wife and wondered why she did not come home. In the evening, his grandmother asked where she was; she had been away so long after water. He said nothing, but just smiled. The sun went down, and it was dark. Next morning, the boy followed his wife's tracks to the water hole. There he saw the man's tracks. Then he saw that these were the tracks of the person who had taken his wife. Then he went back and told his grandmother. 'Someone took my wife away. The tracks show a very rough foot.'

The old woman said: 'I know that man. He is Matahaya. He stole your wife.'

'I'm going to follow him,' said the boy. Then he went to the south, following the tracks, until evening, when he reached someone's house. This was Niza's (Spider's) house. Niza fed him and he spent the night.

Niza said: 'Someone got your wife. He wants to play with you and gamble. You'd better be careful when you play with him, for he beats people just to kill them and eat them.'

Next morning the boy followed the tracks. He arrived at Matahaya's home, looked in, and saw his wife inside with Matahaya. She saw him. In a little while Matahaya lifted his eyes and saw him. Matahaya said: 'Hello, cousin. You came over here. Come in.' He entered and sat beside the fire.

Matahaya said: 'I'll play with you right now.'

The boy said: 'Yes.' They went out to play turabi (ring and pole game). The boy won and kept taking Matahaya's property. It looked as though Matahaya was making good throws, but the boy always beat him by a little.

A little bird kept flying over to the boy's pole to help him, so that Matahaya never won. The boy won all of Matahaya's property. Then at last Matahaya bet the girl sitting in the house and the boy won.

After the boy had won everything, Matahaya said to him: 'Kill me right now. You have won everything.'

The boy asked: 'What is the matter? Why do you talk that way? Have you anything at all left?'

Matahaya said: 'Yes, only my hair.' He had fine hair on his head. Matahaya said: 'Let's go on top of the hill.'

The boy said: 'Yes. All right.' Both went on top of the hill and stood there.

Matahaya said, 'You throw your hair first.'

The boy said: 'No, you throw yours first.' Matahaya threw his hair first, rolling it up. As he threw it, it unrolled and covered the hillside. It was still fastened to his head. It unrolled down to the edge of the Verde river.

The boy then threw his rolled hair. It spread across the river and up the other side. Matahaya said: 'You beat me all right. Get your knife and stab me in the stomach.'

The boy said: 'No. You do it first. Stab me.' Matahaya stuck his knife into the boy's belly. The boy kept doubling himself and telling Matahaya to stick it in there. Four times Matahaya thrust his knife in from the side. The boy was unhurt for the knife merely entered between the folds of skin. Then Matahaya told the boy to try. The boy took his knife and thrust at Matahaya's side. Matahaya tried to draw back, but the knife pierced him. Matahaya ran a ways, fell belly down, and died.

Inside Matahaya's house were many captives whom the boy released. They scattered to their homes. He went to Matahaya's body, pulled his arm off and threw it to the east. He threw the other arm to the south. He said: 'The wind shall come from different directions.' He pulled off a leg and threw it west. He pulled off the other leg and threw it north. He said: 'The wind shall come from the east, the south, the west, and the north.'

He returned to the house and got his wife. He started back to his grandmother's. He stopped at Spider's in the evening on the way home. Spider said: 'You killed the wind.'

The boy said: 'Yes.'

Spider said: 'Build a house with rock here and a big wind will come and tear it down.' The boy built the house and the wind came to blow it down, but failed. The wind blew hard, but failed. Next morning the wind stopped. The boy and his wife went on to his grandmother's.

His grandmother told him about an evil man named Chewasistesik-kaamcha (enemy going around). 'Well, I'll go over and see him,' the boy said.

'Be careful. He wants to fight with someone so as to kill him,' his grandmother said.

'Well, I'll go over,' he said. Then he went.

As he climbed up the round hill in the rain, he saw the evil man with a long knife. He had owl feathers on his head, but was otherwise naked. They looked at each other. He said to the boy: 'I saw you first.' The boy said nothing. The man met him on top of the hill and said: 'I'm going to fight with you here.'

The boy asked: 'What do you mean by saying that the first time you meet me?'

The man asked: 'What are we going to do?'

'This is the first time we have met. Take me home and feed me first,' the boy said. The man consented and took him home.

To get to his home they had to go underground. The meat was boiling in his house. The boy pretended to eat, but dropped it inside his buckskin shirt, because he did not want to eat for fear of being poisoned. He pretended to eat much until his belly was big. The man said: 'Let's go outside and fight.'

The boy asked: 'Why do you talk that way all the time?'

The man said: 'That is the only way I do.'

The boy said 'All right.'

Both went out through the tunnel. They fought with knives. The man tried to stab him in the belly, but only got the knife into the meat placed inside his shirt. After a while the boy stabbed him in the back.

The man ran around and fell dead. The boy turned his body over to see if he was dead. Then he returned to his grandmother. He told her 'I killed him all right. Everything seems hard, but it is easy for me. I killed him all right.'

The boy asked his grandmother where to get cane (arrow reed). She answered: 'Somewhere over by the Redrock country in a canyon. It belongs to Mawata (Bear). He keeps the cane.'

The boy said: 'I want to go over there and get some.'

His grandmother warned: 'Be careful. He is a bad man and might kill you.'

He went over and arrived at the cane place. He had cut two or three, when he heard Bear coming. Bear wanted to catch the boy, who said: 'Don't catch me. I want you to marry my grandmother.' Bear stopped and helped the boy cut cane with his stone knife.

Then they set out together for the boy's home. They arrived at the old woman's house. The boy immediately made arrows, fixing two with stone points. On a few he put shaped charcoal points.

Bear was sitting there and saw the boy use charcoal for an arrowpoint. Bear said: 'Why do you use that charcoal for an arrow. It is too soft. You can kill nothing with that. You shoot something and it is not hurt.'

The boy said: 'Well, if you want to try it, let's test it. You stand over there and let me shoot at you.'

Bear said: 'All right,' and he took a position; but the boy said:

'Too close. Go farther away,' for he did not want Bear to see the stone points on the two arrows he had fixed. Bear went away about fifty feet. The boy did not use a charcoal-pointed arrow, but took a stone-pointed one.

Bear asked: 'Do you want to shoot me in the front or back?'

The boy said: 'Turn your back. I'll shoot you in the back.' Bear did so. The boy took a stone-pointed arrow and shot Bear in the back. Bear turned and ran at the boy, the arrow sticking in him. He fell dead four or five feet from the boy. The boy had fooled him by making a charcoal-pointed arrow so Bear could see him at work. The boy cut off Bear's hide, which he kept for a blanket for his bed.

The boy asked his grandmother where to get arrow foreshaft wood. 'Where will I get that kind of wood for foreshafts?' he asked.

She replied: 'There is good wood down there by the canyon, but someone is living there who owns it. Be careful of that person.'

The boy went to the canyon and came to the place where the wood grew. He tried to cut off the stems, when the owner saw him and came toward him. The owner was Yuu (Great Horned Owl). He tried to catch and kill the boy. The boy said: 'No. Don't catch me. I came after you to marry my grandmother.'

The man said: 'All right,' and helped him to cut the wood for foreshafts.

Owl went home with the boy. They arrived. The boy said to his grandmother: 'I want you to feel for Owl's heart. Feel all over his body till you find it.' She did this and Owl thought she was playing with him, tickling him. She tickled him all over, but could not find his heart. She tickled the sole of his foot. Owl now felt it and the boy observed that he did. The grandmother had now found where his heart was.

She told her grandson, who said: 'All right. It is coming night. You lie with him.'

When night came the two lay there together. Owl went to sleep. The boy, when he observed Owl fast asleep, got out an arrow with a stone point. He shot Owl in the sole of his right foot. Owl had hidden his heart there, as he feared the boy would kill him. The arrow travelled up his leg into his body. Owl died.

The boy wanted to get mulberry wood for a bow. He asked his grandmother. She said: 'Yes, there is a nice smooth tree down the canyon, but you can't go in there because the vertical canyon walls at the entrance keep closing and opening.'

The boy asked: 'Can't I crawl in?'

She replied: 'Yes, but the rock walls coming together will kill you.'

'Well, I'll go over and see,' said the boy.

He went over to the canyon. When he arrived he saw the high vertical rock walls of the narrow entrance. Inside he saw a good tree for bow wood. He tried to enter, but the walls started to draw together. He saw them coming and when halfway, he set a deer antler crosswise so as to prevent them touching. He crawled in under the antler which held the walls apart. He cut wood for four bows. He returned between the walls still held apart by the antler and went to his grandmother's. Now he had a good bow and arrows.

The grandmother told the boy about his father, the sun. 'The sun is your father,' she said. The boy wondered why his grandmother told him this and he wanted to go to where his father lived. He went toward the east where his father appeared in the morning.

It was a long journey. Many days he travelled. Sitting in front of the door of his father's house he could look into it. There he saw his father. His father saw him as he was coming out of his house and they talked. Inside was a woman, the sun's wife.

The woman said to the sun: 'My, is this your son, who has come way over here?' for she was jealous of the boy's dead mother.

A fly came to the boy's ear and said: 'This man, your father, might kill you. He will try to kill you in his sweat house. He'll put you in and put a hot stone in there; it will be so hot you will die. That is the way he kills many people. If he wants you to go in, go ahead. I'll go with you; you will not die.' The fly stayed in the opening of his ear.

The sun said: 'Let's go in the sweat house.'

The boy said: 'All right.' He went in. The sun brought in a red hot stone from the fire outside. The sweat house became very hot. The boy was just barely alive in the heat. However, he did not die. Four times the sun put the hot rock in there, but the boy did not die.

Then the sun called the boy out of the sweat house. The sun said: 'You are really my son, my real son, because you did not die.' They walked along together looking for the sun's horse. The sun said to the boy, 'I've got the horses over here. You select whichever one you want to ride home.' The boy saw horses of different colours. He wanted a gray horse. The sun said: 'All right. Take it.' He got it and mounted it to test it. It ran far with him four times. The horse was made of cloud. He took it over to his grandmother's.

She said: 'I know that horse, too, made of cloud. The sun keeps them.'

His grandmother told him there was a man lying by a rock in the Redrock country. That man was killing people. The boy wanted to go and see. He went over there and saw that man lying right there on the big rock. The man's name was Iilapatohomai, Cliff-person-kickdown. His wife was Yuvempakitskwandja, Daughter's-eyes-kill-people.

The boy came to where the man was lying. He brought with him a small blue fox. The boy talked with the man. He put the fox near the man where he could not see it. When the fox did get in view the man tried to kick it down the cliff, but missed it. The boy saw this but said nothing. The fox came back and the man kicked at it again, but it jumped aside. The boy said: 'What is the matter that you kick at my pet? It belongs to me.'

The man said, 'I didn't kick him; I was just straightening my leg.' The boy told his fox to go near the man again. The man tried again to kick it, but it jumped aside.

The boy said : 'You see now, you kicked him again.' The boy took a rattlesnake out of his shirt and threw it toward the man, saying: 'Now, you kick this one.'

The man said: 'I don't like to see that kind. Take it out. Get it away from me.' The man tried to get up, but his back toes rooted to the earth.

The boy asked: 'Did you kick this snake down by the rock?'

'No, I am afraid of snakes,' the man replied.

The boy said, 'All right,' and he pulled his stone axe from his belt. 'I'm going to cut you loose and throw you down the cliff.' Then he chopped the man loose and shoved him over the cliff.

The boy went around to get to the bottom of the cliff. When he came to the place he saw that other people lived there. He came to six or seven women standing there. The women were looking at the boy. After a bit he got a pain in the face. They were trying to kill him. He saw the remains of the man who had fallen off the cliff. The women had eaten all the flesh. Nothing was left except the bones. He saw the fire where they had cooked his flesh. A little bit was left, namely the stomach. He picked up the stomach and threw it in the fire. He talked to the women, telling them to watch what he did. They watched the stomach which he threw into the fire. A little boy was lying in the house covered with a buckskin. The little boy said: 'See what is in the fire.' The stomach swelled up until it burst. The little boy said to the women: 'Look out, this thing is going to burst.' He was looking through a tiny hole in the buckskin cover. The stomach burst. The contents flew into the eyes of the women. They held their hands over their eyes and went around in a circle. The boy pulled out his stone axe and killed the women. The women had been accustomed to eat the flesh of the people whom the man kicked over the cliff.

The boy looked into the house and saw the little boy still lying there. He went in and picked him up and started home with him. After a bit he told the little boy to stay where he was, while he went into the bush to empty his bowels. He stayed behind a bush a while, while the little boy stayed on the other side. The little boy after a time ran away and the boy ran after him as he entered a cave just as the boy was about to catch him the little boy entered a rock hole. He grabbed him by the heels of his boots which pulled off. The boy went back and got a stick. Then he said to the little boy: 'Come out, let's go.'

He did not come out, so the boy prodded him with the stick. 'If you don't come out, I'll build a fire and suffocate you. Come on, let's go.' He did not come out.

Close to sundown the boy got kindling wood to build a fire. He put pinon pitch on the wood and lighted the fire. The fire was going into the hole. He looked up and saw the little boy on top of the cliff. The little boy said: 'I'm going to eat you up. Then I'm going away to the south.'

'Come down, let's go home before the night comes.' He did not come down, just stayed up there. The boy tried to run around and climb up to him. But the little boy entered a hole again and went to the bottom of the cliff. The boy stood there and looked down into the hole, but could not see him. The fire was still burning at the base of the cliff and the little boy came out by it. The little boy looked up at him as he stood on top of the cliff. The boy could see the little boy standing by the fire. When the boy came down the little one went into the rock hole again. The boy looked in. The little boy climbed up again and the boy saw him on top of the cliff. 'Come on down; let's go home before the night.'

The little boy replied: 'Hastauwa, Hastauwa (Dripping-water, Dripping-water, in reference to the boy's conception). Matkinyabakaamcha (Nobody-person-going-around), go away south gone. Little-water, I'm going south and I'm going to eat you up.'

The boy said: 'Come on down. Let's talk it over here before night.' The little boy did not come down, so the boy climbed up again to the top of the cliff. The little boy went down his shaft and hole again. The boy from the top could see him below again. The little boy taunted him again. The boy ran down again. The sun went down and the fire died down. The boy wanted to go home. The little boy was too clever for him.

The boy stayed there thinking. Then he got a live rattlesnake and put it in front of the hole. He told the snake: 'Watch this hole. If that little boy comes out, you bite him on the foot so that he dies.' He got another rattlesnake, which he put on the other side of the hole with similar instructions.

The boy went home to his grandmother. He told her of what had happened. 'I killed that man lying on the cliff, and the women at the bottom of the cliff. I got the little boy to bring home, but he ran away from me and went into the rocks. I lost him. I tried to get him, but could not. The sun went down, so I left my snakes there and came home. I think the snakes will catch him tonight.' Thus he told his grandmother.

He went to bed. Next morning he went over to see. His snakes were still in place. Both snakes were asleep. He saw the little boy's footprints where he had emerged from the hole and walked away. He became angry at his snakes, and said: 'You two are no good to let that little boy walk by you. Did you see that little boy walk by you here?'

One snake said: 'No. I could not see him; I was asleep over here.' Then the boy killed his two snakes with a stone. Their blood scattered and today there are many snakes over there.

The boy tracked the little boy toward the south. About one and a half miles away the little boy had built a fire. He took a piece of white rock, heated it and broke it open and another little boy came out. They thus made two sets of tracks. The boy still followed, following the double tracks. About one and a half miles farther, the little boy put blue rock in a fire and took another little boy from it. Now three tracks, men's size, were made. All three little boys had become men. At about one and a half miles further he made another fire and put red rock in it and took out another man. Altogether there were four now. The boy kept following the tracks. He had not yet overtaken them.

They kept building fires every one and a half miles and adding to their number. Now there were five men. The boy did not see them, just saw their tracks.

Still he followed the tracks. They put another rock in the fire and took a man out; total six men. The boy did not find them. Another fire and seven men, but the boy could not see them. Another fire and two or three men became. The boy could not see them. Another fire and two or three more men. The boy did not see them, but still followed their tracks. At the next fire many people became. The boy could see tracks, but no men. Next fire and more people. The boy had not seen them yet. The sun went down and the boy returned to his grandmother. He told her what happened.

She said: 'Now let him go. He'll become our enemy. You can't get all of that body of men who are going south.'

Next morning he said: 'Well, I'll go over and see.' He followed the tracks. More and more tracks appeared the farther he went. In the afternoon about four o'clock he came to a wide open space and there he saw the people camped. He stood and looked and counted many, many men. Then he went back to his grandmother's. He told her: 'I saw many people camped over there.'

His grandmother said: 'That's the way I told you.'

The boy said: 'Tomorrow morning I'm going over there early and try to kill all.'

He went to get his father-in-law Gila Monster to accompany him. He lived near Redrock also. About midnight they set out. They arrived at the camp of men before dawn. They started shooting them with bow and arrow. They killed many people, but more kept coming. He did not finish killing them until evening, when his father-in-law got killed. All day long they were killing them. In the evening he returned to his grandmother's. As he went he saw white clouds over the Redrocks. He thought his father-in-law had come back alive because of this sign.

He went to his father-in-law's house and saw him sitting inside the house. He laughed at him. 'You already came back.'

'Yes.' The boy went on to his grandmother's place. He told her what had happened. 'From early morning I killed them all day long. My father-in-law got killed. But I did not kill them all. More and more people came, and I got tired. Coming home, on the way, I saw the clouds over the Redrocks, a sign my father-in-law had come home safely. I went there and saw him there already home.'

His grandmother said: 'I told you to let him go. You can't kill him.'

The boy said: 'I'm going over there again.'

His grandmother said: 'I told you to let him go. There will be more people this time. Better stop now.'

The boy said: 'All right. I'll quit. I know I can't finish them, because there are more people now.' He stayed with his grandmother.

The Burning of the World

Two families lived to the east of Mayer. One man was Sun, the other was Coyote. These two men played the hoop-and-pole game. Sun won all sorts of things from Coyote: buckskin, boots, leggings, hides, pots, baskets, dolls, deer meat, shell beads, etc.

The last time Coyote bet his son and daughter and lost to Sun. Then Coyote bet his wife and lost. Then he bet one of his legs and lost. Sun cut Coyote's leg off. Coyote made a wooden leg for himself. Then he went away.

He went up into the mountains where there were pine trees. He saw the people who lived there. Coyote entered the house of one man named Mipuskachuakba (Arizona Tree Squirrel), the 'high man' of that place.

Coyote told Squirrel: 'I want you and your people to go over there and play the hoop-and-dart game with Sun. Sun won all my goods, my children, my wife, and my leg,' and he exposed his wooden leg. 'You see how very poor I am now. I've got one leg, that's all.'

Squirrel said: 'All right,' and he went around and talked to his people.

Some days later the men came to Squirrel's house in the evening. They smoked. Coyote told about Sun. Squirrel said: 'Our friend is very poor and has only a wooden leg. We'll go over there and play against Sun and win the things back for this man.'

Sometime later all went over to Sun's house. Coyote went too. They camped a mile or two away from Sun's house. Squirrel sent a man over to look at Sun's house. When Sun saw him he was to return to camp. Sun had two houses of stone, one higher than the other. In the higher one he was watching. He saw this man and shouted: 'Already I see you. You'd better turn around and go back.' The man did so.

Squirrel sent a different man toward Sun's house. Sun saw him before he reached the house and sent him back like the first man.

Squirrel sent more than ten men altogether. Each one was seen and sent back by Sun. Finally Squirrel sent Chipmunk to see Sun's house. Chipmunk made a hole in an Opuntia cactus to peek through, but Sun saw him. 'Already I see you peeking through that cactus hole. You go away.' Chipmunk returned to the camp.

Squirrel said: 'I wonder how we'll reach his house. It is pretty hard to get over there. I'll try sending Hummingbird.'

Hummingbird said: 'Yes. I'll go.' He flew far up in the air, high in the sky. Then he came straight down. Sun was lying on his back on his house but did not see Hummingbird, who was conning very fast. Hummingbird lit on one of Sun's eyelashes. Then he looked around the house. Sun did not see or feel him. After a while Hummingbird darted upward. Sun heard the humming noise and then knew someone had come over and spied on him and had gone back.

Sun said: 'That was Hummingbird who came to my house. I wonder where he came from. I looked around all over, so he must have come from the sky, because I did not see him in any direction. All right. He won.'

Hummingbird flew up, then down to the camp. He reported to Squirrel: 'I got over there all right. I lit on his eyelash. I looked around at the house, and saw how the people go in under the houses. I saw how big the houses were and what the ground looked like inside.' Hummingbird was a shaman.

Squirrel said: 'Well, my mind is to dig under the ground and come up inside Sun's house. It is a good thing Hummingbird got over to Sun's house. I think he'll be lucky playing with Sun. You people dig a tunnel under the ground, so we can go over to Sun's place unseen.'

Badger started digging, others helped. They completed the tunnel. Sun lying in the upper story of his house did not know they had tunnelled into the ground floor. They all entered his house and sat there. Sun still lay on the second story. He heard a noise downstairs. Then he knew the people had entered his house. He knew without looking.

Sun had his helper (another Coyote) go down: 'Go downstairs. The people have already entered my house.'

Coyote went down. There he saw many people in the spacious house. He saw the fine things the people had brought in the way of clothes, beads, bows, arrows, etc. He went up and reported to Sun: 'The people have filled up the downstairs. They brought much fine property. You will win all those fine things when you play with them.'

Sun knew that wooden-legged Coyote had brought these people over. Sun said to his helper Coyote: 'Go over there and fetch some water for those people.' Coyote went for the water and brought it over in clay pots for the people.

Squirrel would not drink it and told his people not to. 'If you drink this water, we'll lose the game.'

The people threw out the water which Sun's helper had brought them. Sun said to Coyote and to his (Sun's) wife and daughter: 'Let's get some maize and squashes for those people. Bring them over and boil them for those people.' They brought the maize and squashes and cooked them for the people. Squirrel ordered his people not to eat, lest they lose the game. The people threw the food away.

Squirrel asked wooden-legged Coyote: 'Do you know the Sun's sitting place? Which side of the house?'

Wooden-legged Coyote said: 'He sits on this side of the house in that one place.'

Squirrel said: 'I'll sit in Sun's place.' He did so.

Sun came downstairs to see his visitors. He saw Squirrel sitting in his place. Sun said: 'Move over this way. You are in my place.' But Squirrel did not move. Three or four times Sun asked him to move.

Squirrel told him: 'Sit over there; there is more room.'

Sun said: 'I know that is a good place. But this is the old man's place where you are sitting. You move over there and let me have my place.'

Squirrel said: 'That other place is good for an old man.' Sun sat over there without replying.

Evening came. They started to play nohobi, the game of hiding a disk of yucca root in a pile of earth. Sun was a good player; he never missed. Neither did Rabbit of the other side. Rabbit never missed, just like sun. Back and forth the disk went between them neither winning nor losing. Near the middle of the night, Sun got tired and weak-minded and missed a number of times. Rabbit thus won from Sun.

Sun said to his people: 'Go tell my two daughters there is a young man here who is a great player. Have them come and take him away and lie with him.' The girls came and attempted to beguile Rabbit. In a little while they took him out, away to the maize field. He stayed with the girls and did not return.

Some other good players took his place. Sun lost many things, and in the morning he lost his house, garden, and maize field. Sun had many people; these he bet too, and lost. He bet his Coyote helpers, wife and daughters, too. He lost. He bet Coyote's leg which he had won before. He lost it.

Rabbit remained with the girls in the maize field, one lying on each side of him. Sun had bet his daughters and wife and lost. Morning came. He said: 'All right. Right now, kill me.'

Squirrel said: 'Well, cousin, I did not understand what you said. We are only playing. We don't want to kill you, but you said "Kill me." That is not good. Is that all you had?'

Sun said : 'Yes. That is all I had. You've won everything.'

Squirrel asked: 'Have you anything left at all that you want to gamble?'

Sun said: 'I have a few sons left down in the valley. You people can foot race my sons. Go far south and then back. If you win you keep my sons and kill me.'

That morning at daylight, the visitors started racing Sun's sons toward the south. Sun went up in the sky. Sun's wife went to the maize field to get some ears of corn to boil for her family. Squirrel was still lying in Sun's house.

Sun's wife saw her daughters lying with Rabbit in the maize field. She said: 'What is the matter? All of the people are foot-racing toward the south. But you sleep over here very late.' Rabbit woke up, jumped far away, and ran back to the house. At the house was nobody except Squirrel.

Squirrel said: 'They are foot-racing toward the south.'

Rabbit said: 'I'll follow.' Just a little way from the house Rabbit made a high place where the racers would have to climb or stop. Then he made a barrier of atatkashula cactus, which the racers would have to pass. Also he made a mud hole in the race course. Then he followed the other racers. He went south very rapidly and caught up with the hindmost racers. He did not catch up with the fastest racers, the Sun's sons.

Jackrabbit and Rabbit were both in the race. The foremost racers turned back at the south and started for home. Rabbit could not overtake Sun's sons. When they reached the mud hole they went over it easily. Similarly they broke through the cactus barrier. But the cliff they could not climb. The racers were kicking a buckskin ball. This they could not get over the cliff.

Rabbit said to Jackrabbit: 'You kick it first. I'll follow it to the middle of the cliff and then kick it the rest of the way over.' Jackrabbit kicked it first, but did not reach the top, so the ball came back part way. Rabbit met it halfway and kicked it all the way over and to the goal.

At that time Sun came back and lay down beside the opposing high man, Squirrel. Rabbit kicked the ball so vigorously that it fell between the two leaders. The Sun saw it and said: 'This is my son's ball.' Then he got a big knife with which to kill Squirrel.

Squirrel picked up the ball and looked at it. 'This belongs to Rabbit and Jackrabbit,' he said. 'See this ball over here. It is marked with Rabbit's teeth. I know it belongs to him.' They argued. Then Rabbit appeared at Sun's house.

Sun said: 'I have lost again. This is the end of my life.' Squirrel picked up a little stone axe. He hit Sun on the temple with it. He struck again and again to kill him. Sun died.

Then Squirrel pulled off Sun's arm. 'Sun is not staying in this world any more.' He threw the arm in the air and it encircled the sky. It has done so ever since, as the sun.

The other people arrived. The dead man's sons ran away. They did not return to their father's house. Only Squirrel's people returned. They cut the skin from Sun's body like flaying an animal. Squirrel said: 'Don't drop a particle on the ground. Keep it good.'

All the people cut off pieces of Sun's body. Coyote got a piece of Sun's stomach. He put it on a rock pile. Many of the people returned to Squirrel's place. As they went they looked back toward Sun's place and saw the smoke coming out.

The people said: 'We knew that Coyote left some of the body over there.'

The people asked Coyote: 'Did you leave anything over there?'

'Oh my! I left a little piece of stomach over there. I put it on top of the rock, but I forgot it,' Coyote said.

The fire started from the stomach. It spread and became larger and larger. The fire was burning everything. The people said: 'How are we going to save our lives?' They were in a broad open valley. The fire spread over there and the ground was burning. It was burning the world. It killed all kinds of people and animals and everything. All the people burned up. They turned into red ants. Coyote had made trouble again.

The Human Bear

After the burning of the world, new people came, but we do not know whence. This was the fourth generation or creation. Miamatkahuwa (mia, heaven; matka, other side or up above; huwa, sit over there) began this world. Miamatkahuwa had several brothers and sisters. Coyote was the friend of Miamatkahuwa, one of whose sisters married Coyote.

Miamatkahuwa was the youngest. He had older brothers and sisters. His older brothers went deer hunting daily. Coyote stayed home all the time. He did not do anything. The older brothers brought meat. All ate meat. Any bad meat they gave to Coyote always. Coyote said to his wife as they lay together: 'What's the matter with your brothers? They don't give me anything good to eat; just a little piece and rotten.'

His wife replied: 'My brothers don't like you.' She was angry at her brothers. These brothers went over there and hunted deer daily.

Miamatkahuwa stayed home continually. His brothers brought him deer meat all the time. He had good meat every evening; Coyote received only bad meat.

Sometime later, the brothers were hunting over there again (above Black Canyon). There was a big cliff visible far below. One went home and told his brother-in-law Coyote. 'I came after you, my brother-in-law. I saw a big cliff far below and a mountain sheep lying there, but I could not see very well. I want you to come and look down over there. Maybe you can see better. I think you can look down there and tell me. Then I'll shoot it.'

Coyote said: 'Yes,' and they went together over there.

Arrived at the cliff, they asked Coyote to look over to see if a mountain sheep was below. Coyote objected: 'I'd get scared. I can't stand by the edge of that cliff. I might fall over the edge.'

'Go ahead. Stand right there. I'll hold you,' they assured him. One held him by the shoulder, while Coyote leaned over. He shoved him over the cliff. He fell to the bottom dead. His brothers-in-law wanted to kill him, but Coyote was unsuspecting.

The brothers returned home. They said nothing to their sister. She asked: 'Where's my husband?'

One said: 'I saw him way over there on the other side of the mountains. I thought he came home first but he is not here yet.'

She waited and waited until the middle of the night, still thinking. She thought: 'My brothers did not like him. They never gave him good meat. Maybe they killed him over there somewhere and hid his body.'

Next morning, the brothers went hunting again. The sister (Coyote's wife) went to her little brother Miamatkahuwa and said: 'You stay here while I go looking around for my husband.' She went. The little fellow stayed home until evening. She came home. The brothers came home after a while. They brought meat and skinned it. Next morning they went hunting again. Every morning it was the same way. The sister went on the second morning to look for Coyote. The little fellow stayed home always. In the evening she came home. She went every morning. Sometimes at night the little fellow would see his sister lying there scratching her side. There was something like an arrow which she pulled out of her side and hid in the ground under the bed. Next time, she scratched the other side; next time, her back. She did this four or five times, all in one night.

Next morning the brothers went hunting. The sister went out too. Only the little fellow was left at home. He thought about what he saw his sister put in the ground. 'I'll go and see it,' he said. He scraped the earth aside with a stick. He found four or five pieces of arrow several inches long. He put them back and covered them again.

That evening when his sister came home, he did not ask her about the pieces of arrow. The brothers came home with venison. Next morning the brothers went hunting. The sister said: 'Come on, little brother, and go to the edge of that river and make a sweat house.' He went with her and made a sweat house. She went in, he sat outside, not near the door, but around in back. In a little while, he came around and peeked in. It was hot inside and her body was perspiring. He saw his sister scratch her side and get out a piece of arrow which she stuck under a rock.

He got scared. He thought maybe people were shooting her when she went out each day. He thought, 'I'll tell my brothers this time.' She came out of the sweat house and took a plunge. She clothed herself and then they started for home. They went home.

After a little while the brothers all came, bringing meat. They had supper. In the early morning the sister went out in the wilderness. The little fellow told his brothers what he had seen, showing them the pieces of arrows. 'One night I saw her take them out here. Yesterday I saw her do the same thing at the sweat house.'

The oldest brother said: 'Our sister goes out to kill people (by the hand or biting) on account of her husband being dead. People shoot at her.'

The little brother said: 'Sometime she'll kill us too.'

The brothers went out to hunt. They came back in the evening. The sister came back.

Early in the morning the sister went out first. The older brothers said: 'All of us stay right here.' They put the little fellow in a hole in the ground. 'Now we're going away. Our sister will kill us over there. You stay here and keep alive.' They put a big rock over the hole.

They departed. About noon the little fellow heard his sister come and ask: 'My little brother, where are you?' He did not answer her. She walked around and around calling him. He did not answer. After a while she moved the rock aside and found the little fellow in the hole. He came out.

Her body was trembling and her face was different. 'Where are my brothers?' she asked the little fellow.

'I don't know,' he said. 'They put me here under the ground. I don't know where they were going.'

She said: 'I'll circle around the house till I see their track.' She found it. She said: 'I've found your brothers' tracks and I'll follow them. Little brother, you stay home.'

He saw her running along their track. A little while after he saw Turkey Vulture flying. He came to the little fellow and talked to him. He said to him: 'Your sister is following your brothers and wants to kill them. She has been going around the wilderness killing people. Now she has started after your brothers, following them over there. Every time your sister goes into the wilderness she changes into a bear. She came over here a little while ago and talked to you. Then she went over there and changed to a bear and is following your brothers. She has followed your brothers and has caught them already. All your brothers got in a hole in a log and started shooting at the bear. But she killed them all. Now she'll come over here and eat you too.' Turkey Vulture went away.

The little fellow cried as he walked around the house. In a little while Blue Jay came to him and said: 'Your sister has killed and eaten your brothers. She is coming now. She left her heart right there. See it! She has covered it with grass. That is how she can go out in the wilderness and never die, because her heart is over here. She's coming back already. She'll want to eat you too. There is a little knife over here. You heat it in the fire.' He did as told. 'When she comes you take that knife and cut her heart in half,' Blue Jay said. 'I'll watch from right over there and shout when she appears.' In a little while Blue Jay shouted. The boy looked and saw her approaching in bear form.

He took the red hot knife and cut her heart. She shouted: 'Don't cut my heart, little brother.'

Blue Jay said: 'Don't listen to her, but cut her heart in two. Otherwise she will eat you.'

He cut the heart in two. Bear fell dead. After that he walked around inside his house, all alone. He slept inside the house. Next morning he followed his brothers' tracks. He followed them where they climbed the mountains, to the other side of the mountains. He found their bones, some with flesh on. He looked around and saw their bones. He thought as he walked around. After a little while, he gathered the bones. He cleaned the ground. He cleaned all the weeds and grass off. No bushes or any vegetation were left on the plot of ground. In the centre of the clearing he built a hut. He made a door on the east side. He put their bones inside the house and closed it. Some distance away he built another house. He lay in that himself.

After four days he heard something in the bone house. He went over to look into it. There was nobody in there, only the bones. He went back to his own house.

After four more days he heard a sound like people talking in the bone house. He went over again. He stood looking inside. There was nobody there. He returned to his own house. After four days he heard something again in the bone house and went over to look. He saw the bones had turned to men. He returned to his house. Next day he went to the bone house and looked in. The people had become alive. They remained inside. He went back to his house without speaking to them.

Next day, he heard noises all day in the bone house. He went over again to see. The people were walking around inside the house. They had horses inside the house. He stood by the door and he saw people making saddles, leggings, and shirts. He went back to his own house. Next day, he heard the noise of hammering. He went over to the bone house to see. He saw a rifle inside the house. Someone inside had a hat like a white person's. He entered to talk to the people.

'I want you people to make horses.' They paid no attention to him. He said: 'I want a rifle made for me.' They paid no attention to him. He went back to his own house and lay there thinking.

Next morning, the people took the horses outside one by one. There were many different people. They mounted the horses, one by one, and rode off. The little fellow came out of his house to the people. He said: 'I made you people. I'm the one that made you people. Make something for me.' They paid no attention to him. They started riding away to the east. They scattered to all different places.

The little fellow went and lay inside his house. In a little while something like lightning came from the sky down to the ground. This pulled him quickly from the earth to the sky. Nobody knows where he is in the sky.

The Laughing Wives

A man with two wives lived in Verde valley to the south of the Redrock country. He lived over there. He and his wives travelled to the northwest, up Verde valley. The man said: 'My garden is over there in which I planted red and white spotted maize. You women camp over there some distance from the maize, while I go around the other way looking for deer.' The women went toward the garden. They rested not far from the maize, waiting for their husband.

In a little while the older wife said to the younger: 'I'd like to go over there and examine the maize.' The older one went over, but the younger remained. The old one got close to the maize. The maize laughed like a person. The older wife began to laugh, too. The younger wife then ran over. She came over and started to laugh. Both went running around in the maize field. After a time they were running around naked. In a little while they were going around in the air above the maize field.

The husband came. He saw a burden basket there with food in it, but did not see his wives. He looked for their tracks and saw they led toward the maize. The tracks went through the maize in every direction. He went around and around in the maize field, looking for his wives, whose tracks he saw everywhere.

In a little while he heard laughing up in the air. He looked up and saw his wives flying around in the sky.

He went out and camped beside the garden. He planted a dogtail tree. He also planted a wild grape vine which grew up the tree. The tree grew up into the sky. The man climbed up it. He arrived in the sky.

There he saw his wives running around, laughing. Both laughed at their husband, though they did not come close to him.

He chased around trying to catch his wives. He caught them and brought them down the tree. They reached the ground at his camp.

Sometime later the women recovered from their laughing spell. They stayed over there with their husband.

Coyote Resurrects Mountain Lion

A man named Mountain Lion and another man named Coyote lived northwest of the Redrock country. Mountain Lion hunted deer every day. Coyote went out to gather seed. After a long time, Mountain Lion dreamed that an enemy came, killed him, and took his scalp.

Coyote said: 'It is not true, that which you are dreaming.'

After a long time, Mountain Lion was still hunting deer. A little while after that Mountain Lion stayed home and Coyote went out gathering ripe things. Mountain Lion heard some people coming. They circled around his house. He saw that they were Bear people. There were more than ten of them. They killed Mountain Lion and took his scalp. They went back to their country.

Evening time and Coyote came home. He saw his friend dead, lying right there. He remembered Mountain Lion's dream. Coyote saw the big footprints around the house. He saw his friend's body had been scalped. He slept in the house.

Next morning he followed the enemy's tracks. He wanted to get back Mountain Lion's scalp. He followed their tracks west, then east. Far away, in the afternoon, he saw an old woman (Bear) walking. He caught up with her. Coyote talked to her: 'Where are you going?'

She was partly blind and replied: 'I don't want to tell you. I know you, man, you are Coyote. You stayed with Mountain Lion, I heard.'

Coyote said: 'No. I did not live with Mountain Lion. I lived in the west. I don't know anything about this place over here. I was just looking around when I saw you. Do tell me about the places and people over here. I want you to tell me where the different people live. I'll go with you to where you live.'

She said: 'Yes. My people were just going over here and they left me because I could not walk fast enough. I'll reach their camp in the evening.'

Coyote asked: 'Where were your people coming from?'

'My people were just over to Mountain Lion's place. He lived over there a long time. They killed him at his place and got his scalp. Last night they had a dance on the way with his scalp.'

'Did you dance too?' asked Coyote.

'Yes, I danced,' said the old woman.

'Did you carry that scalp?' asked Coyote.

She replied: 'Yes. I got that scalp and carried it around in a circle and I sang. They are dancing again tonight. This evening when I get over there the people will dance with the scalp and I will do the same way as last night.'

Coyote asked her many questions as they walked together along the trail. The sun was going down, when Coyote said: 'When we get over there will the people have a dance?'

The old woman replied: 'Yes. Perhaps they have already started dancing now.'

Coyote asked: 'When we get over there what are you going to do? Are you going to lie down and rest or are you going right into the dance?'

She replied: 'No, I'm not going to rest. I know the people are having the dance already. When I arrive I shall shout with my hand over my mouth like that. That's the way I did last night and the people let me have that scalp. I danced around over there in a circle. In a little while I took the scalp off the stick and put it on my head and danced close around the fire. I'll do the same way this evening.'

Coyote said: 'Good, my nipi (man's father's sister). Better walk a little faster so we can get over there right away.'

She walked faster; Coyote followed. On the way Coyote saw a cleft in a rock. He pushed her down into it. Then he got a stick and beat her to death. He flayed her, put on her skin, then followed the trail. By the river they were making the scalp dance.

Coyote saw the people dancing. He approached wearing the old woman's skin. His face was well covered and he imitated her walk. The people were circling around. He went close to them, then shouted with his hand beating against his mouth. The people opened one side of the circle to let him in, thinking it was the old woman.

He went in. Some people gave him the scalp. He carried it on a stick. After a time he took it off and put it on his head. He sang as he danced around the fire with it. He watched, as he danced, for a place to squeeze through the line of people and escape. In a little while his opportunity came and he darted through. Away he went, very fast. The people now remembered the Coyote who lived with Mountain Lion. They followed him and hit him with stones and pieces of wood. After following him a short distance, it became dark. They lost track of him. As he ran he had pulled off the old woman's skin in pieces, shouting: 'This is your mother's skin. This is your grandmother's skin.'

Coyote returned home and took the scalp back to the dead body of his friend. He put the scalp in place. He built another house a little way from the old one; in this he stayed, leaving Mountain Lion's body in the old house. Every morning Coyote listened for sounds from the dead man's house. The second night he thought he heard a voice in Mountain Lion's house. On the third night, he heard plainly the talking. The fourth night he heard walking inside the house. In the morning he went over to see. He found Mountain Lion alive.

Coyote Juggles His Eyes

Coyote was looking for cactus and seeds to the eastward. He was in low hill country. His body felt sleepy. He saw a good shady place and lay down to sleep. For a long time he slept. He woke up and heard the noise of people walking. He sat up and saw a lot of people going by. These people were juggling with their eyes as they walked along. That was the noise Coyote heard.

Coyote started thinking: 'I wonder why they do that. It looks very good. Well, I'll go over there and ask those people to teach me, so I can do the same way.' So he arose and went.

He came to the people and asked how they did the eye-juggling. The people said: 'No, we will not teach you. You are Coyote and different from us. If we teach you; you might do it wrong sometime and then you would die.'

Coyote did not believe those people and asked again and again. The people finally said: 'Yes, we'll teach you.' So they took both of his eye's and threw them a ways and they came back in place.

The people said: 'Now, do it yourself.' Coyote did and they came back all right.

After they came back, Coyote said: 'I see better now.' Then Coyote went home. There he juggled his eyes. Then he threw them up again and turned his head the other way. His eyes landed on the ground. He lost his two eyes. He had to grope with his hands.

Bat's Wives

Bat lived south of the Redrock country. He went far to the east, hunting deer. He had two wives, who accompanied him on the hunt. He started four or five deer, shot at them, but missed. Then he killed a fawn. He went to look at it. It was very small, lying there dead. The women came with their pack baskets and put the fawn in one of them. They brought it home and boiled the meat.

Next morning Bat went hunting. He came home late in the evening. He kept doing this every day, always getting home late in the evening. He kept telling his wives not to be building a fire because it was too light, but when dark they might build one. The two wives were not bats. They were a different kind.

One evening he came back late. He brought something and put it right there. It was only a paunch. The wives said: 'We'll make a good fire, so as to see what kind of a husband it is who always likes a dark place.' One wife went out the door and looked to see what Bat had brought. She found only ice. Bat called it meat. The wife did not feel good. One wife stayed inside the house and made ready to make the fire when Bat came in. She had dry grass to start the fire with. She carried it in her hand.

Bat entered and sat down. His wife put dry grass in the fire to make it blaze. The other woman was standing there. Both wanted a good look at the man. The fire burned up brightly. The two wives saw their man. He had eyes like a bat. Those women began talking to each other about him. They said: 'What a funny face he has. Let's go away from him.' Both ran away.

Bat did not know they had run away, so he started talking to them. No one answered him. Then he knew they had left him, so he went outside. He followed the women. He did not find them. He travelled around in the dark.

The women had gone far to the east. He never found them. He turned into a bat and travelled around in the dark.

CHAPTER 35

Zuni

The Flood

There was some reason that the earth or 'ocean' got angry and all the little springs became larger and this land began to be full of water, and then all the people with all the elletteliwa ran up to the mesa. They lived there. The water got higher all the time. It filled up and almost went up to the mesa, and all the animals that lived in the water were in the water and kolowisi was lying on top of the mountain now called nose face. He lay on that point looking towards this side and crying out, and the water almost reached the top of the mesa. And the people did not know what to do. At last they looked for a boy that knew nothing about girls and a girl that knew no boys. They were the children of the priest. When they found them, all the people made telikyanawe for them. When they finished, they took them out from their house and said, 'Now, our children, you are to go in the water to save your people.' So they took them to the north side and there they gave them a large bundle of feather-sticks. So they sent them down both at the same time. As they went down into the bottom, the water would lower each day. Where the suds stopped at the rock you can see the white rocks, and the marks of the heels of the two children you can see in the rocks. Where the water got very low there the two were standing. They had turned into the rocks which are now standing at the base of the mesa. They call them the youth and girl. The girl stands at the north, the boy at the south.

The Hopi Boy and the Sun

A poor Hopi boy lived with his mother's mother. The people maltreated him, and threw ashes and sweepings into the house in which they lived. They were very unhappy. One day the boy asked his grandmother, 'Who is my father?'

His grandmother replied, 'My poor boy, I do not know who your father is.'

'I want to find my father, because all the people treat me so badly. We cannot continue to live in this place.'

Then his grandmother said, 'Come, grandchild! You must go and see the Sun; he knows who your father is.'

On the following morning the boy made a prayer-stick and went out. Many young men were sitting on the roof of the kiva. When they saw him going by, they said, 'See where that little boy is going!'

One of them remarked, 'Don't make fun of him! I believe the poor little boy has supernatural power.'

The boy took some sacred meal made of cornmeal, pounded turquoise, coral, and shell, and threw it up. When he looked up, he saw that the meal formed a trail which led upwards. He climbed up; but when he was half way up, the trail gave out. Then he threw more of the sacred meal upwards, and a new trail was formed. After he had done so twelve times, he came to the Sun. But the Sun was so hot, that he was unable to approach him. Then he put new prayer-sticks into the hair at the back of his head, and the shadow of that plumes protected him against the heat of the Sun.

He asked the Sun, 'Who is my father?'

'I only know children who are conceived in the daytime, for all children conceived in the daytime belong to me.'

Then the boy gave to the Sun a prayer-stick, and turned to go back. He fell down from the sky, and landed in the Hopi village.

On the following day he went westward; and when he came to Holbrook, he saw a cottonwood-tree. He chopped it down, and cut off a piece of the trunk of his own length. He hollowed it out, and made a cover at each end. Then he went home. There he took some sweet cornmeal and prayer-sticks. He carried them to his box and entered it. Then he closed the door. He had a small hole in the door through which he could peep out. Then he lowered the boat into the river and drifted down.

He drifted for four days and four nights, and finally the box drifted ashore at the place where the two rivers join. He felt the box striking the shore, and tried to get out; but he was unable to open the door. Then he took the plug out of his peephole and looked out. It was about the middle of the forenoon. All his efforts to open the box were in vain, and he thought he would have to die inside.

In the afternoon a Rattlesnake Girl came down to the river. When she discovered the box, she took off her mask and looked into it. She asked the boy, 'What are you doing here?'

The boy replied, 'Open the door! I cannot get out.'

The girl asked, 'How can I open it?'

'Take a stone and break the door.'

Then the girl broke the door with a stone, and the boy came out. The girl said, 'Let us go to my house!' She took him along; and when they entered, he saw many people inside – young men, girls, and old people. They were all rattlesnakes.

They asked him, 'Where are you going?'

The boy replied, 'I want to find my father.'

The girl replied, 'I will go with you; you cannot go alone.'

She made a small tent of rattlesnake-skins. She carried it down to the river, and then entered it. Then they travelled in the tent for four days and four nights. Finally they reached the ocean. There they saw a meteor, which fell into the sea and entered the house of the Sun. They asked the meteor to take them along, and in this way they reached the Sun's house.

When they entered, they saw an old woman who was working on turquoise, coral, and white shell. When she saw them, she fainted. She was the Moon, the mother of the Sun. After a little while she awoke; and the boy asked, 'Where is my father?'

The Moon replied, 'He has gone out, but he will soon be home.'

In the evening the Sun came home, and the old woman gave him venison and wafer-bread to eat. After he had eaten, he asked the boy, 'What do you want here?'

The boy replied, 'I want to know my father.'

The Sun replied, 'I am the father of the whole world. I think you are my son. When I go into the other world, you shall accompany me.' Early in the morning he said, 'Let us go!' He opened the door in the ground, and they went out. He sat down on a stool of crystal. He took a fox-skin and held it up. Then daylight appeared. After a little while he let the fox-skin down, and took the tail-feathers of the macaw and held them up. Then the yellow rays of sunrise appeared. After some time he let them down, and said to the boy, 'Now let us go!' He sat down on his stool, and made the boy sit down behind. Then they went out into another world. After they had travelled for some time, they saw people with long ears. When they went to sleep, they covered themselves with their ears as with blankets. The Sun said to the boy, 'Look at those people! When the droppings of bluebirds fall on them, they die.'

The boy said, 'How is that possible? How can people be killed that way? Let me kill the birds!'

The Sun said, 'Go ahead! I shall wait for you.' Then the boy jumped down, took a small cedar-stick, and killed the bluebirds. Then he made a fire and roasted them and ate them.

The people shouted, 'Look at this boy! He is eating Navajos!'

'No,' said the boy, 'these are not Navajos, they are birds.' Then he went back to the Sun.

They went on. About noon they came to another town.

The Sun said to the boy, 'Look! here the Apache are coming to make war on the people.' The boy saw a whirlwind moving along; and when wheat-straw was blown against the legs of the people, they fell down dead.

The Hopi boy said, 'How can people be killed by wheat-straw? Let me go down and tear it up.'

The Sun said, 'I shall wait for you.' The boy jumped down, gathered the wheat-straw, and tore it up.

The people said, 'Behold this boy, how he is killing the Apache!'

The boy replied, 'These are not Apache. That is wheat-straw.' Then he went back to the Sun.

They came to another town. There he saw people with very long hair reaching down to the ankles of their feet. They had a large pot in which thin mush was being cooked, and onions were tied to its handles. The mush was boiling over; and when it hit a person, he died. The Sun said, 'Look at the Jicarilla Apache, how they kill the people!'

'No,' said the boy, 'These are not Jicarilla Apache. It is mush. I will go down and eat it.' The Sun said,

'Go! I shall wait for you.' Then the boy jumped down. He dipped the mush out of the pot, took the onions from the handles to which they were tied, and ate the mush with the onions. The people said,

'Behold, how this boy eats the brains, hands, and feet of the Jicarilla Apache!'

The boy said, 'These are not Jicarilla Apache! It is corn-mush. Come and eat with me!'

'No,' they said, 'we are no cannibals. We do not eat Apache warriors.' Then the boy went back to the Sun, and they went on.

Finally they came to the house of the Sun in the east. There the sister of the Sun waited for them, and she gave them venison-stew for supper. After they had eaten, the Sun said to his sister, 'Wash my son's head.' She took a large dish, put water into it, and yucca suds; she washed his head and his body, and gave him new clothing, the same kind as the Sun was wearing, buckskin trousers, blue moccasins, blue bands of yarn to be tied under the knees, a white sash and a belt of fox-skin, turquoise and shell earrings, a white shirt, silver arm-rings, bead bracelets, and a bead necklace. She put macaw-feathers in his hair, and a sacred blanket over his shoulder, and she gave him a quiver of mountain-lion skin.

Then the Sun said to him, 'Go ahead! I am going to follow you.' Then the boy went ahead. He took the fox-skin, held it up, and the dawn of day appeared. Then he put it down and raised the macaw feathers. He held them up with the palms of his hands stretched out forward, and the yellow rays of sunrise appeared. Then he dropped his hands and went on into the upper world. When he came up, the people of Laguna, Isleta, and the other eastern pueblos, looked eastward and sprinkled sacred meal. The

Sun said, 'Look at the trails (the life) of the people! Some of them are short, others are long. Look at this one! He is near the end of his trail; he is going to die soon.' Then the boy saw an Apache coming, and within a short time he killed the man whose trail had appeared so short. He saw everything that was happening to the people. The boy said to the Sun,

'Let me go and help the people!'

Then he jumped down and went to the place where the Laguna people were fighting against the Apache. He told the people to wet their arrow-points with saliva, and to hold them up to the Sun, who would then help them. He killed ten of the warriors. Then the boy went back to the Sun.

They went on, and saw a number of Navajos who were going to make war upon the Zuni. He killed them. Then he saw his own people, the Hopi.

A Mexican was playing with his wife. When the Sun saw them, he threw the Mexican aside, and cohabited with the woman. He said to the boy, 'I do not need a wife, for all the women on earth belong to me. If a couple cohabit during the daytime, I interfere as I did here. I am the father of all the children that are conceived in the daytime.'

In the evening the Sun entered his house in the west. The boy wanted to go back to his own people. Then the Sun's mother made a trail of sacred flour, and the boy and the Rattlesnake Woman went back eastward over it. At noon he came to the house of the Rattlesnakes. The Rattlesnake Woman who accompanied him said, 'I want to see my father and my mother. After that let us go on!' They entered the house, and she told her relatives that the Hopi boy was her husband. Then they went on.

In the evening they arrived in Hopi. There the boy went to his grandmother. An old chief said, 'Behold, a handsome man is going into the house of these poor people!' He invited him to come into the chief's house.

The boy, however, replied, 'No, I am going into this house.'

The war-chief said, 'We do not want you to enter this dirty house.'

Then the boy replied, 'Tell your people to clean the house. It is mine. When all of you treated me badly, I went up to the Sun, and he helped me.'

On the following evening the chief called a council. The boy went there and told all that had happened to him. He said to them, 'You shall teach the people how to act rightly. The Sun told me to instruct you to forbid all bad actions.' The people accepted his instructions. They went to clean his house, and all worked for him. The boy gave peaches, melons, and wafer-bread to the poor. Every evening after sunset he gave them to eat. The women would come with their dishes, and he gave them venison-stew and peaches. He said to the chief, 'I teach the people how to act. Even if you are my enemy, I must show you how to act rightly.'

After some time, twin children were born to his wife, a boy and a girl. They had the shape of rattlesnakes. The youth's sister used to carry them on her back. When any children saw them and kissed them, the rattlesnakes would bite them, and the children died.

Lanco Blala

A long time ago there was a king (Leya) who was very rich. He had six thousand sheep and four thousand cattle and horses. He had a beautiful daughter. He said, 'If anyone can shear all my sheep in one day, he may marry my daughter.' All the young men tried it, but nobody succeeded.

The Sun heard about this, and thought he would try. He became a man and went down to Old Mexico. Then he travelled westward; and after he had passed the top of the White Mountains, he came to a spring. There he took his bow and his lightning arrow and shot into the spring. In the fourth world below, his arrow hit some saliva, which was transformed into a person, who came out of the spring and sat down on the ground. The Sun saw him. He was a small dark man, and looked like a Zuni. The Sun said, 'Are you here, my son? I want you to go to Old Mexico to the daughter of the king. If anyone is able to shear his sheep in one day, he is to marry his daughter. You shall do so.'

'I will try,' said the boy.

The Sun said, 'Somebody shall go with you. Be sure not to eat anything that the king may give you. Wait until you come to a lake in the southeast. There you will find a large white horse which belongs to me. The king's daughter will like to have it. Do not eat until after you have caught the horse and taken it to her.' The boy promised to obey. 'You must stay there for twenty-five years. Then come back here, and I will send you home.'

The boy started on his travels through Old Mexico. Finally he came to a mountain. There he met a mountain lion, who asked, 'Where are you going?'

The boy replied, 'I am going to Old Mexico to marry the king's daughter. I am going to shear his sheep.'

The mountain lion said, 'May I go with you?' The boy accepted his offer, and they went on together.

After some time he met a bear, who asked, 'Where are you going?'

The boy replied, 'I am going to Old Mexico to marry the king's daughter. I am going to shear his sheep.'

The bear said, 'May I go with you?'

The boy said, 'Come along!' and they went on.

After some time they met a wildcat, who asked, 'Where are you going?'

He said, 'I am going to Old Mexico to marry the king's daughter. I am going to shear his sheep.'

'May I go with you?'

The boy said, 'Come along!'

After they had gone some time, they met a wolf, who asked, 'Where are you going?'

'I am going to Old Mexico to marry the king's daughter.'

'May I come along?' The boy accepted him, and they went on westward. The boy was carrying some sacred meal. Every now and then he would swallow a little of it, but he did not eat anything else. Every night they camped, and in the morning they went on.

On the fourth day they reached the top of a large mountain. There the mountain lion said, 'Tomorrow morning at sunrise we shall reach the king's house.' They camped, and early the following morning the animals called the boy.

They said, 'Now you must have a name. How shall we call you?' None of the animals knew how to call him.

After some time the wolf said, 'I shall give you a name. Sit down on top of the mountain! When your father the Sun rises, I shall call you. Then answer!' The boy sat down on the top of the mountain and looked eastward. When the sun rose, the wolf shouted, 'My son, Lanco Blala.

The boy replied, 'What do you want? I like that name.' Then they went down the mountain.

At the foot of the mountain the animals said, 'We shall stay here. You go on!'

Early in the morning Lanco Blala arrived at the king's house. He saw that the people had tied together the feet of the sheep and were shearing them. Some were shearing five sheep, others six sheep. He looked into the corral and saw the foreman shearing the sheep. While Lanco Blala was standing there, the foreman turned around and saw him. He asked, 'What do you want? Do you want some work? What can you do?'

'I can help you shear the sheep.' The boy entered the corral, and they gave him a rope to tie up the sheep. He, however, took a sheep between his knees and sheared it. Then he caught another one and did the same. In one hour he had sheared many sheep. Then the foreman went to the king and told him about it.

He said, 'Come and look at this boy!'

The king came, and said, 'You are a good workman. You can shear sheep well.' Then six flocks of sheep were driven into the corral, and he sheared them. The king asked, 'What is your name?'

The boy replied, 'My name is Lanco Blala.'

'I never heard of such a name,' said the king. The boy continued, and sheared many sheep. One flock after another was driven into the corral, and he sheared them all. He succeeded in shearing the six thousand sheep all in one day.

Then he went to the king's house. The king's daughter brought him his supper; but he said, 'I am not hungry.' She urged him to eat, but he refused. He stayed in the house, and the king's daughter wanted to marry him.

She said, 'I should like to have you for my husband.'

But he refused her, and said, 'Wait a while.' He said, 'It is too warm for me in the house. I shall sleep outside.' He carried his bed to the corral, and put it down among the sheep and pigs. The following morning at breakfast time the people looked for him, but could not find him. His bed in the corral was empty. Finally they found him lying among the pigs, where he had slept.

They said; 'Get up! Breakfast is ready.' He, however, swallowed a pinch of sacred meal; and when the king's daughter invited him to eat, he refused.

She said, 'You must eat something!' but he replied,

'I am not hungry.'

After some time the king's daughter asked for wood for her fire. He went out and carried wood for her. He put the wood into the stove and helped her cook. After some time she saw the people going into the corral. He asked, 'What are they doing there?'

She said, 'I do not know. Maybe they are marking father's cattle.'

He said, 'I shall go and see.' She wanted him to stay, but he refused. Many irons were in the fire, and the people branded the steers and marked their ears. There was one wild steer of which the people were very much afraid. They asked the boy whether he would mark the steer. He said, 'I can do it.' They told him to mount a large white horse and to catch the steer. 'No,' he replied, 'I cannot ride; the horse might fall, and the steer might gore me.' He went into the corral. The steer was pawing the ground. Then he talked to him, spit on him, took him by the horns and threw him. He called one of the men to come with a hot iron and to brand the steer on the side.

The people became angry, and said, 'You branded him on the wrong side. You must brand him on the left side.'

'No,' said Lanco Blala, 'that is wrong; this side is better.' He continued, and branded many cattle. He finished this work in one afternoon. Then he went home.

When the king saw the strength and ability of Lanco Blala, he wanted him to marry his daughter; but the young man refused. The king said to him, 'You must get my white horse in the southeast. For five years I have tried, but nobody has been able to catch it.'

Lanco Blala said, 'Wait for four days. You must give me one man, who must drive a post into the ground four feet deep, and you must give me a long rope.' Then the king brought a long rope and gave it to him. The king's daughter made biscuits, cakes, and pie for him; and she gave him meat and eggs, potatoes and coffee, and fork, knife, and spoon. He took these along. He camped at night, and after four days he came to the lake; and there, a short distance away, he saw the horse sleeping.

As he went along, he saw some gophers, who asked him, 'Where are you going?'

'I want to catch the horse.'

The gophers said, 'We will awaken the horse. Three times he will run around the lake; the fourth time he will pass close by you; then catch him with your lasso. Stand between two cedar-trees.' Then Lanco Blala made a fire and prepared breakfast, but he did not eat. Meanwhile the gophers made a burrow towards the horse. They came up under him and bit his side. The horse jumped up and ran once around the lake. Lanco Blala was holding the lasso in his left hand. Three times the horse ran around the lake. The fourth time it passed close to the boy. He threw his lasso and caught it. The horse fell on its side, and he quickly hobbled its fore and hind legs. Then the gophers said to him, 'Now you must get its saddle.' Lanco Blala went to the lake, and there he met Old Woman Spider, who said to him,

'Have you come?'

'Yes,' he said, 'I want to get the saddle for the horse.'

She replied, 'Come in here, step into this spider-web, and close your eyes! I will let you down into the water, and don't open your eyes until you get there!' Lanco Blala obeyed, and he entered the water in the spider-web. Then he found himself in another world. When the spider web stopped, he opened his eyes, stepped out, and turned to the east. There he saw a large white house, which he entered. In the house was a large white saddle, a white bridle, white shoes, spurs, saddlebags, and a saddle-blanket and clothing – trousers, shirt, and hat. He took all of these, put them in the spider web, and shook the rope. Then Old Spider Woman pulled up the rope. When he came out of the water, Old Spider Woman said to him, 'Now open your eyes!' She continued, 'Take this!' When he looked to the north, he saw much gold, which he put into his saddlebag. When he looked to the south, he saw much silver, which he put into the other saddle bag. The Spider Woman asked him, 'Did you take everything?'

'Yes,' he replied. Then he went to the horse. He saddled it, took off the hobbles, and made the horse rise. Then he said to the gophers, 'Now eat all that I have cooked! I am not going to eat.' The gophers thanked him. He mounted the horse, and it started running towards the lake.

The gophers shouted, 'Pull him back!' Then he pulled the left side of the reins, turned the horse's head, said goodbye to the gophers, swung his hat, and rode home. The horse ran like lightning. At night he came home. He put the horse into the stable and took off the saddle. Then he went to the house. The king's daughter gave him supper, but he refused it.

He said, 'I have caught the horse,' and told her all that had happened.

On the other side of the street lived a poor Mexican who had raised a pig for his many children. He said, 'Let us put our pig into the field in which Lanco Blala's horse is! The horse will kill the pig, and we are going to get money for it. Then we can buy something good to eat.' They took their pig out and put it into the field. On the following morning it was found that the horse had killed it. Then the old man said to Lanco Blala, 'Why don't you put your horse into the corral, so that it cannot kill my pig?' The king's daughter heard his complaint, and sent out to inquire what the trouble was. The poor Mexican said, 'Lanco Blala's horse has killed my pig. He shall pay for it. Where is he? Call him out!'

Then they called him out; but he said, 'Tell the man to come in.' When the poor man came in, he said, 'Your horse has killed my pig: now you shall pay me.'

'What do you want for it?' he asked.

The poor man said, 'Five dollars.' Then the king's daughter opened her trunk and gave the five dollars to Lanco Blala.

He replied, 'No, I don't want your money: I shall pay him with my own money.' He went to his saddle bag, and said to the poor man, 'Five dollars is not enough for you, you need more.' He took out two handfuls of gold and gave them to him, and he gave to his children silver money. He said to the children, 'Save this money, so that you may have some when you are grown up.' Then he turned to the old man, and said, 'I know that you took your pig to my horse in order to have it killed. Why don't you come to me and ask me for money? I am perfectly willing to give it to you.'

Then the man was ashamed. The poor man said to him, 'Now you may keep my pig, skin it, and eat it.'

'No,' said Lanco Blala, 'I do not want your pig. You can skin it, and eat it with your children.' Then the poor man went home. He bought beans and sugar and flour for his children. He bought new furniture. He skinned his pig, and ate it with his children.

Lanco Blala still refused to sleep in the house, but went out and slept with the pigs.

One day another king sent a letter, and asked that Lanco Blala help him against a giant. Lanco Blala agreed. The king's daughter prepared food for him. He wrote to the king that he would be there in four days. He started, and arrived at the king's house. The king said to him, 'When you go to fight the giant, I shall send my soldiers with you.' He gave him six wagons of hay and corn for his horse. 'If you do not kill the giant and bring me his scalp, I am going to cut off your head. If you do kill him, then you may cut off my head, and those of my wife and daughter.' Lanco Blala replied, 'If you grant that agreement, then let us make it in writing! and you, your wife, and your daughter must sign.' The king did so. Then Lanco Blala started with the soldiers. After he had gone some distance, he left the soldiers behind, and camped by himself. Then his animals – the lion, the bear, the wildcat, and the wolf – came and joined him. They said to him, 'The house of the giant is one mile away from here. Tell your soldiers to go to sleep, because tomorrow they are going to fight.' Lanco Blala did as the animals asked him, and after an hour all the soldiers were asleep.

Then the lion told him, 'Now kill all the soldiers! Cut off their heads!' The soldiers were in bed, always two in one bed. With one stroke he cut off the heads of each pair of men, and he killed all their horses and mules. Then the animals told him to go to sleep. When day dawned, the lion said, 'When the sun rises, call the giant.' Lanco Blala started, and stopped at an arroyo. Shortly after sunrise the giant came out of his house. He looked around, and Lanco Blala called him. The giant tried to find who had called him, and went around the mountain. Then Lanco Blala called again. The lion spoke to him, and said, 'Go a little farther along! Maybe he will see you then.' Lanco Blala went on, and shouted again.

He called to the giant, 'Come down! I want to fight you.' Then the giant saw him, and came. Lanco Blala said, 'You are a strong man. Let us see who is the stronger! If I am stronger than you, I shall kill you.' They began to wrestle. After a little while Lanco Blala became tired, and called to his animals for help. Then they bit the giant. The bear tore open his side and tried to kill him.

The giant said, 'You cannot kill me. My heart is in my house. If you find it, then I shall die.' The animals went into the house. There they saw a large hammer hanging over an anvil. Lanco Blala asked the giant,

'What is this?'

He replied, 'If I do not succeed in killing a person who comes here, I take him into the house and kill him with this hammer.' He placed a human bone on the anvil and released the hammer, which shattered the bone. He said, 'That is the way that I kill people.'

At another place a large saw was hanging. They asked him, 'What is this?'

He replied, 'If I do not succeed in killing people outside or with my hammer, I kill them with this saw.' He placed a human bone under the saw, pulled a rope, and the saw came down and cut the bone to pieces.

In still another room he had a large stove. The animals asked, 'What is this?'

He said, 'If I do not kill people before they come here, and if my hammer and my saw do not kill them, I put them in the stove. Then I roast them and eat them. Now look for my heart! If you do not find it, you cannot kill me. The animals looked for the heart, but they could not find it. And he said, 'If you do not find it; you are going to die.'

In one of the rooms there was much yellow corn. They searched among it. Among the corn they found a coral as large as fist. That was the giant's heart. When Lanco Blala took it up, the giant died. Then they went out. The lion said, 'Now go and take all his cattle!' Lanco Blala turned around, and in a canyon near by he found horses. In still another one he found mules. He released all of these. All these animals were cannibals.

He told them, 'From now on, eat grass and yucca and brush, but do not eat human beings!' Then he went back to his animals.

The lion said to him, 'Now we have done our work. Tell us where to go.'

Lanco Blala said to him, 'Go northward, up the mountain, and kill deer, which shall be your food.'

'Thank you,' said the lion, and went away.

Then the bear asked him, 'Where shall I go?'

'Go northward and live on the high mountains, and eat black ants, weeds, and roots.' He said to the wildcat, 'Go southward and live on rabbits.' To the wolf he said, 'Go to the east; kill antelopes, eat their flesh, and drink their blood.' Then the animals left him.

The giant, however, came back to life; but he was blind, and could not find the door of his house. While he was stumbling about, he fell into the door of his stove. The wood in the stove was burning, and his body was consumed. His heart burst, and a large fire came out of the mountain.

Lanco Blala was riding back to the king's house. The scalp of the giant was dangling from his arm. He travelled as fast as he could. Suddenly he saw the fire from the mountain pursuing him and coming nearer and nearer . He threw a comb back over his shoulder. It was transformed into a large lake, which detained the fire. Gradually, it found its way around the lake. When it came near again, Lanco Blala threw a hairbrush back over his shoulder. It was transformed into a canyon and mesas, and it took the fire a long time to pass these. When it came near again, he threw his sword down, which became a long river. After some time the fire crossed the river too. Then Lanco Blala said, 'I do not know what to do now.'

Then his horse said to him, 'Ask your father to help you.' Then he took a dollar gold piece, wet it in his mouth, and held it up to the sun. He asked him for help. At once a cloud came down; and when the fire came near him, a heavy rain poured down, which extinguished the fire. Then he filled his hands with water four times, and gave it to his horse to drink; and he himself also drank four times from his hands.

In the afternoon he reached the king's house. When he arrived there, he asked one of the servants to call out the king. He said to him. 'Here is the giant's scalp. Now I am going to kill you. I am going to cut off your head.' He told him that the giant had killed all the soldiers, and that they were not worth anything.

The king replied, 'I have lost my life.' Lanco Blala said to him, 'Now look up to the sun for the last time! Soon you are going to die.' The king looked up and cried. Lanco Blala took hold of his head. He took a large knife and pretended that he was about to cut his throat.

Then the king said, 'Wait a moment! Keep me as your slave. Let me work for you! I will cut wood for you and do whatever you tell me.'

'That is good,' said Lanco Blala. 'Then I am not going to kill you.'

The king called his wife, and Lanco Blala threatened to kill her; but she also offered to work and wash for him. She said, 'I do not want to die, because my husband is foolish.'

Then they called their daughter. She wept, and said, 'Do not cut off my head! rather marry me!' Lanco Blala replied, 'I have a wife.'

'That does not matter, you might as well have two wives.'

'If you are willing to treat my wife as a sister, I will take you.' Then he took the king, his wife, and his daughter along to the other king's house. He went ahead, and they walked behind him. When he arrived at his house, he took the saddle off his horse, and he asked his new wife to take it into the house. He said to her, 'If you cannot lift it, you are no longer my wife.' She tried to lift it, but it was too heavy. Then Lanco Blala said, 'You are weak, I don't want you.' He lifted the saddle and carried it in.

Then his new wife said, 'Let me carry your saddle blanket!'

'No,' he replied, 'you are too weak;' and himself carried it into the house. Then he said to his new wife. 'You are too bad, you try to kill people. You must not do so. If a man wants to marry you, why don't you take him? My wife is soon going to come.'

Then the first king's daughter, his wife, arrived. He showed her the giant's scalp. She cooked for him, and now he ate. For five years he stayed with his wife. Then he went back to the White Mountains. When he arrived on top of the mountain, he sat down near the spring at which he had originated. The Sun came down and asked him what he had done, and he told him everything that had happened. The Sun said, 'I am glad to hear this. Now the Mexicans are going to be better. They will not act as they have done heretofore.' He took the boy and shot him back into the spring from which he had come.

Santu

It was in 1899, at the time when the Santu Dance is held behind the church. The chief, the governor, and the tenientes were present. The Santu was standing on a table on blankets, and boys and girls were dancing for him. It was in the afternoon, after dinner, when one of the tenientes nudged me, and said, 'Blood is coming out of the Santu's head.' Then I saw how a little swelling appeared at the temple of the head of the Santu, and a drop of blood came out. The face of the Santu changed colour, and looked very pale, like that of a dead person. I thought at first that it was not blood. A hole appeared which was nearly an inch deep, and I thought that the paint was coming off because the image had been wet; but I put my finger on and smelled of it, and it smelled like blood. It looked as though the Santu had been shot. I felt very badly. This lasted a little while. Then suddenly the hole disappeared, and the Santu looked as before. He was no longer pale, but had his regular colour, and his eyes were quite vivid.

The dance continued for four days. This happened on the fourth day. The following night we were sitting in a house, and were talking about this matter. There were twelve men there, all principals.

In the same year, during the harvest dance, the people were distributing peaches, apricots, and other fruits. The people were shooting with six-shooters, as was the custom at that time. Then they hit one boy in the shoulder, and my niece was hit in the abdomen. She died the following day. I believe the Santu wanted to tell us that this was going to happen. Nobody knows who fired the shots. Since that time the officers have forbidden shooting . If a person shoots, he is put into jail.

The Mexicans call the Santu 'Santu Linio'. If a Mexican wishes to pray to him, the keeper of the Santu has to bring him out. The Mexican may pay him fifty cents or twenty-five cents; rich people, as much as five dollars; or they may give him some calico. This money is given to the sacristan.

During the Santu Dance everybody pays him. The paying is not demanded by anybody; but the people, not only from Zuni, but also from other pueblos, give to the Santu whatever they like, money or candles. Whenever the Santu is exhibited, candles must be lighted for him.

When a Mexican is sick and asks for the help of the Santu, the sacristan must bring him out, and the Mexican prays to him. The Santu is carried into the living-room, and candles are lighted. The Catholics and Americans do this, but not the Zuni.

In December, at the end of the year, the Santu is exhibited for eight days in the house. Then the Zuni make little sheep out of clay, also pumpkins and ears of corn. They bring these to the Santu, and pay money to him. For eight days these are left there in the house of the sacristan. After this time the people who made the clay figures take them away. They make a hole in the ground, in the house or the corral, and bury the figures there. Then their corn and their stock will increase. During this time also two candles are left burning next to the Santu.

Juan Without Fear

A long time ago a Mexican priest lived in Zuni. A Mexican girl cooked for him. One morning after she had prepared breakfast, she called the priest; and while he was sitting at the table with the girl, he said to her, 'You are going to give birth to a child.'

'No,' she said, 'that is not true.'

The priest continued, 'You are going to have a wise son.'

The girl replied, 'You are no seer. How do you know what is going to happen?'

'I know it,' he retorted. She, however, laughed at him, and would not believe him. However, after a month the young woman gave birth to a boy. She hid the baby in a trunk. Then she washed herself, put on new clothing, and prepared the breakfast for the priest. When the priest was sitting at the table, the infant knocked against the trunk with his feet; and the priest asked, 'What is in that trunk?'

The young woman replied, 'Maybe it is a cat.'

The priest did not say anything. After a little while the noise was heard again, and he asked again, 'What is in that trunk?'

The young woman replied, 'It is a cat.'

He, however, said, 'That is no cat, it is a child. Take him out!'

The young woman asked him, 'How do you know that?'

The priest repeated, 'Never mind! I know it. Take him out!' Then she opened the trunk, and the child was standing there. He looked like a six-year-old child. He was standing, and holding with his hands to the sides of the trunk. The priest said, 'You are a wise child.' The boy grew up quickly; and one day the priest said to him, 'Stand in the doorway.' While the boy was standing there, looking out of the house, the priest went quietly up to him and suddenly clapped his hands, in order to frighten the boy. The child, however, was not afraid. 'Indeed,' said the priest, 'he is a boy without fear.' He said to the young woman, 'I'll bet that he will not have the courage to go at midnight to church to ring the bells. If he does so, I will pay you much money.'

The boy heard it, and said, 'I am not afraid. If I win, you shall give me an undershirt and drawers, trousers and stockings, a hat and a kerchief to tie over my hat, a mule and saddle, and an axe, canteen, pan, cup, knife and fork, and also give me some bacon and potatoes. If I lose, then you may have all that my mother has, and you can keep the money that you owe her.' They made the bet in writing, and signed it.

Sunday night the boy wanted to go to the church; but his mother said, 'No, first go to sleep, and do not start until twelve o'clock.' The boy lay down and slept.

During this time the priest went to the churchyard and took a body out of a grave. He carried it up the ladder of the steeple, placed it there, and he said to the dead man, 'When the boy comes to ring the bells, frighten him. Do not let him pass.' Then he went home.

A little before twelve o'clock the mother called the boy; and she aid to him, 'Now go and ring the bells.' He put on his hat, and tied the kerchief around it. He went up the ladder as quickly as he could. When he had almost reached the top of the church, he saw somebody on the ladder.

He said, 'Who are you?' Then the dead one let a green light shine from his eyes, his nose, and his mouth, and tried to frighten the boy. He, however, said, 'Doesn't that look nice? Let me see it once more!' And again the green light shone from the dead man's face. The boy said, 'That is remarkable. How do you do that? Let me see it once more!' He made him repeat this four times. Then he said, 'Now go out of my way! I have to go up to ring the bells.'

The dead man said,' Never mind! I will make room for you. You can pass by me.'

'No,' said the boy, 'maybe you will push me down.'

Then the dead one said, 'No, I only wanted to frighten you; but you do not know any fear.'

The boy asked, 'Who sent you here?'

'The priest did. He told me to frighten you. Come up here! I am not going to do you any harm.'

But the boy mistrusted him, and said, 'Maybe you will throw me down. Come down, or I am going to kill you with my axe.'

'Where is your axe?'

'I have it at home.' The boy jumped down the ladder and ran home.

When the priest saw him coming, he said, 'He did not ring the bells. He is afraid. Now you have lost your money.'

The boy, however, merely asked his mother, 'Where is my axe?'

She took it out of the corner, and said, 'What do you want to do with it?'

He replied, 'I want to kill someone with it.'

He ran back to the church; and the dead man asked him, 'Where is your axe?' The boy, however, simply took it and cut up the dead man. He merely said, 'I am already dead, I cannot die twice.' But the boy passed without hindrance, and rang the bells.

When the priest heard, it, he said, 'I knew he was a wise boy. He is not afraid. He is ringing the bells.'

When the boy came home, he said to his mother, 'Call the priest and let him pay us.'

His mother said, 'Oh, he will pay us tomorrow.'

'No,' retorted the boy, 'I want to have the money now.' The priest heard him, and gave him the money that he had lost.

When the boy grew up, he said to his mother, 'Make some bread for me. I am going out to look for work.' His mother baked bread for him; and on the following morning, after breakfast, he asked the priest for a mule. The priest took him to the corral where he kept his mules and horses.

He said to him, 'Take this small mule. It is the best one I have. When you are grown up, you may take a bigger one.' The priest saddled the mule, and said to it, 'At noon, when the boy takes dinner, kick him once and kill him.'

The mule asked, 'Where shall I kick him?'

The priest said, 'Kick him in the testicles.' Then the priest put on the saddle, and he gave to the boy a canteen and bread and whatever he needed.

The boy mounted the mule, and rode to Calistea Canyon. He rode up some distance, and at noon he started a fire and prepared his dinner. He took the saddle off the mule and tried to hobble it. Then the mule put back its ears. The boy said, 'Maybe you want to kick me.'

'Yes,' said the mule, 'I am going to kick you in the testicles.'

'Who told you to do so?'

'The priest did.'

Then the boy said, 'Wait until I put on my new clothing.' He put on his overcoat, and tied his kerchief over his hat. Then he tried again to hobble the mule. The mule kicked and hit him in the testicles. Then the boy fell over in a faint.

After a while he woke up; and the mule said to him, 'Now you may hobble me.'

'No,' said the boy, 'you are going to kick me again.'

The mule replied, 'No, the priest told me to kick you only once, and so I am not going to kick you again.' Then the boy hobbled the mule. He made coffee and fried bacon and potatoes. Then he ate dinner.

After dinner he took off the hobbles, and said to the mule, 'Now I am going to ride you. I am tired.'

'No,' said the mule, 'I am going to run into the arroyo and throw you. Then you will die. Nobody has ever ridden me.'

'Oh,' said the boy, 'if you try to leave the trail, I am going to beat you with my stick.'

'Well,' said the mule, 'try it.' Then the boy buttoned up his overcoat, and tied his kerchief over his hat, and mounted. The mule tried to leave the trail, but the boy beat it until it turned back When the mule tried to turn to the left, he beat its head on the left-hand side; and when the mule bucked, he knocked it right on the head. Finally the mule fell down.

The boy said, 'What is the matter with you? I think you are hungry,' and he offered the mule biscuit. But the animal did not stir. The boy said, 'It looks to me as though you were dead.' Then he cut off four posts with forked tops, and two long poles. He put up the posts, and laid the long poles across them. Then he took the mule's forelegs and placed them over one of the long poles, and he took the hind-legs and put them over the other poles, so that the mule was hanging in the air. Then he said, 'Now I am going to ride you,' and he sat down on its back. He made a whip and beat its feet, but the mule did not stir. Then he beat the left side, and the mule began to stir a little. Then he struck again the other side, and the mule stirred a little more. 'Soon you are going to wake up,' said the boy. 'Now, look out!' When he struck the fourth time, the mule jumped off from the poles and ran the whole day without stopping. Finally the boy became very tired, and said, 'Stop, you fool! Stop! I am hungry. I want to eat.'

The mule replied, 'I am going to run on until I come to a spring where there is nice grass. Let us eat there!' The boy wanted to stop, but the mule ran on, and after some time they arrived at the spring. Then the boy jumped off and started a fire. He made coffee, fried bacon, and ate. After dinner they went on.

In the afternoon they came to a mountain. There he saw a number of Mexican men coming from the southwest. He met them at a crossing of the roads. They asked him, 'Where are you going?'

He replied, 'I am looking for work.'

The men said, 'We are also looking for work. Let us go on together!' He asked them to put their loads on the mule, and they went on. When it was near sunset, they reached the Rio Grande. The men were going to camp there; but the boy said, 'No, let us cross the river tonight!'

The men said, 'No, it is too late.' But the boy insisted. Then the men got ready. They took off their shoes and trousers, and began to wade across the river. While they were in the water, the sun set. Meanwhile the boy was still on the eastern side of the river. They said to him, 'You are too slow, you will never get across tonight.'

When it was dark, the boy started. He sent the mule ahead; but since it was dark, he lost it, and was unable to find it. He called the mule, and it answered from the east. Then he said to the mule, 'I am not going to drive you across, I am going to ride you across.' He mounted, and rode into the water. Meanwhile it became quite dark; and he said to the mule, 'Let us stop here in the water until tomorrow morning!'

'How can we do that?' asked the mule. 'I am going to sleep sitting on your back, and you sleep standing in the water,' said the boy.

'Let us do so!' said the mule.

When the boy awoke the following morning, they went on and crossed the river. There the boy saw a white house. The two men who had accompanied him had gone into the white house the night before. When the boy rode near, he saw a number of people who carried their dead bodies out of the house. They took them to the Plaza; and the boy asked, 'What has happened to these people? How did they die?' And when he came near, he recognised his companions. The people told him that the house was haunted, and that whoever stayed there overnight was found dead on the following morning. The boy, however, had no fear, and rode his mule to the white house. He took off its saddle and hobbled it. Then he entered. The house was entirely empty. He looked around and found a fire place. The house was quite clean. Then the boy said, 'I shall make a fire here, and I am going to sleep next to the fireplace.' He carried the saddle into the house, and started the fire. The people in the town saw smoke coming out of the chimney.

When the governor heard about this he said to his teniente: 'Go and see who is there! Tell him to come out. If he stays in that house overnight, we shall have to bury him tomorrow morning.'

The teniente went to the house and found the boy. He told him that everybody who slept in the house was killed; but the boy replied, 'Why should I die in this good house? I am going to stay here.'

And the teniente replied, 'If you insist, you will be dead tomorrow morning.'

'No,' said the boy, 'I am not going to die.' He could not be induced to leave the house. In the evening he fried potatoes and bacon. When supper was ready, he placed the dishes on the floor. He poured out his coffee and began to eat. Then he heard above in the chimney a noise which sounded like wind. The boy said, 'I think a gale is coming up.' But presently a man's shoulder and arm fell through the chimney. The boy said, 'What does that mean? Whoever has done that?' And he threw the arm and shoulder into the corner, and rearranged his fire. After a little while he heard again a noise, and said, 'Who is coming now?' Then the right shoulder and arm of a man fell into the fire. 'Why do they always fool me?' said the boy, and he threw the arm and the shoulder into the corner. He arranged his fire, and continued to eat. Soon he heard a new noise. 'Who is coming now?' said he. 'Soon we shall have enough people here.' Then the right leg of a person fell down into the fire, and almost extinguished it. The boy became angry, and said, 'Who is the stupid fellow who throws these bones into my fire?' He took the leg and threw it into the corner, and rearranged his fire. It was not long before the noise began again, and the left leg of a person fell down into the fire. He threw it into the corner, and rearranged his fire. When it just began to blaze up again, the head and trunk of a person fell down. The boy threw them into the corner, and started his fire again. Suddenly he saw a large Indian standing in the corner of the room.

He said, 'You are a brave boy. I thought you would die of fright when the bones came down the chimney. Other people who see it die.'

The boy replied, 'Well, they must be very stupid.'

Then the tall man said to him, 'Now we will wrestle. One of us must die, and the one who survives shall own the house.'

The boy said, 'Wait until after I have eaten. When I am hungry, I am weak.'

The boy ate as though nothing had happened; and after a while the large man said, 'Are you done now?'

'Wait a little while. First I have to put away my dishes.' Then he put on his overcoat, and tied his kerchief over his hat, and said, 'Now I am ready!' and they began to wrestle. The man was so large, that the boy could not put his arms around him; and he said, 'Wait a little while, I have to stand on my saddle.' Secretly he pulled out his little axe. Then he said to the man, 'Now I am ready!' When the man put his arms around him, the boy took his axe and struck him with it, and the large man fell.

He said to the boy, 'You are fortunate. Now the house belongs to you. Here are the keys, but do not open the doors until tomorrow morning. If you do so tonight, you will die. When you are dead, the people come tomorrow morning to bury you. When they carry you out, the priest will stand on one side; and after he has thrown the soil into the grave, then get up and come into the house through the east door.' Then he gave him the keys. Immediately after this a whirlwind came and carried away the large man. The boy sat down to take a rest. Then he made his bed and went to sleep. He slept until midnight.

Then he woke up, and said, 'The big man is a liar, I am not dead.' He went to sleep again, and woke up again before sunrise; and again he said, 'The big man is a liar. Why should I die?' He woke up again shortly after sunrise, turned over, and went to sleep again; but when he went to sleep the fourth time, he died.

In the morning the people from the town came to the house, and they found him dead. They said, 'Let us dig a grave and bury him!' After they had dug a grave, a number of men came and carried him out. They covered him with a blanket, and carried him to the graveyard. They put the body down into the grave, and threw soil on top of it.

After a while the priest asked, 'Are you done now?' and the people replied in the affirmative. Then they went away. Immediately the boy arose and ran back into the house.

When the people saw it, they were surprised, and said, 'Who is this boy running into the house?' He prepared his breakfast, and after that he opened all the rooms. In one of the rooms he found a bed. A sword lay on it, and under the bed was much money – silver, gold, and paper. Then he opened another room, which was full of all kinds of medicines. He had a small cut on his hand, and decided to try the medicine. He put some on it, and at once the cut was healed up. He went into another room, and found a bay horse, a carriage, corn and wheat, oats, and a brush. Then he took his mule and put it into the stable and gave it to eat.

After some time the people of the town had a celebration. He asked himself, 'Shall I go there?' He cut off his left leg with his sword. Then he applied the medicine to the wound, and it healed up at once. He carried his left leg in his hands. He put on poor clothing. His coat and his trousers were torn, but his pockets were full of money. He went where horse races and foot races were being held, and where a cockfight was going on. 'Is there anybody who can run very fast?'

'Yes,' said the people. He bet a thousand dollars against the runner. The other man started; and when he was way ahead, the boy began to jump. He moved along in somersaults on his hands and his one leg, and reached the goal first. The people asked, 'Who are you? What is your name?'

And the boy replied, 'I am Djamisa.'

The people said, 'How can we get our money back? Let us have a horse race! He cannot possibly ride with his one leg. Let us ask him whether he will run a race!' The boy agreed, and they gave him a large saddle horse. The boy staked all his money against that of another man. The horse which he was to ride was very wild, and six men had to hold it. He took the rope and spoke to the horse. Then he put his fingers into the horse's nose and on its ears, and the horse stood there quietly. The people said, 'Formerly, when anybody touched the horse, it kicked. Certainly we are going to lose now.'

The people told Djamisa to saddle the horse; but he said that he would ride bareback without a bridle, and only with a rope and a halter. He made a noose in his rope, and put it on the horse's neck. He let the rope drag behind, jumped on the horse, which started at once. It ran about in circles, and the boy came back to the people. Then he called the owner of the horse to sit behind him. He said, 'The horse won't do you any harm. If it should kick you, I will give you all my money.' Then the other jumped on the horse, and the two rode around the town. When they came back, the boy told the owner, 'Now this horse has been broken. If it should ever kick again, I will give you all my money.'

After a while Djamisa asked the people, 'Where does the king live?'

One man said to him, 'Do you see the soldiers near that cottonwood tree? The king's house is near by.' He went there. When he came to the cottonwood tree, the boy left his property in the branches of the tree. He reached the soldier, who forbade him to go on.

Djamisa said, 'I came to see the king.'

'You cannot see him.'

'Why not?'

'People must pay much money if they want to see him. It costs a thousand dollars.'

'Well, I will give you a thousand dollars.' He paid the money to the soldier, who allowed him to pass. In the first room of the house, he found another guard, who would not allow him to pass. The boy said, 'I came to see the king.'

'You have to pay five hundred dollars if you want see him.' The boy paid it, and was allowed to pass. In the following room there was another guard, who demanded two hundred and fifty dollars; and after the boy had paid him, he came to a fourth one, who demanded one hundred and fifty dollars. Finally the king's cook came out.

The boy said to him, 'I want to see the king,' and the cook went in to call him. Djamisa was talking to the king when he was called to dinner. Djamisa asked him, 'How much must I pay you in order to be allowed to eat with you?'

The king said, 'Fifty dollars.' He paid the money, and the king and Djamisa ate together.

In the afternoon he said to the king, 'Now I must go home, but I am going to come back to see you.'

The king said, 'I should like to know who he is. He must have a great deal of money. He shall marry my daughter.' He sent out his soldiers to search for him. Meanwhile Djamisa had put on his leg. He wore overalls, and carried a small bundle on his shoulder. Thus he walked across the street.

The soldiers asked him, 'Did you see the man who visited the king?'

'How does he look?'

'He has only one leg.'

'Which one?'

'The right one.' The boy said that he did not know the man. The soldiers went back, and he continued on his way. He walked around the town to his house, and there he stayed for several days. Then he went back to the king. The king asked him whether he would help him find the boy, and he asked five dollars a day as pay. The king's soldiers had looked through all the houses in the town without finding the man.

Then the king thought, 'Maybe he lives in the white house.' The soldiers went there. Then Djamisa dressed himself like a soldier, and stood guard in front of the house, and did not permit the soldiers to go in.

He asked them, 'What do you want?'

They said, 'We want to see whether the man lives here who dined with the king.'

'You cannot see him. It costs too much money. You have to pay a thousand dollars.' The soldiers paid a thousand dollars, and the boy repeated everything that had been done to him at the king's house.

Finally the soldiers reached him, and delivered the king's letter. He read it, and said, 'I do not want to marry the king's daughter.' He wrote an answer, and sent it back through the soldiers. They took the letter to the king; and when he had read it, he replied, insisting again that Djamisa should marry the king's daughter. The soldiers took the letter there, but again he declined. The king sent three letters; and when the boy continued to decline, the king finally wrote,

'If you do not marry my daughter, I am going to put you into prison.' Then Djamisa replied, saying that he would marry the king's daughter the following week on Monday. When the king received this letter, he ordered the cooks to prepare for a great feast. They killed cattle and made cakes and pies, and after a week the marriage was celebrated. Djamisa took the king's daughter to live with him in the white house. He was very rich. He had many sheep and cattle, and herdsmen to take care of the herds.

One day his wife received a letter from her mother, who had died some time before, and who was now in heaven. She wrote to her that a festival was going to be celebrated in heaven, and she asked her and her husband to come. Djamisa did not want to go, but finally he was persuaded. For four years he and his wife stayed in heaven. When he came back, his sheep and cattle, horses and mules, were scattered, and he was quite poor.

The Rebellion Against the Spaniards

The Mexicans were plotting to kill all the Zuni on Sunday after church. A young war chief overheard them, and understood what they were talking about. Therefore he informed the chief, and at night a council was called. There the young war chief told the assembled people that the Mexicans were planning to kill them. There were forty or fifty war chiefs in the assembly. They decided to kill the Mexicans before they had a chance to attack them.

On the following Sunday they hid their bows, arrows, and war clubs under blankets, and went to church. After the sermon, when the people were singing a Mexican song, the war chiefs arose. Ten or fifteen of them stood next to the door, and they called the boys and girls and told them to hurry out of church. When all were out, they shut the door and killed all the Mexicans. One man, a Mexican, ran into one of the adjoining rooms. There were ten or fifteen rooms on each side of the church. The priest was sitting on the altar at the feet of the Santu and crossed himself. The war chiefs did not attack him. They tied his hands on his back. The Mexican who had escaped into the adjoining room crept up the chimney and made good his escape.

After this had happened, the Zuni from all the seven towns left their pueblos and went up Corn Mountain.

When the people of the Rio Grande Pueblos heard what had happened, they held a council. They had learned that the Mexicans were to send an expedition against the Zuni, and the Rio Grande Pueblos were summoned to accompany them. One young man, a good runner from Laguna, ran with all speed to the Zuni who were on Corn Mountain, and told them of the approaching war party. The chief of the Zuni invited the runner in, and gave him to eat and to drink. He told him not to drink any of the water from the springs in the valley, because the water had been poisoned. He also advised him that the Laguna people, who were compelled to accompany the Spaniards, should hold juniper branches in the mouth, and that then they would not attack them. Before the Laguna runner left, he promised to send word to Zuni ten days before the warriors should start.

Ten days after this, six or eight people from Laguna came on their mules. They made a camp at the foot of Corn Mountain. The Zuni chief sent down to inquire who they were. When the Laguna met them, they wept, because they thought that the Zuni were going to be killed and told them that the Spaniards were coming with a large army. When the chief of the Zuni heard the message, he sent word to them, warning them not to drink, because all the springs had been poisoned. Then the members of the Shell Society went into their *kiva*, in which they stayed for eight days. After eight days the Spanish army arrived. The soldiers were on horseback. They rode four abreast. They encamped at the place where the reservoir now is. After they had eaten, they attacked the mesa. The Zuni defended themselves with bows and arrows, while the Spaniards had muzzle-loading guns. At that time the head of the Shell Society came out of the *kiva*. He had long hair. He was painted black around the eyes. His forehead and chin were painted white. He had eagle-down on his head. His body was painted red, and white lightning was painted on his clothing. He held a shell in his mouth. He had no bow and no other weapons. He stepped right to the edge of the cliff; and when the Spaniards shot at him, he just blew out of his mouth. Then the bullets could not hit him, and the soldiers tumbled about as though they were drunk. Blood flowed out of their eyes, nose, and mouth, and they died. Only a few were left. Then the Spaniards, with the people from the Rio Grande Pueblos, went back.

After a month they came back again with a new army. The Laguna sent word again, telling them that the soldiers were coming. They made their camp at the same place as before. After they had eaten, they came to attack the Zuni.

Then the priest, who had stayed with the Zuni, said, 'I will write a letter to them and tell them that you have not killed me.' But he had no paper and no ink; therefore they took a rawhide, spanned it over a frame, and he wrote on it with charcoal. He wrote, 'I am still alive, but I have no clothing.' Then they put a stone to the frame and threw it down. A soldier picked it up and carried it to the commander. He read it, and gave orders to the soldiers to stop fighting. They sent a priest's dress, paper, and ink to the father, and asked him to return with them to Mexico. He, however, replied, saying that he could not wear the dress of dead people; that he wanted to stay with the Zuni and wear their clothes. Then the Zuni came down from the mountain, and the soldiers went back.

Acknowledgments

Lukai Nez collected the story of the origin of the Manygoats clan, and his text is used with his permission. The story of Boy and Girl Rock was collected by Keith and Kathryn Cunningham. All others selections are taken, with permission, from the *Journal of American Folklore*, a scholarly quarterly that has been published since 1888 by the American Folklore Society.

Sources for the individual stories are as follows:

Story	Published in *JAF*	Original Editor
Chapter 1 – Abenaki, p. 25		
Heroic Deeds of Glooscap	1888, p. 85	Edward Jack
Why the Porcupine and Toad Have No Noses	1888, p. 85	Edward Jack
Chapter 2 – Achomawi, p. 27		
Pine Marten Marries the Bead Sisters	1909, pp. 283–4	Roland B. Dixon *from the collection of Jeremiah Curtin*
Kangaroo Rat Races with Coyote and Others	1909, pp. 284–5	Roland B. Dixon *from the collection of Jeremiah Curtin*
Chapter 3 – Acoma, p. 30		
The Flaming Horse	1930, pp. 79–83	Ruth Benedict
Kaupata	1930, pp. 62–7	Ruth Benedict
The Kobictaiya Are Challenged to the Test of Lightning	1930, pp. 61–2	Ruth Benedict
Windows of the Fox	1930, pp. 77–9	Ruth Benedict
The Travels of Salt Woman	1930, pp. 59–61	Ruth Benedict
Paiyatyamo and Yellow Woman	1930, pp. 67–70	Ruth Benedict
Greasy Boy Recovers His Wife	1930, pp. 71–7	Ruth Benedict
Careful Burden Carrier	1930, pp. 85–7	Ruth Benedict

Story	Published in *JAF*	Original Editor
Chapter 4 – Arapaho, p. 60		
On the War Path	1912, pp. 46–7	H. R. Roth
The Woman and the Buffalo	1912, p. 44	H. R. Roth
The Man Who Gets Advice from the Skunk	1912, p. 44	H. R. Roth
The Origin of the Pleiades	1912, p. 44	H. R. Roth
Origin of the Buffalo	1912, pp. 45–6	H. R. Roth
The Mother's Head	1912, pp. 48–9	H. R. Roth
Origin of the Medicine Arrows	1912, p. 46	H. R. Roth
The Frog and the Woman	1912, p. 44	H. R. Roth
How a Bird and an Alligator Saved Two Children	1912, p. 50	H. R. Roth
The Cannibal and the Fox	1912, p. 48	H. R. Roth
Bad Robe Resurrecting a Buffalo	1912, pp. 44–5	H. R. Roth
The Bear Girl	1912, p. 49	H. R. Roth
Why the Bear Has a Short Tail	1912, pp. 49–50	H. R. Roth
The Alligator Boy	1912, p. 47	H. R. Roth
The Boy Who Was Carried off by the Wind	1912, p. 43	H. R. Roth
Chapter 5 – Blackfoot, p. 70		
Legend of Red Coulee	1890, p. 298	John McLean
The Legend of Sheep Creek	1890, pp. 296–7	John McLean
Legend of Tongue Creek	1890, pp. 297–8	John McLean
Chapter 6 – Carrier, p. 73		
The Giant's Grandson	1934, pp. 99–114	Diamond Jenness
A Big Frog	1934, p. 255	Diamond Jenness
The Trickster	1934, pp. 204–12	Diamond Jenness
Coming of the White Man	1934, p. 257	Diamond Jenness
Caribou Man and the Sekani	1934, pp. 245–6	Diamond Jenness
Origin of Crest Sleepy	1934, pp. 219–20	Diamond Jenness
The Revenge of the Mountain Goats	1934, pp. 155–7	Diamond Jenness
The Flood	1934, pp. 141–3	Diamond Jenness
The Dead Woman's Son	1934, pp. 149–54	Diamond Jenness
The Man Who Ate His Wives	1934, pp. 170–4	Diamond Jenness
The Origin of the Tribes	1934, pp. 240–1	Diamond Jenness
The Monstrous Bear	1934, pp. 193–5	Diamond Jenness
The Bear Wife	1934, pp. 199–200	Diamond Jenness
Porcupine	1934, pp. 250–2	Diamond Jenness

Story	Published in *JAF*	Original Editor
Chapter 7 – Cheyenne, p. 122		
Falling Star	1921, pp. 308–13	George Bird Grinnell
Chapter 8 – Chipewyan, p. 130		
Naba-Cha	1903, pp. 80–4	James Mackintosh Bell
Big Bird Story	1903, p. 77	James Mackintosh Bell
White Bear Story	1903, pp. 78–9	James Mackintosh Bell
Chapter 9 – Comanche, p. 137		
Origin of Death	1909, pp. 279–80	R. H. Lowie *from the collection of* H. H. St. Clair
Chapter 10 – Coos, p. 139		
The Country of the Souls	1909, pp. 37–9	Leo J. Frachtenberg *from the collection of* H. H. St. Clair
The Underground People	1909, pp. 40–1	Leo J. Frachtenberg *from the collection of* H. H. St. Clair
The Woman Who Married the Merman	1909, pp. 27–8	Leo J. Frachtenberg *from the collection of* H. H. St. Clair
The Revenge on the Sky People	1909, pp. 32–4	Leo J. Frachtenberg *from the collection of* H. H. St. Clair
The Man Who Married the Bird	1909, pp. 30–1	Leo J. Frachtenberg *from the collection of* H. H. St. Clair
Chapter 11 – Cree, p. 148		
The Birth of Lake Mistassini	1905, pp. 139–40	Fred Swindlehurst
The Painted Canoe	1905, pp. 140–1	Fred Swindlehurst
The Story of Katonao	1905, pp. 141–2	Fred Swindlehurst
The Biter Bit	1905, p. 143	Fred Swindlehurst
Chichipischekwan (Rolling Head)	1929, pp. 309–11	Rev. E. Ahenakew
The Flight of Wesakaychak	1929, pp. 311–13	Rev. E. Ahenakew
The Younger Boy Becomes a Wolf	1929, pp. 313–14	Rev. E. Ahenakew
Wesakaychak Destroys the Great Moose	1929, pp. 316–19	Rev. E. Ahenakew
Wisakitcax and Buzzard	1921, pp. 320–1	James A. Teit

Story	Published in *JAF*	Original Editor
Chapter 12 – Eskimo, p. 161		
The Woman Who Was Fond of Intestines	1905, pp. 215–20	F. A. Golder
A Sea Otter Story	1905, pp. 221–2	F. A. Golder
The Sad Woman	1905, pp. 215	F. A. Golder
The Man and Woman Who Became Sea Otters	1905, pp. 220–1	F. A. Golder
The Woman Who Became a Bear	1909, pp. 10–11	F. A. Golder
The Old Man of the Volcano	1909, pp. 11–14	F. A. Golder
An Aleut with Two Wives	1909, pp. 14–15	F. A. Golder
Woman Without a Nose	1909, pp. 15–16	F. A. Golder
The Woman with One Eye	1909, pp. 16–17	F. A. Golder
The Boy with Seal Flippers	1909, pp. 20–1	F. A. Golder
Ughek	1909, pp. 23–4	F. A. Golder
The Brother and Sister Who Became Hair Seals	1905, p. 222	F. A. Golder
The Loon and the Blind Man	1954, pp. 65–8	Robert F. Spencer and W. K. Carter
Chapter 13 – Flathead, p. 183		
Coyote Makes Spokane Falls	1901, pp. 240	Louisa McDermott
Coyote and the Woman	1901, pp. 244–5	Louisa McDermott
Coyote and the Medicine Trees	1901, pp. 245	Louisa McDermott
Coyote and the Crying Baby	1901, pp. 244	Louisa McDermott
Coyote and Rock	1901, pp. 245–7	Louisa McDermott
Coyote and the Buffalo Country	1901, pp. 247–9	Louisa McDermott
Coyote and the Two Shells	1901, pp. 241–2	Louisa McDermott
Coyote Kills the Giant	1901, pp. 240–1	Louisa McDermott
Coyote and Fox Separate	1901, pp. 249	Louisa McDermott
Coyote and the Little Pig	1901, pp. 250–1	Louisa McDermott
Chapter 14 – Fox, p. 193		
Dispersion	1911, pp. 229–31	William Jones
The Blackhawk War	1911, pp. 235–7	William Jones
The Origin of the Sauks and Foxes	1911, pp. 211–12	William Jones
Witchcraft	1911, pp. 216–20	William Jones

Story	Published in *JAF*	Original Editor
Chapter 15 – Hopi, p. 200		
The Emergence	1929, pp. 3–6	Alexander M. Stephen
After the Emergence	1929, pp. 10–11	Alexander M. Stephen
Witch and Coyote Establish Death	1929, pp. 7–10	Alexander M. Stephen
Birth of the Twins	1929, pp. 13–14	Alexander M. Stephen
The Twins Slay Kwatoko	1929, pp. 15–18	Alexander M. Stephen
Early Monsters	1929, pp. 14–15	Alexander M. Stephen
The Twins Slay Chaveyo & Giant Elk	1929, pp. 18–20	Alexander M. Stephen
Pyuukanhoya Slays Chaveyo and the Nataska	1929, pp. 20–1	Alexander M. Stephen
Salyko	1929, pp. 55–7	Alexander M. Stephen
The Jamestown Weed Maids (Toothed Vagina)	1929, pp. 28–30	Alexander M. Stephen
Kwatoko, the Woman Stealer	1929, pp. 21–5	Alexander M. Stephen
The Sipapu Is Sought by the Birds	1929, pp. 6–7	Alexander M. Stephen
The Migrations of the Eagle Clan	1929, pp. 70–2	Alexander M. Stephen
The Migrations of the Horn Clan	1929, pp. 67–70	Alexander M. Stephen
Chapter 16 – Huron, p. 232		
The Making of the World	1888, pp. 180–3	Horatio Hale
Chapter 17 – Iroquois, p. 235		
Three Brothers Who Followed the Sun under the Sky's Rim	1910, pp. 474–8	Arthur C. Parker
Chapter 18 – Mandan, p. 238		
No Tongue	1913, pp. 331–7	George F. Will
Chapter 19 – Mojave, p. 245		
Story of the Flood	1921, pp. 320–1	M. K. Gould
Fire Myth	1889, pp. 188–9	John G. Bourke
Chapter 20 – Navajo, p. 248		
Origin of the People	1930, pp. 88–100	Alexander M. Stephen
Coyote Makes Songs for the Hills	1923, p. 371	Elsie Clews Parsons
Coyote Burns up Her Children	1923, pp. 371	Elsie Clews Parsons
Mock Plea	1923, pp. 372–3	Elsie Clews Parsons
Coyote at the River	1923, p. 370	Elsie Clews Parsons
Coyote Sets Fire to the Earth	1923, pp. 370–1	Elsie Clews Parsons
Coyote Plays Dead	1923, pp. 371–2	Elsie Clews Parsons
Coyote Invites Wildcat to Eat	1923, p. 369	Elsie Clews Parsons
Coyote & Wildcat Scratch Each Other	1923, pp. 369–70	Elsie Clews Parsons
Origin of the Manygoats Clan	Not published	Lukai Nez

Story	Published in *JAF*	Original Editor
Chapter 21 –Ojibwa, p. 267		
An Adventure of Wenabuzu	1911, pp. 249–50	Truman Michelson
Chapter 22 – Papago, p. 269		
Montezuma	1921, pp. 255–67	J. Alden Mason
Some of Coyote's Adventures	1909, pp. 340–1	Henriette Rothschild Kroeber
Chapter 23 –Piegan, p. 282		
The Woman Who Turned into a Bear	1911, pp. 244–6	Truman Michelson
Old Man and the Geese	1911, p. 248	Truman Michelson
How the Beaver Bundle Was Introduced	1911, pp. 238–44	Truman Michelson
Chapter 24 – San Luisenos, p. 291		
Creation Myth	1904, p. 185	Mary C. B. Watkins
Chapter 25 – Shasta, p. 292		
Origin of Death	1910, pp. 19–20	Roland B. Dixon
The Dead Brought Back from the Other World	1910, p. 21	Roland B. Dixon
Urutsmaxig	1910, pp. 364–8	Roland B. Dixon
The Race with Thunder	1910, p. 368	Roland B. Dixon
The Captive of the 'Little Men'	1910, p. 25	Roland B. Dixon
Coyote and the Rogue-River People	1910, pp. 25–7	Roland B. Dixon
Chapter 26 – Shawnee, p. 302		
Huron Legend of the Snake Clan	1909, p. 321	J. Spencer
Legendary Origin of the Kickapoos	1909, pp. 325–6	J. Spencer
Chapter 27 – Shoshone, p. 304		
Cosmology	1909, pp. 272–3 *from the collection of H. H. St. Clair*	R. H. Lowie
The Star Husband	1909, pp. 268–9 *from the collection of H. H. St. Clair*	R. H. Lowie
Weasels and Owl	1909, pp. 272 *from the collection of H. H. St. Clair*	R. H. Lowie
The Eye-Juggler	1909, pp. 269–70 *from the collection of H. H. St. Clair*	R. H. Lowie

Story	Published in *JAF*	Original Editor
Chapter 28 – Sioux, p. 309		
Ben Kindle's Winter Count	1930, pp. 350–2	Martha Warren Beckwith
Chapter 29 – Tahltan, p. 311		
The Man with the Toothed Penis	1921, pp. 245–6	James A. Teit
The Three Sister Rocks	1909, p. 318	James A. Teit
Story of Dcandui	1921, pp. 224–5	James A. Teit
Story of Gonexhataca, The Snail	1921, pp. 229–30	James A. Teit
The Sisters Who Married Stars	1921, pp. 247–8	James A. Teit
The Man Who Fooled the Cannibal Giant	1921, pp. 351–2	
Story of the War Between the Tahltan and the Taku	1909, pp. 314–18	James A. Teit
The Woman Stolen by the Ducine	1921, p. 354	James A. Teit
The Story of Tcizqa; or The Hunter Who Could Not Kill Game	1921, pp. 225–6	James A. Teit
The Deserted Woman	1921, pp. 232–3	James A. Teit
The Cannibal Women Who Lured Men	1921, pp. 241–2	James A. Teit
Big-Man and the Boy	1921, pp. 346–9	James A. Teit
The Bad Man and His Son-in-Law	1921, pp. 235–6	James A. Teit
Chapter 30 – Tewa, p. 328		
Water Jar Boy	1943, pp. 69–70	Gladys A. Reichard *from the collection of Elsie Clews Parsons*
Tewa Goat	1921, p. 221	J. Sullivan
Chapter 31 – Ute, p. 331		
Nowintc's Adventures with the Bird Girls and Their People	1910, pp. 322–35	J. Alden Mason
Coyote Juggles His Eyes and Becomes Blind	1910, pp. 314–16	J. Alden Mason
Chapter 32 – Western Mono, p. 348		
The Making of the World	1923, pp. 305–6	Edward Winslow Gifford
A Visit to the World of the Dead	1923, pp. 340–1	Edward Winslow Gifford
Walking Skeleton	1923, pp. 313–18	Edward Winslow Gifford

Story	Published in *JAF*	Original Editor
The Adventures of Haininu and Baumegwesu	1923, pp. 333–8	Edward Winslow Gifford
The Coyote Called 'Another One'	1923, pp. 345–6	Edward Winslow Gifford
Chapter 33 – Winnebago, p. 362		
The Man Who Visited the Thunderbirds	1909, pp. 288–300	Paul Radin
Origin of the Thunderbird Clan and of Their Spirit Abode	1909, pp. 307–13	Paul Radin
Chapter 34 – Yavapai, p. 380		
Origin Story	1933, pp. 349–64	Edward Winslow Gifford
The Burning of the World	1933, pp. 373–7	Edward Winslow Gifford
The Human Bear	1933, pp. 377–81	Edward Winslow Gifford
The Laughing Wives	1933, pp. 372–3	Edward Winslow Gifford
Coyote Resurrects Mountain Lion	1933, pp. 369–71	Edward Winslow Gifford
Coyote Juggles His Eyes	1933, pp. 371–2	Edward Winslow Gifford
Bat's Wives	1933, p. 372	Edward Winslow Gifford
Chapter 35 – Zuni, p. 408		
The Flood	1923, p. 161	Elsie Clews Parsons
The Hopi Boy and the Sun	1922, pp. 62–6	Franz Boas
Lanco Blala	1922, pp. 76–84	Franz Boas
Santu	1922, pp. 96–7	Franz Boas
Juan Without Fear	1922, pp. 84–95	Franz Boas
The Rebellion against the Spaniards	1922, pp. 97–8	Franz Boas

The Folklore Society

What is folklore? Folklore has been defined as 'traditional culture', but no one phrase can do justice to the subject. It embraces music, song, dance, drama, narrative, language, foods, medicine, arts and crafts, religion, magic and belief. Folklore is the way that people fill their lives with meaning, through the stories they share, the daily rituals they perform. Folklore can be both the expression of our individuality and the source of a sense of community. From standing stones to biker gangs, from ancient riddles to the latest joke craze, from King Arthur to the playground, from birth to death, folklore is the stuff of life.

The Folklore Society: who we are. Since 1878 The Folklore Society has provided a meeting-ground for both academics and enthusiasts eager to learn about popular culture and traditional life. The Society promotes awareness of folklore within universities, museums, festivals, in fact wherever traditional culture is discussed and researched.

The Society has an elected committee which aims to be responsive to its members' needs. It therefore embraces a number of specialist groups, such as the East Anglia Folklore Group, to make the Society accessible to all.

The Folklore Society: what we do. In order to encourage awareness of folklore the Society organises events, prizes and research projects. It runs at least one conference a year, and hosts the annual Catharine Briggs memorial lecture.

The Society publishes its own academic journal, *Folklore*, in association with Routledge. It also produces numerous monographs and pamphlets, either under its own imprint, *FLS Books*, or in conjunction with other publishers.

In addition to the journal *Folklore*, members receive a regular newsletter, *FLS News*, through which they can call on the expertise of the entire Society. They also have access to a specialist library with both reference and lending facilities and a substantial archive. The library constitutes a unique resource for the study of folklore, old and new.

The Folklore Society: how to contact us. For details about how to join The Folklore Society and about our forthcoming activities and publications, contact: The Folklore Society, University College London, Gower Street, London WC1E 6BT

Telephone: 020 7862 8564 (with voice mail) or 020 7862 8562
E-mail: folklore.society@talk21.com
Website: www.folklore–society.com

The Folklore Society is a Registered Charity No.1074552